The Role of Chromosomes
in
Development

The Twenty-Third Symposium
The Society for the Study of
Development and Growth

Amherst, Massachusetts, June 1964

The Role of Chromosomes in Development

Edited by

Michael Locke

Developmental Biology Center
Western Reserve University
Cleveland, Ohio

1964

ACADEMIC PRESS, New York and London

ACADEMIC PRESS INC.
111 Fifth Avenue, New York, New York 10003

United Kingdom Edition published by
ACADEMIC PRESS INC. (LONDON) LTD.
Berkeley Square House, London W.1

LIBRARY OF CONGRESS CATALOG CARD NUMBER: 63-14493

PRINTED IN THE UNITED STATES OF AMERICA

Contributors and Presiding Chairmen

Numbers in parentheses indicate the pages on which the authors' contributions begin.

R. ALEXANDER BRINK, Department of Genetics, University of Wisconsin, Madison, Wisconsin. (183)
Chairman: HERBERT STERN, University of Illinois

HARRIS BUSCH, WESLEY C. STARBUCK, ERIC J. SINGH, and TAE SUK RO, Department of Pharmacology, Baylor University College of Medicine, Houston, Texas. (51)
Chairman: HEINRICH URSPRUNG, The Johns Hopkins University

JAN-ERIK EDSTRÖM, Department of Histology, University of Gothenburg, Gothenburg, Sweden. (137)
Chairman: JOSEPH G. GALL, Yale University

T. C. HSU, WERNER SCHMID,* and ELTON STUBBLEFIELD, Department of Biology, The University of Texas M. D. Anderson Hospital and Tumor Institute, Houston, Texas. (83)
Chairman: HANS STITCH, Queens University, Ontario, Canada

E. B. LEWIS, Division of Biology, California Institute of Technology, Pasadena, California. (231)
Chairman: DONALD POULSON, Yale University

CLEMENT L. MARKERT, Department of Biology, The Johns Hopkins University, Baltimore, Maryland. (1)

MONTROSE J. MOSES and JAMES R. COLEMAN, Departments of Anatomy and Zoology, Duke University, Durham, North Carolina. (11)
Chairman: CARL P. SWANSON, The Johns Hopkins University.

DAVID L. NANNEY, Department of Zoology, University of Illinois, Urbana, Illinois. (253)
Chairman: PHILIP GRANT, National Science Foundation

WALTER S. PLAUT and DAVID NASH, Department of Zoology, University of Wisconsin, Madison, Wisconsin. (113)
Chairman: DAVID M. PRESCOTT, University of Colorado Medical School

EDWARD REICH, The Rockefeller Institute, New York, New York. (73)
Chairman: CHARLES THOMAS, The Johns Hopkins University

LIANE B. RUSSELL, Biology Division, Oak Ridge National Laboratory, Oak Ridge, Tennessee. (153)
Chairman: JACK SCHULTZ, The Institute for Cancer Research, Philadelphia, Pennsylvania

---

* Present address: Kinderspital Zürich, Zürich, Switzerland.

72001

OSCAR SCHOTTÉ

Dedication

It is especially fitting that we should meet at Amherst College upon the invitation of Professor Schotté to discuss the role of the chromosomes in development. One of the first rays of light to be shed upon this question, and still one of the brightest, issued from the results of Oscar Schotté's xenoplastic transplantations conducted in the laboratories of Hans Spemann and Ross Harrison. His experiences in those laboratories and in that of Guyénot came in one of the most exciting periods in the history of embryology. It was an excitement that was to prove contagious, for it has been communicated through Professor Schotté with an effervescent enthusiasm to his brood of scientific children.

Twice a speaker before the Growth Society and twice its host, Dr. Schotté has devoted the major part of his scientific career to the discovery and elucidation of the physiological correlates of regeneration in the amphibian limb. He has uncovered a wave of changing competence in the anuran limb during metamorphosis, and physiologically distinct phases in the regeneration process itself. The actions and interactions of nerves, of stress, and of the hormones of the pituitary and adrenal glands have been illumined by his probing scrutiny.

It is in grateful tribute to Professor Schotté and to his contributions as an investigator, his inspiration as a teacher, and his congenial passion for the study of development and growth that this volume is dedicated to him.

"The Growth Society"

June 1964

Contents

The Role of Chromosomes in Development

CLEMENT L. MARKERT

Department of Biology, The Johns Hopkins University, Baltimore, Maryland

After the recognition at the beginning of this century that the chromosomes were repositories of hereditary potentialities there soon came the realization that they must also be fundamentally involved in embryonic development. Adult structures could scarcely be inherited independently of their embryonic precursors from which they arose by a long process of orderly development. Like the adult, each preceding stage in development represents a fully integrated and functioning individual whose characteristics must ultimately be traceable to the inherited endowment present in the fertilized egg. Analysis of the zygote reveals two distinct kinds of inherited material, the chromosomes and the surrounding protoplasm of the nucleus and cytoplasm. It is important to realize that the continuity of life narrows between generations not to the chromosomes but rather to an exceedingly complex cell, the zygote, containing a vast array of substances free in solution or arranged in complex specific patterns in gels, membranes, fibrils, macromolecular aggregates, and organelles, each rivaling in complexity many simple organisms. Only some viruses are reduced to the bare minimum of a strand of DNA linking one generation with the next. And even these must use the complex machinery of living cells in order to reproduce themselves. All higher organisms retain a complex cell as the minimal link between generations.

Although studies in genetics have long traced inherited characteristics to the genes on the chromosomes, it was initially perplexing to note that during cell division each daughter cell received an apparently identical set of chromosomes, so that later differences between individual cells or between the organs they composed could not be ascribed to differences in gross genetic makeup. Several explanations have been offered for the diversification and specialization of cells occurring during development.

1

(1) Although the chromosome sets seem identical in each cell of a metazoan, perhaps 5 or 10% of the genes might be destroyed in each cell, enough to account for the differences between cells without being microscopically visible. On this view, cellular differentiation would be based upon a selective loss of parts of the genome, and indeed a few early cytological studies, e.g., of *Ascaris,* seemed to point to such a mechanism. Studies of regeneration, dedifferentiation, and nuclear transplantation, however, have shown that irreparable loss of parts of the genome, even very small parts, cannot be a general explanation for cellular differentiation. (2) A more likely mechanism is suggested by the observation that the cytoplasm of zygotes is typically very heterogeneous, and daughter cells receive qualitatively different aliquots of this cytoplasm during cell division. The differences in this cytoplasm have been advanced as the essential condition for cellular diversification, and indeed they are. Many analyses over several decades have repeatedly demonstrated that the cytoplasmic inheritance of a cell can determine its fate. (3) Another view is to suppose that the chromosomes undergo some programmed change which is unrelated to their protoplasmic milieu and which enables them to specify the constellation of properties characterizing each adult cell. Such chromosomal autonomy is excluded however by the results of experimental transplantation of cells from one area of a developing embryo to another area. When transplanted at a sufficiently early stage, such cells develop characteristics suitable to their new location and quite different from those they would have acquired if not transplanted. Such experiments demonstrate the dependence of differentiation on the cellular environment and clearly reveal the genome of the cell to be in a dependent, responding position rather than to be the autonomous director of the cell's activities.

It seems obvious that any acceptable explanation for cellular differentiation must involve some mechanism by which the function of the genome is, in effect, regulated by the surrounding protoplasmic environment. Our current understanding of molecular biology enables us to recognize several steps from the gene to terminal character, any one of which might be subject to regulation in such a way as to produce the specialized properties of adult cells. These properties commonly stem from the presence in the cells of particular proteins in characteristic relative quantities. The synthesis of a protein might be regulated by controlling the synthesis of ribonucleic acid (RNA) at the level of chromosomal deoxyribonucleic acid (DNA) or by controlling the activity of the various types of RNA involved in the synthesis of protein; the function of protein as an enzyme, for example, is further subject to a variety of metabolic controls.

For many years the prevailing view was that genes were active all the time in each cell with diversification occurring at some later step. In contemporary molecular terms this would mean that the initial messenger RNA population would be the same in all cells. This we now know is not true. Although regulatory mechanisms may operate at many levels of cellular organization, certainly one of the most important operates at the level of the gene itself. Moreover, these regulatory mechanisms must determine not only which genes are to function but to what degree as well. Most investigations on gene regulation have made use of bacteria or other microorganisms, and much useful information has been obtained, some of it no doubt applicable to higher organisms as well. There are, however, fundamental differences in the biological expectations of gene regulation in bacteria and in metazoa. These differences stem from requirements of immediacy, stability, and durability. The whole bacterium responds to environmental conditions in an immediately adaptive fashion through reversible gene action that displays great sensitivity to transient stimuli. By contrast, gene regulation during the development of higher organisms involves persistent responses to transient stimuli. Genes are turned on that will continue to function for many years in environments quite different from the one that turned the genes on in the first place. Moreover, these genes may be turned on in only a few cells. In all other cells they are turned off throughout the life of the organism.

The regulation of genes in metazoans seems quite different from what we have come to expect in bacteria. This difference in gene behavior is paralleled by and quite possibly attributable to the quite different organization of the genetic material into chromosomes. Although we speak of bacterial "chromosomes," these bear little resemblance to chromosomes of higher organisms. They do have in common the DNA which encodes their genetic potentialities, but bacterial DNA is essentially naked and free in the protoplasm, exposed to the immediate chemical environment, and responsive to fluctuating metabolic conditions. Metazoan DNA, on the other hand, is part of a complex chromosome containing large amounts of several varieties of proteins as well as other less abundant substances. In addition, it is relatively isolated within the nucleus from the larger part of the cell that is outside in the cytoplasm.

Before restricting our attention to the chromosomes it is important to note that all hereditary potentialities may not reside in the chromosomes. There are two views of the relationship of genes to cell structures as mediated by proteins. One holds that the primary structure of proteins—the linear sequence of amino acids composing them—determines all subsequent properties, secondary, tertiary, and quaternary structure, and through these the physiological activity of the molecules and their assemblage into larger aggregates and cell organelles. Moreover, all other organic molecules are synthesized in the organism through the activity of these proteins. This view, then, relegates the complex organization so evident in living systems to a purely derivative position. Given the genes and the environment in which they can function, the organism will eventually be formed completely. The proper environment for the genes is considered to be the product of the preceding generation of genes; so, in effect, the genes are everything. Supporters of this view give a resounding "yes" to the question paraphrased from Harvey *"Omne vivum E DNA?"*

The alternative view, while acknowledging the central role of DNA as a code for protein, regards the cell as the smallest unit of life and presumes that the cell contains arrangements of parts that cannot be directly or completely derived from the activity of DNA. Specifically, the presence of some of the complex membranes or organelles may be necessary in order that more of the same can be made out of the macromolecules synthesized under the aegis of DNA. Such structures may act as essential templates for the assemblage of their constituents and, once formed, would be self-perpetuating. If so, historical accidents which led to their initial formation would have thenceforth been encoded in the structures themselves rather than in DNA. The best examples have been presented by Sonneborn (1964) in his studies of the ciliary patterns and external organelles, such as the mouth and anus, of *Paramecia*. Mitochondria and plastids are also candidates for self-replicating structures not under the direct control of DNA, although some evidence for the presence of DNA in these structures casts doubt on their autonomy.

Though one may question that the chromosomes are the source of all that is significant in the organism, no one can deny their central role both in governing the finished characteristics of the organism and in specifying the multitude of steps along the way from the fertilized egg. Accordingly, this symposium was organized to focus attention on the structure and function of chromosomes during development.

Despite decades of cytological observations the structure of the chromosome is still poorly understood, although we can feel some confidence concerning our knowledge of the major chemical constituents. In the introductory paper of the symposium Moses and Coleman summarized the evidence on the comparative morphology of chromosomes particularly as revealed by the electron microscope. A morphological common denominator of chromosomes is a microfibril about 100 Å in diameter. This fibril is composed of DNA and protein. The role of the DNA is clear, but the function of the protein component is still not resolved. Histones, rich in lysine and aginine, are always present on the DNA and have been the most extensively studied of the chromosomal proteins—because of ease of isolation and characterization and because of the expectation that they may play a key role in regulating the function of DNA. It seems clear that histones of one variety or another can inhibit DNA-dependent RNA synthesis, but this capacity does not make them gene regulators during development. In fact, genes appear to be inactive during early cleavage stages and only become active later in development after the appearance of acidic proteins on the chromosomes (cf. chapter by Busch *et al.*). This suggests that the histone inhibition of DNA heterosynthetic activities may be removed through the activity of a more acidic type protein; but these proteins have been little studied and, consequently, there are few constraints on speculation.

The work of Edstrom clearly demonstrates that inactive genes cannot be due to the presence of RNA, for only a small minority of the bands on dipteran salivary gland chromosomes contain any RNA and these appear to be the active regions. Furthermore, RNA is absent from the chromosomes of sperm, that must be almost completely inactive. When RNA does appear, it probably is one of the three kinds of recognized RNA—mRNA, tRNA, or rRNA—any one of which would indicate the activation of DNA rather than its inhibition. Moreover, since RNA is an immediate product of gene function, it does not seem to be a logical contender for the role of gene activator. Both the repression and derepression of gene function appear to involve proteins—probably histones to repress and acidic proteins to derepress or activate.

The nature of the combination between DNA and various kinds of protein is not clear, although it seems probable that the histones combine through salt linkages between their arginine and lysine amino groups and the phosphate groups of DNA. Little is known of the combination between acidic proteins and DNA and essentially nothing as to what might underlie the apparent specificity of such combinations. However, the work of Markert and Ursprung (1963), Ursprung and Markert (1963), and Kimmel (1964) on the effects of proteins injected into frog eggs demonstrates some affinity between these nonhistone proteins and the chromosomes. In their experiments abnormal combinations presumably occurred between injected protein and DNA leading to failure of normal replication together with the production of breaks in the chromosomes. In any event, the chromosomes were not able to fulfill their normal roles at the time of gastrulation as shown by the cessation of further embryonic development. Several lines of evidence point to gastrulation as the time in embryonic life when genes first become active and essential for further development. Any interference with the normal programming of gene function at that time would probably lead to serious abnormalities or, as in the cited experiments, to complete cessation of development. Partly in an effort to gain insight into the combining properties of DNA with protein, Reich has carried out an extensive examination of the combination of actinomycin with DNA. This peptide interferes with the synthesis of mRNA through an inhibitory combination with DNA. Unfortunately, one of the limitations in applying an analysis of actinomycin behavior to gene regulation is that it inhibits mRNA synthesis. What is needed is a molecule that will stimulate RNA synthesis, i.e., to release the DNA from its normally inhibited state. Of course, the more we know about the chemical basis of inhibition the more likely we are to gain insight into possible mechanisms of stimulation.

Both Hsu and co-workers and Plaut analyzed the discontinuous labeling of DNA with tritiated thymidine during cell division. They demonstrated that the chromosome is not in a uniform state from one end to the other, nor does it replicate as if it were simply a very large and very long bacterial "chromosome." Rather the chromosome behaves as if it consisted of a longitudinal series of linked DNA molecules, each replicating independently. The replication, however, seems to follow a consistent pattern since the same regions on homologous chromosomes replicate synchronously, thus pointing toward control mechanisms affecting the same genes alike even though on different chromosomes.

Perhaps the most significant point to be gained from these observations is that the physical state of the chromosome may regulate gene function. During the intermitotic period when genes are functioning and RNA is being synthesized (see chapters by Edstrom and Hsu *et al.*) some parts of the chromosomes remain condensed or tightly coiled. These heteropycnotic regions are inactive in transcribing the DNA code to RNA and lag behind in the synthesis of DNA as the time for cell division approaches. Although molecular events must underlie gene regulation, it is apparent that these events may be implemented by changes in the steric conformation of the chromosome, thus regulating its ability to function as a template both for RNA and for DNA synthesis. The cytologically evident conformational changes in the chromosomes do not permit any estimate as to what fraction of the genome may be inactive at any one time. Several lines of evidence (Hoyer *et al.*, 1964), however, point to the conclusion that only a small part of the genome of any cell is functional at any one time (cf. also Edstrom). Thus the normal state of the gene appears to be one of inactivity, probably because of its combination with histone even though this is not evident as heteropycnosis. Certainly many genes, perhaps nearly all, are inactive in the early cleavage stages of an embryo. Progressive changes in the chromosomal environment eventually turn on certain genes in the proper sequence. These newly functioning genes synthesize products which lead to the activation of additional genes and perhaps also to the inhibition of some of those previously functioning; such a dynamic cyclical interplay between genes and environment is logically adequate as a mechanism for driving the cell along the pathway of differentiation. Once specialized adult status is reached cells generally exhibit great stability in their differentiated characteristics, but this stability may only reflect the constancy of the cellular environment. When removed from their normal environment, as when transplanted to culture, cells commonly lose many of their specialized characteristics, particularly after several division cycles have been completed. Thus the differentiated state of the chromosomes is ultimately dependent upon a stable protoplasmic environment. The degree and immediacy of this dependence must, however, vary widely from one chromosomal region to another. Perhaps the clearest and most conspicuous example is provided by the mammalian X chromosome (see chapter by Russell). In the female embryo, one of the two X chromosomes in most cells soon becomes heteropycnotic and thereafter through succeeding cell generations gives rise only to additional heteropycnotic chromosomes. The conformational state of the chromosome and its descendants remains fixed even though other properties of the cells change enormously. Here the regulatory mechanisms are not directed at each individual gene separately but at large sections of the X chromosome. A wave of inhibition seems to spread along the chromosome, or in the reciprocal view a wave of activation may spread in the opposite direction. Since additional X chromosomes in a cell do not become active and since the initial condition is one of inactivity, the hypothesis most consistent with the general view expressed here makes the partial activation of one X chromosome the positive event in the cell. Whatever molecular events may be involved, they appear sufficient from a quantitative view to act on only one chromosome; all others remain inactive.

Perhaps most significant is the observation that the control, whether activation or inhibition, acts at the chromosomal rather than at the gene level. Whether a gene functions or not depends upon its location in the X chromosome and not upon its own characteristics. Translocated to an autosome, it functions, or translocated from an autosome to an appropriate part of the X chromosome, it is inhibited from functioning.

In many ways this behavior of the X chromosome resembles variegated position effect. Some change in the chromosome, spreading along it to varying degrees, alters the function of the genes encountered. This change is evident in the heteropycnotic character of the inactive region which involves a physical change in the conformation of the chromosome and possibly also extensive chemical changes. That the functioning of the genes may be affected by adjacent regions of the chromosome may also be illustrated in the paper by Brink on paramutation at the R locus in maize. This puzzling phenomenon results from a persistent modification of gene behavior as a consequence of the temporary presence of a chromosome bearing alternate alleles. Although an explanation in molecular terms cannot be provided yet, it is obvious that one region of a chromosome must be influencing another. How far such influences may spread seems to follow no general rule. *Cis-trans* arrangements are important in the bithorax mutants of *Drosophila* studied by Lewis, but many degrees of interdependence between chromosomal regions have been established in studies of different organisms. The bithorax genes seem to act as repressors of alternate systems of cellular differentiation, but this apparent specific repression may only reflect the canalization of development arising out of mutual exclusion in the activation of sets of genes.

A similar all-or-none choice in gene activation is illustrated during nuclear differentiation of ciliates (see chapter by Nanney). The macronuclei of these organisms are composed of many subnuclei, the properties of which become fixed at a precise time in the life of the organism. This fixation involves the activation of one of the alleles in each subnucleus coincident with a repression of the alternate allele.

This genetic behavior during nuclear differentiation emphasizes a basic and common characteristic of cellular differentiation, i.e., its all-or-none character. The cell types represented in a complex metazoan like ourselves do not compose a continuous spectrum ranging from one type through fine gradations to an alternate type. Rather each cell type falls into a clearly recognizable discrete category sharply set off from other cell types. This behavior seems to imply, on a genetic level, that as one set of genes is turned on another set is, through a closely linked process, turned off. The molecular and chromosomal basis of this mutual exclusion may prove to be more accessible to investigation in ciliates than in metazoan cells, but we must be cautious in extrapolating from ciliates to man. The phenomenon may be similar only superficially and may stem from quite different molecular events.

Although the symposium presented an interesting, and even exciting, analysis of the structure and function of chromosomes in a wide variety of organisms, it was nevertheless very clear that their role in development cannot yet be described except in vague and general terms. To be sure, most evidence now available points directly at differential gene function as the primary underlying cause of cellular differentiation. One may reasonably expect that an understanding of the molecular basis for regulating gene function, for turning them on or off, will emerge from a physicochemical analysis of chromosomes. At least this field of investigation, at present so little populated by investigators, looks exceedingly attractive and promises to reward the perceptive and diligent investigator with deep insights into the central problem of contemporary experimental biology—the molecular basis of cellular differentiation.

REFERENCES

HOYER, B. H., McCARTHY, B. J., AND BOLTON, E. T. (1964). A molecular approach in the systematics of higher organisms. *Science* **144**, 959-967.

KIMMEL, D. L., JR. (1964). Embryonic development and chromosome complements of protein-injected and of hybrid amphibian embryos. Ph.D. thesis, Johns Hopkins Univ., Baltimore, Maryland.

MARKERT, C. L., AND URSPRUNG, H. (1963). Production of replicable persistent changes in zygote chromosomes of *Rana pipiens* by injected proteins from adult nuclei. *Develop. Biol.* **7**, 560-577.

SONNEBORN, T. M. (1964). The differentiation of cells. *Proc. Natl. Acad. Sci. U. S.* **51**, 915-929.

URSPRUNG, H., AND MARKERT, C. L. (1963). Chromosome complements of *Rana pipiens* embryos developing from eggs injected with protein from adult liver cells. *Develop. Biol.* **8**, 309-321.

Structural Patterns and the Functional Organization of Chromosomes

MONTROSE J. MOSES
AND JAMES R. COLEMAN

Departments of Anatomy and Zoology, Duke University, Durham, North Carolina

Over the past 10 years the acuity of the cytologist's understanding of chromosome structure and function has been greatly enhanced by rapid advances in knowledge of the molecular organization of genetic systems. Largely because of the essentially simple, macromolecular nature of the more elemental "chromosomes" of bacteria and viruses, their functional mechanics are rapidly being recognized as those of the double-helix deoxyribonucleic acid (DNA) molecule. But, a sizeable gap exists between the more complex and diversified "classic" chromosomes of higher animal and plant forms (*eukaryotes* of Ris and Chandler, 1963) and the DNA molecule that must be the ultimate common denominator of all primary genetic systems. It is a gap not only of dimensions, but also one involving chromosome-associated ribonucleic acid (RNA) and protein, together with considerable morphological variety and structural complexity. Whatever the differences, and however simple or complex the structures in which reside the primary genetic information, the presence of both DNA and the basic mechanisms for fulfilling genetic functions must be common to all of them.

The hereditary apparatus, be it DNA or complex chromosome, must first be a repository in which the genetic information is conserved and maintained in a fixed sequential order; second, it must serve as a replicator by which a precise duplicate of a gene thread is synthesized and segregated for transmission to the next cell generation; third, it must serve as a transcriber by which the genetic message may be read as many times as necessary for controlling the metabolic activities of the cell through the synthesis of specific proteins; and finally, it must provide a system in which a limited amount of variation may occur.

The way in which the DNA molecule accommodates these responsibilities is becoming understood from studies on genetic mechanisms at the molecular level largely in viruses and bacteria (*protokaryotes*—Ris and Chandler, 1963). The genetic information is sequestered in the long, double-stranded molecule by the linear sequence of complementary purine and pyrimidine base pairs, probably coded in triplets. During replication, the two strands of the molecule separate and new complementary strands are produced along the separating strands. The old strands serve as matrices for the new strands, and thus, during replication, complementary strands are paired, insuring their stability. From this, two identical hybrid molecules (each half old and half new—but each with a different "new" strand) are formed and are physically separate (semiconservative replication). The forces responsible for complete segregation and distribution to daughter cells are probably not inherent in the DNA molecule. It is not known how this occurs in protokaryotes. As predicted by Crick (1958), the genetic message is transcribed to a less permanent and expendable "messenger" strand of RNA which in turn is assembled as a complementary strand on one of the DNA strands. The latter thus serves as a message template. The message template strand is thus left undisturbed and free to synthesize more RNA messages. Finally, genetic variation occurs either through intra- or intermolecular rearrangement. In one sense such variations may be called errors, since they represent failures to maintain precisely the original order; but they nevertheless represent the foundation on which genetic diversity and evolution ultimately rest. The simplest mutation might be a change in one amino acid resulting from a substitution of one base for another in the DNA template. Other variations may result from loss or gain of one or several bases, or from deletions, repetitions, and exchanges of entire segments of the molecule. Interstrand exchanges may occur between like single chains of immediately adjacent duplex molecules. If these strands happen to differ slightly in their genetic message, the exchange will effect a new combination of sequential characters. This is apparently the basis of genetic recombination and of crossing-over in meiosis in higher forms.

This discussion will be concerned mainly with the functional aspects of chromosomes of eukaryotes. In these forms, a single chromosome is a unit genetic structure and may be composed of many thousand molecules of DNA. Much of the complexity of the chromosome is undoubtedly the consequence of adaptation for marshaling such a bulky complement of genetic material.

It appears likely that the varied morphological transitions of the chromosome are structural accommodations for particular functional states. This is most obvious, for example, in the gross variations of the chromosome during the mitotic cycle: in the unfolded state at interphase for transcription and replication, and in the condensed state at metaphase and anaphase for preservation and segregation. Other more specialized morphological states serve more specialized functions, as exemplified by lampbrush and polytene chromosomes. Whatever the variations, and the functions they serve, there must be a single underlying structural scheme which serves to handle large amounts of DNA during all genetic functions. The involved secondary and tertiary chromosomal structures that may be superimposed upon the primary pattern undoubtedly serve not only to adapt the unwieldy genetic complex of DNA to its functional activities, but also to integrate these activities with the demands of the cell. The unique puffing patterns of the polytene chromosomes of dipteran larvae (Beermann, 1959, 1963), for example, may be more than a device for exposing a maximum amount of particular template material and for facilitating the production of an abundance of selected gene product (messenger material). It probably also serves as a means for exposing particular genetic sites in response to the demands of the cellular environment and thus for providing a quantity of specific messenger to govern production of a specific protein, which in turn shifts the metabolic balance of the cell. It is now well recognized that cellular differentiation may depend largely on a sequence of such feedback cycles. Fortunately, in the dipteran larvae, the cytological aspects happen to be exaggerated and highly specialized.

Whatever the fundamental organizational pattern of the chromosome or of chromosomal DNA may be, it is obscured by the large size and structural complexities of the chromosome attending its functional differentiations. So far, the higher resolution of the electron microscope has not yielded an unequivocal picture of the pattern. But, from the present trend of comparative cytological studies of the chromosome in its various functional states there should eventually come recognition and proof of the underlying common organizational scheme.

Two outstanding cases of extreme chromosomal differentiation have lent themselves to very promising cytological studies of transcriber function: these, of course, are the lampbrush chromosomes of amphibia and the afore mentioned dipteran polytene chromosomes. Both have been elegantly discussed before this group in recent years; the former by Gall (1963) and the latter by Beermann (1959; see also the more recent survey, 1963). We would therefore like to consider some comparative morphological aspects of the chromosome in three other functional conditions: in replication, as repository, and in recombination.

Replication

Any hypothetical plan of chromosome organization has restrictions imposed on it by previous experimental observations. In particular, the autoradiographic analyses of chromosomal DNA replication that follow the distribution of tritium-labeled thymidine (H^3-TDN) in chromosomes in successive cell cycles (see summary and references in Taylor, 1963) have set forth clearly defined requirements. Two conclusions have emerged: (1) The DNA of an unreplicated chromosome is organized in two side by side units along the length of the chromosome. (2) One DNA unit differs from its sister in that it is restricted from physically exchanging with it (in the sense of breakage and recombination), but it may do so with its like daughter unit. Thus, the chromosome, at least with respect to its DNA, behaves as though it were a giant DNA molecule (double helix). Taylor has extended this hypothesis by using it as the basis for constructing a model of the chromosome (after Freese, 1958) which is essentially a long chain of DNA double helices held together with hypothetical linkers. This is indeed the simplest hypothesis, and in many ways the most attractive, but the data do not exclude the possibility of side by side multiple molecular strands of DNA, provided that a mechanism is invoked for holding them together and ordering them so that they behave as single units (Steffensen, 1961). Taylor's observations seem firmly established at this point, although they have been subject to criticism on the basis of the experimental design in which colchicine, which was used to keep the chromosomal products of replication together in one cell, may have affected the distribution of label (LaCour and Pelc, 1958; see discussion in Lima-de-Faria, 1962). But, the subsequent experiments of Woods and Shairer (1959) and of Prescott and Bender (1963) confirm Taylor's essential observations.

It is now also apparent that DNA replication, which occurs over several hours during the synthesis (S) period of interphase, does not occur simultaneously at all loci in the nucleus. In fact, replication is markedly asynchronous along and among the chromosomes and, indeed, even between homologous chromosomes (summary in Lima-de-Faria, 1962). Lima-de-Faria (1959; see also Taylor, 1958), for example, observed that the heterochromatin of grasshopper spermatogonia replicates at the end of the S period. It is also apparent that replication does not necessarily proceed sequentially along the chromosome, nor does it necessarily occur at the same rate in different loci. In one locus, replication may be complete in a very short period of time, whereas in another, it appears to occur almost throughout the entire S period. From a purely pragmatic point of view, the pattern of asynchrony offers a unique opportunity to examine the distribution of chromosomal strands in interphase.

In cultured HeLa cells labeled with a 2-minute pulse of tritiated thymidine (H^3-TDN; 25 mC per milliliter) three kinds of distribution of label were observed in light microscope autoradiographs (Moses, 1964a). Grains were either arranged around the periphery of the nucleus, scattered throughout the nucleus, or arranged as chains or spokes radiating from the central nucleolus. These evidently represent three phases of asynchronous replication, although we do not yet know which comes first. After exposure for 30 minutes, or approximately one-tenth of the S period, perinuclear and perinucleolar labeling is greatly enhanced. Distribution of label after a 2-minute pulse followed by 30 minutes in cold thymidine resembles that after the 2-minute pulse alone, except that the label is heavier, indicating that there is a labeled precursor pool that is not diluted by cold thymidine. Localization of grains in electron microscopic autoradiographs (EM-ARGs) parallel those observed in the light microscope. It may be added parenthetically that appreciable cytoplasmic incorporation has also been observed, which may represent thymidine precursor being transported to the nucleus (Moses *et al.,* 1962; Moses, 1964a), and also conceivably cytoplasmic DNA.

In EM-ARGs of cells exposed to H^3-thymidine for 30 minutes and allowed to be in contact with the emulsion for sufficient lengths of time, the intense replication activity of specific areas is apparent (Figs. 1 and 2). Such "hotspots" may be followed in serial sections (Fig. 1) and appear to be knots of activity usually associated with dense clumps of chromatin, rather than chains or threads. Such areas are often, though not always, apt to be associated with the nuclear envelope. There is nothing about their organization that readily distinguishes them from similar areas which are not labeled.

The question of whether there is a characteristic morphology associated with DNA replication can, however, be approached with higher EM-ARG resolution by either underdevelopment of the exposed silver grain (Moses, 1964a) or by the use of physical developer (Caro and Van Tubergen, 1962). A closer approximation to the point of origin of the tritium β-particle in the section may be arrived at in this manner. Under the

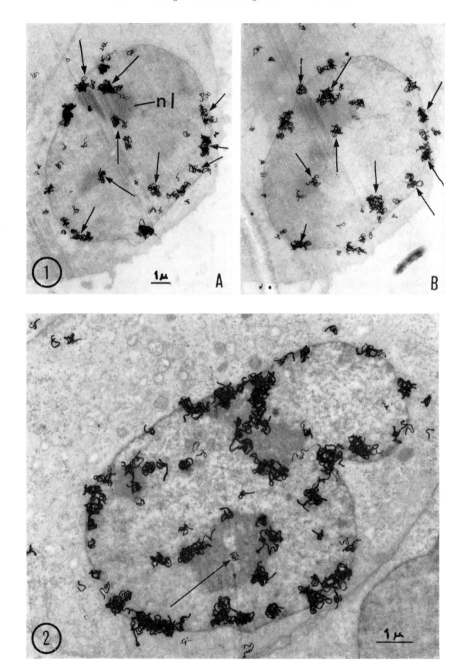

best conditions, Caro (1962) estimates this resolution to be of the order of 100 mμ. Using such methods, it is apparent first that the distribution of grains in the nucleus parallels that seen after coarse development. Second, it is observed that grains are restricted from certain characteristic areas, the composition of which is not known, but which are usually characterized by an abundance of small granules. It is also obvious that grains are in close contact with microfibrillar structures (Figs. 3 and 4). This observation has been noted before (Revel and Hay, 1961; Hay and Revel, 1963). It is not surprising in view of the indirect evidence that the microfibrils contain DNA (Moses and Lafontaine, 1961; see also Dales, 1960). On the other hand, the nucleus is mainly filled with microfibrils, and there are few areas in which a grain could lie that are not microfibrillar.

One consistent observation does seem to be emerging from our studies so far. The punctate grains, of which two or even three may arise from a single crystal, appear very often to be localized over relatively clear areas of the nucleoplasm (Fig. 3). Occasionally, in some nuclei the grains tend to be localized over the dense fibrillar masses bordering the clear areas. But, as a qualitative observation, it seems that a preponderance of the grains are in contact either with what might be called the border of the fibrillar masses or with spaces outside of them. None of these areas is

---

Fig. 1.   Electron microscopic autoradiographs of two serial sections of HeLa cell exposed to H3-thymidine for 30 minutes. DNA (1 mg per milliliter) was present during the incubation in an effort to elevate cytoplasmic incorporation, but no significant difference in either localization or distribution of grains attributable to the DNA was noted. The grains lie predominantly around the periphery of the nucleus; clusters are also found near the edge of the nucleolus (nl). Heavy clusters of silver grains indicate relatively high concentrations of incorporated thymidine. In a number of instances such areas of active DNA synthesis, or "hot spots," can be followed from one section to the next (arrows) indicating that replication is occurring in a relatively large structure included in both sections. A number of grains can be seen scattered in the cytoplasm. The knife marks may be used as markers to identify comparable replicating areas in the two sections. Sections stained with uranyl acetate; coated with Ilford L-4 emulsion, exposed 2 months, and developed in Microdol-X.

Fig. 2.   Electron microscopic autoradiograph of HeLa cell nucleus as in Fig. 1. Areas of very active synthesis around the nuclear periphery are indicated by dense clusters of grains. Such areas are also associated with the periphery of the nucleolus. There are a few grains that are not associated with one or the other of these areas. That some replication is occurring in the internum of the nucleolus is indicated by the presence of a grain over a clear area in the center of the largest nucleolus (arrow). Note also cytoplasmic incorporation. Autoradiograph as in Fig. 1.

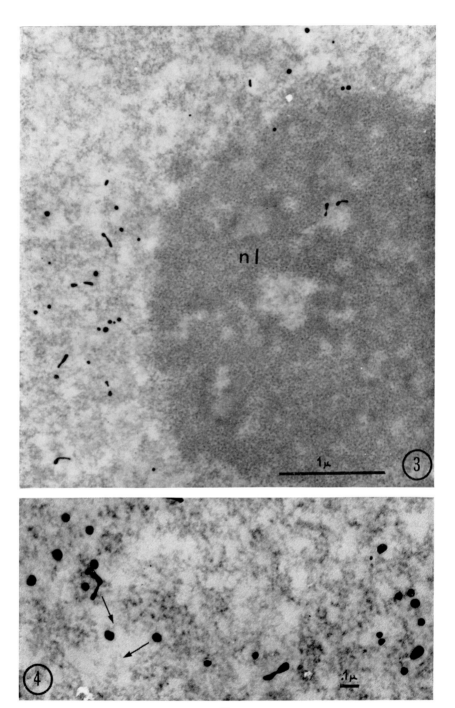

nl

1μ

③

④

.1μ

completely free of fibrils; usually a number of fine filaments, more attenuated and less dense than those in the masses, are seen to occupy these regions (Fig. 4). Although a precise measurement has not yet been possible, the finer filaments have a thickness of the order of 50 Å or less (within the radius of resolution of 100 mμ around each silver grain, several such fibrils can usually be observed). On the other hand, grains have not yet been observed over the regions that contain small particles, whether these be arranged as separate granules or accumulated adjacent to the fibrillar masses. Silver grains are occasionally found over the nucleolus. Where this structure is involved, grains are usually localized near the periphery. When they are found over the nucleolus, they are often, though not always, associated with clear patches in which fine filaments may again be seen (Fig. 3). In all likelihood this represents the nucleolar associated chromatin, which, in some forms may be clearly seen as Feulgen-positive fingers extending into the nucleolus (e.g., Lafontaine and Chouinard, 1963, in *Vicia*). Such an attenuated strand of chromatin is not apt to be seen as a Feulgen-positive structure in the light microscope.

Our observations so far on the distribution of punctate grains suggest that replication is mainly associated with fibrils that are of a smaller dimension than the 100–200 Å ones associated with the bulk of the nuclear chromatin. If replication is occurring preferentially in these fine strands, then the grains over the masses could be due to peripheral strands that replicated early during the 30-minute exposure to H³-TDN and then migrated inward to the chromatin mass to assume some other function. One could then assume that the thicker strands associated with,

---

FIG. 3. Electron microscopic autoradiograph of a portion of a HeLa cell nucleus exposed to H³-thymidine for 30 minutes as in Figs. 1 and 2. This autoradiograph was prepared by exposing the emulsion (Ilford L-4) to the section for 2 months and then developing with a physical developer (Caro and van Tubergen, 1962). Each silver grain is represented by a punctate or apostrophe-like grain. Each exposed halide crystal may produce one, two, or three such grains. The resolution of such a preparation is estimated to be better than 0.15 μ. Note that a majority of the grains lie over "clear" patches, and many of them are adjacent to the denser fibrillar masses, but do not actually lie on them. Two grains are found over the nucleolus, again associated with a clear patch in which fine fibrillar material may be discerned. It is assumed that this represents replicating DNA in part of the chromosome surrounded by nucleolar material.

FIG. 4. Higher magnification of an area of the nucleus similar to that shown in Fig. 3. Note again that most of the grains lie over clear patches or are adjacent to the dense fibrillar masses. Very fine microfibrils may be seen traversing the clear areas, and in some cases they lie directly under the grains (arrows).

and possibly coated with other material, are engaged in different functions and are not replicating.

The replication of DNA in *Euplotes* may well have a bearing on these observations. Replication is not homogeneous throughout the elongate, crescent-shaped macronucleus, but occurs instead in two transverse bands which move from the opposite ends toward the center (Gall, 1959; Prescott and Kimball, 1961). A marked chemical and structural reorganization occurs in these bands. Prior to the beginning of replication, RNA (Prescott and Kimball, 1961) is lost. Replication of both DNA and histone appears to occur simultaneously. Electron microscopy studies (Fauré-Fremiet *et al.*, 1957; Roth, 1957) show that the replication band is composed largely of fine fibrillar material, whereas the pre- and post-replication areas are composed of thicker strands and granular material. After replication, RNA incorporation again occurs. A similar sequence may ensue in HeLa nuclei, in areas where replication is occurring. Regions of chromatin that may be engaged in transcriber functions may lose associated material just prior to replication. Following replication, which may be presumed to occur at the periphery of the mass, the other processes may resume with the fibrils reacquiring their functional accessories. This hypothesis may be tested using shorter pulses of H^3-TDN and by following these with chases of cold TDN. Such experiments are now in progress.

Repository Function

One biological structure that has been especially adapted and preserved in evolution to conserve the genetic message of eukaryotes is the sperm cell. The entire cell is reduced to the barest minimum of highly efficient structure for transmission of the genome intact for fertilization of the ovum. The extremely compact nucleus contains the entire chromosome complement packaged in such a way that it is metabolically inert and evidently protected from external damage. In a sense, the differentiation of the sperm cell is a terminal one, the only component to be perpetuated being the genetic elements. After fertilization, nucleoprotein structures emerge that are capable of resuming their morphological and functional characteristics. It is to be expected that in such a reduced elemental state, one should observe the essential structural organization of the chromosome. But the nucleus of the mature sperm is so compact that it is not amenable to simple morphological observation. With one exception, most of the cytological information about the organization of chromosomes in the sperm has come from studies of the stages of differentiation.

In spermateleosis a general pattern of change has been observed, especially in the nucleus. Profound alterations in the nucleoprotein content occur in the spermatid nucleus. Protein is gradually lost together with RNA, and generally there is either a conversion or replacement of

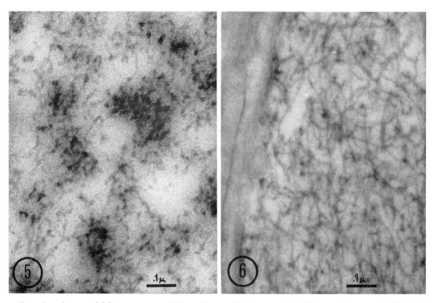

Fig. 5. Area within a spermatid nucleus of the crayfish *Procambarus clarki* fixed in formaldehyde. Dense clusters of microfibrils measuring approximately 100 Å fill this nucleus from which an appreciable amount of accessory material may be assumed to have been lost.

Fig. 6. Nuclear region of a late spermatid of a rat. (Although the animal was treated with estrogen for 11 days for other reasons, the microfibrillar structure is not atypical.) Microfibrils of various thicknesses and densities ranging from 40 to 100 Å may be seen.

histone to produce arginine-rich basic protein associated with the DNA. At the same time, structural changes are also marked. The nuclear contents become denser in both the light and electron microscope and fibrils of the order of 100 Å or less become evident (Fig. 5). In most forms an elongation of the nucleus occurs; as it progresses, smaller (approximately 50 Å) fibrils appear (Fig. 6). Ris (1962) believes that one 100 Å fibril splits to give rise to two of the finer ones. He compares these with nucleoprotamine fibers isolated from trout sperm and shows that 40 Å fibrils tend to associate in pairs to form 100 Å fibrils.

In some cases, a remarkable degree of order is associated with the terminal changes in the spermatid. In certain mollusks and insects elongation is accompanied by a parallel alignment of the microfibrils along the long axis (Grassé *et al.*, 1956; Gibbons and Bradfield, 1957; Rebhun, 1957; Dass and Ris, 1958; Gall and Bjork, 1958; Kaye, 1962; Ris, 1962). The parallel fibrils tend to fuse and arrange themselves in convoluted curtains of honeycomb-like tubules, the spaces between which eventually occlude and finally disappear completely from view as the sperm matures. Studies with polarized light, however, have indicated that there is still a precise orientation of nucleic acid molecules in certain mature sperm (Caspersson, 1940).

The obvious question that arises concerns the way in which the chromosomes are arranged: Are they in tandem, side by side, coiled, or in some other configuration? And what is the pattern of organization of the DNA? A clue to the answer comes from very beautiful observations by Inoué and Sato (1962) with polarized ultraviolet light on the sperm head of the cave cricket. The results indicate that the chromosomes are arranged in tandem, one behind the other in a precise order, and that they are coiled in a spiral. The cave cricket, incidentally, is a form in which the parallel organization of microfibrils occurs during sperm elongation. Recently, Taylor (1964) has confirmed the tandem arrangement in chromosomes of the grasshopper. Sperm nuclei, which are derived from spermatogonia labeled briefly with H^3-TDN, at a time when only the heterochromatic X chromosome (the last to replicate) was labeled, show autoradiographic labeling primarily over one segment along the mature sperm nucleus. Conversely, gonial cells in which most of the chromosomes except the heterochromatic X had incorporated label give rise to sperm which show autoradiographic grains over all but the short length of sperm that apparently represents the X. Whether this arrangement of chromosomes is common to sperm from a wider variety of species has not yet been determined. One other instance, however, is worth noting.

The first clear-cut case of linear alignment of chromosomes in the sperm was reported by Hughes-Schrader (1946) in a study of spermiogenesis in iceryine coccids. In the three species studied, the usual diversifications of extranuclear elements to form flagellum, acrosome, and other accessory apparatus are absent, while the nucleus distinguishes itself in a rather unusual way. During spermateleosis in *Steatococcus tuberculatus*, for example, a papilla is formed at one side of the spermatid nucleus which extends and, together with a cytoplasmic cap, protrudes to form a tube that gradually grows away from the body of the spermatid. The haploid chromosome number in *Steatococcus* is two, and as the papilla forms, both chromosomes emerge from the nucleus proper and pass into the tube, aligned end to end with the shorter of the two chromosomes always in the lead. Eventually, the sperm, consisting now only of a cytoplasmic sheath and the two Feulgen-positive chromosomes still aligned in tandem, breaks away from the body of the spermatid, leaving behind intact Feulgen-negative nuclei. During the elongation of the sperm, the chromosomes also extend, but maintain their relative lengths, and undergo a series of despiralizations and spiralizations, resulting in a mature sperm in which the chromosomal material is extended but spiraled. During the latter stages of development, thirty-two sperm align and become organized into bundles enclosed by a cellular sheath. The bundle itself appears to be coiled, reflecting the spiralization of the individual sperm that it contains. The tightly spiraled nature of the chromosome bundles can be seen by examining living bundles with polarized light (Fig. 7). Nebel (1957) reported briefly on an electron microscope examination of *Steatococcus* sperm. He demonstrated that the individual sperm consists of a sheath of "cytoplasmic tubules" each 150–200 Å in diameter surrounding a dense central core said to correspond to the chromosomal material. In this core he reported about sixty-four microfibrils, the finest of which appeared to measure 30–40 Å. From this he concluded that the basic subunit of the chromosome was a thread ("eltene") and that each chromosome was a 64-stranded structure. Dr. Hughes-Schrader has very generously provided us with *Steatococcus* larval males for a re-examination of the process of spermiogenesis and the fine structure of these sperm with the electron microscope. One observation in particular is pertinent to this discussion.

A transverse section through a sperm bundle from a mature male shows thirty-two circular profiles of individual sperm packed in hexagonal array (Fig. 8). The junction between every pair of sperm is marked by a pair of dense structures with triangular profiles. Each sperm consists of a sheath and a dense central core, presumably of chromosomal material. At higher resolution the sheath can be seen to be made up of three to four concentric rings of structures having the profiles of tubules, each approximately 250 Å in outside diameter, with a less dense center approximately 100 Å in diameter. Because in any transverse section of a bundle only a small segment of the tubular mass shows round profiles, it can be deduced that the tubules spiral around the central core. The

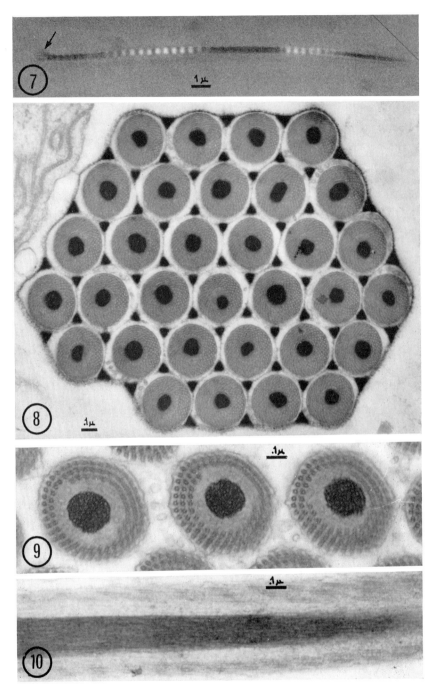

chromosomal core itself is dense and no structure can be discerned within it. Longitudinal sections of this stage confirm these observations and in addition, reveal again the spiralization of the bundles. The gyre frequency appears to vary along the bundle, but the spacings correspond to those observed with polarized light. In an immature (unhatched) adult, more detail of the internal organization of the core can be seen. The core is not consistent in diameter, but appears to taper to very fine strands at the extremities of the chromosomes. At this stage, the individual sperm apparently are not yet completely aligned, and a transverse section of a forming bundle may include cores with various cross-sectional diameters, although the diameter of the sperm itself is roughly constant. In a cross section of maximum diameter an irregular honeycomb-like organization is observed within the core (Fig. 9). The appearance is not unlike that seen in the elongating spermatids of the insects and mollusks mentioned previously. It is difficult to make any estimate of the number of tubules or fibrillar structures that might be responsible for this internal organization. Longitudinal sections of the same stage indicate closely spaced longitudinal striae (Fig. 10). The question immediately arises as to where DNA is localized in this structure.

The indium trichloride method of Watson and Aldridge (1961) provides the most selective heavy-metal staining procedure for the electron micro-

---

FIG. 7. Single sperm bundle isolated from the testis of an adult *Steatococcus tuberculatus* seen in polarized light. Striations probably represent gyres of the enclosed coiled chromosomes. Two such regions may be noted, a short one to the right representing the first chromosome to enter the sperm tube, and a longer one to the left representing the second longer chromosome. At the far left, the bundle is opening and the frayed ends of the individual sperm may be seen (arrow).

FIG. 8. Electron micrograph of a transverse section of a single sperm bundle from a mature male. Thirty-two sperm are hexagonally packed. Each sperm, except those at the periphery of the bundle, is surrounded by six dense triangular bodies and consists of three concentric rows of fine tubules seen in cross section and a dense core representing the chromosomal material. Glutaraldehyde and osmium fixation; stained with saturated uranyl acetate.

FIG. 9. Transverse section of three immature sperm from an 11-day-old third instar. Two complete and one incomplete concentric rings of microtubules surround the dense chromosomal core. In cross section the core is seen to consist of what appear to be tubules more or less of the same order as the tubules of the cytoplasmic sheath. Glutaraldehyde and osmium fixation; stained with saturated uranyl acetate.

FIG. 10. Longitudinal section of a single sperm at the same stage as those shown in Fig. 9. Striae can be seen running longitudinally, especially on the right-hand side of the micrograph where the dense core passes out of the section. Glutaraldehyde and osmium fixation; stained with saturated uranyl acetate.

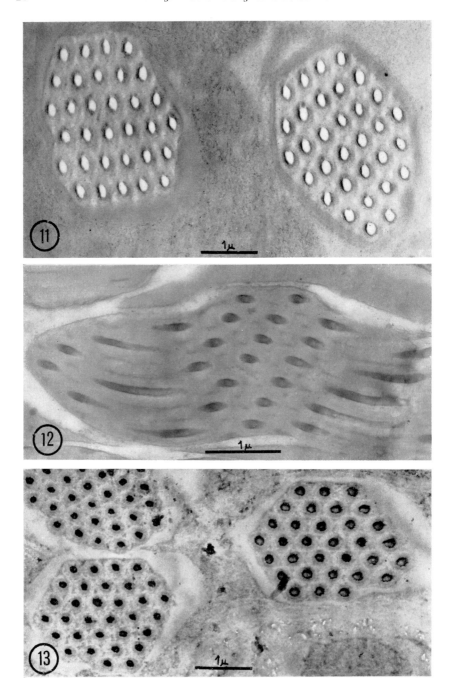

scopic localization of nucleic acids so far available. It owes its selectivity to its ability to make available a maximum number of negatively charged binding sites on the nucleic acid molecule by acetylating amino groups which might otherwise compete with the cationic heavy-metal ion and by suppressing the indiscriminate binding of indium by nonnucleic acid sites. Watson (1962a) has cautioned that the method is not completely specific, but, as will be pointed out later, the selectivity is quite high. Testes of the same stage as the preparation in Fig. 8 were fixed in glutaraldehyde (Sabatini *et al.*, 1963) and stained by the indium trichloride method with a few minor modifications (Coleman and Moses, 1964). One important point is immediately evident in transverse (Fig. 11) and longitudinal (Fig. 12) sections of sperm bundles. The only significant deposit of indium seen in transverse sections takes the form of a circular profile around the periphery of the core of each sperm. The central portion of the core is unstained. In fact, there is not even the faint nonspecific background staining that is characteristic of other cellular areas in indium preparations, as though this portion were completely devoid of matter. This is not the case, however, as can be determined by staining adjacent sections in a nonspecific way with saturated uranyl acetate (Fig. 13). The core is dense throughout and the over-all morphology resembles that seen after osmium fixation and uranyl staining. Thus, the composition of the central portion of the core, including the material that gives the longitudinal striations appears not to be nucleic acid and, while it has yet to be determined with certainty, it is probably protein. On the reasonable assumption that the only nucleic acid present in appreciable concentration is DNA, it may be concluded that this component is localized in a sheath surrounding what may be assumed to be protein microfilaments and is in turn surrounded by several layers of microtubules. Until studies can be completed on the details of formation

---

FIG. 11. Transverse section of two sperm bundles from an immature male; the sperm are at a stage slightly later than those shown in Figs. 9 and 10. Fixed in glutaraldehyde and stained with $InCl_3$, according to Watson and Aldridge (1961). The cores are completely lacking in stain, except for a dense rim around the periphery of each core. Cytoplasmic ribosomes have bound indium.

FIG. 12. Longitudinal section of a sperm bundle from the same testis shown in Fig. 11. The arrangement of oblique sections is the result of coiling of the sperm. The cores are seen to be empty while indium stains their peripheries strongly.

FIG. 13. Section adjacent to that shown in Fig. 11, with three sperm bundles in transverse view. This $InCl_3$-stained section has been further stained with saturated uranyl acetate for 30 minutes, and it can be seen that the dense peripheries of the cores are even more pronounced while the centers have now taken on stain.

of the sperm, the significance of the tubular arrangement of DNA is not clear. At this point, however, it seems advisable to hold in abeyance the notion that this chromosome as it is found in the sperm is composed of a number of microfibrils of DNA-containing chromatin. The fact that each chromosome making up the core appears to taper and become thin and attenuated at the ends leaves some question as to how this chromosome can be a multistranded structure in the first place. On the other hand, a cocoon of DNA is equally difficult to understand at the present time.

The possible functional role of intranuclear microtubules in sperm elongation is exemplified in another bizarre form of sperm. In decapod crustacea, sperm are aflagellate and the nuclear portion assumes a stellate form with long semirigid spines that are Feulgen-positive. In the crayfish *Procambarus clarkii* four nuclear arms radiate from the main body (Moses, 1961). Inside the testis and the sperm ducts the arms are wrapped around the body of the sperm. Sections perpendicular to the plane of symmetry near the center of the sperm cut through a number of cross sections of arms. The distal portions of the arms, i.e., those with the smaller diameters, are seen to be occupied by fine tubules, suggesting that they may be responsible for giving the arms rigidity. Similar tubules have been observed in the nuclei of spermatids at a stage where projection of the nucleus is just beginning. Tubules apparently form and align near the points of extension. The only other structural component of the nucleus of the mature crayfish sperm, which is otherwise vesiculate and empty in appearance, are sparse tangles of thin, wispy, dense threads, ranging from approximately 30–150 Å in thickness. Their chemical composition is not known.

Most of the electron microscope studies of sperm development and fine structure that have contributed information about the organization of nuclear material have utilized the now conventional methods of tissue preparation, i.e., procedures involving fixation (and "staining") with osmium, with further staining for contrast with uranyl, lead, and other heavy-metal salts. The uncertain selectivity of the staining materials used for contrast may very well be responsible for camouflaging the true structural arrangement of the DNA. This, after all, is the essential component on which the organizational pattern of the chromosome depends. If the observations on *Steatococcus* are at all indicative, the structural relationship between DNA and basic protein in sperm is far more complex than would be suspected from the appearance of simple extracted nucleoprotamine microfibrils. The application of truly selective heavy-metal staining procedures and other more specific cyto-chemical methods at the electron microscope level are needed for clari-fication.

Variation

In meiosis three specialized activities characterize the chromosome in prophase of the heterotypic division: failure of sister chromatids to separate (chromatid used here in the sense of half of a replicated chromo-some), precise point by point pairing of homologous chromosomes (synapsis), and chiasma formation associated with genetic crossing-over and evidently the consequence of a physical exchange between homol-ogous chromosomes. The last two activities intimately involve DNA. Thus, if in crossing-over exchange occurs at the molecular level as seems most probable, it is necessary for two homologous molecules of DNA to seek out each other from many thousands of others and to pair. Moreover, some mechanism must exist whereby an exchange of DNA strands may occur. Although these processes are frequently under genetic control, neither the mechanism of crossing-over nor the level at which it occurs is properly understood, and the same is true of chiasma formation.

Pairing of homologous chromosomes in nonmeiotic cells is not un-common, the best known example being the polytene chromosomes of dipteran larvae, where the precision of juxtaposition is at least at the level of the bands and is visible in the light microscope. The forces responsible for the pairing are, however, not understood. Genetic ex-change between homologs in somatic cells also occurs (see review by Pontecorvo and Käfer, 1958) but at a low frequency which might be accounted for on the basis of random contact. Physical exchange between chromatids has been clearly demonstrated by Taylor (1958); this is assumed to occur at replication, however, when the exchanging strands are physically close and aligned.

Meiotic pairing in synapsis is unique, however, in that it occurs at prophase and generally, though not always, leads to crossing-over. Pritchard (1960) distinguishes "effective pairing" as being a condition in which crossing-over occurs as opposed to other paired states where it does not. It could very well be assumed that synaptic pairing may actually occur on two levels: a "coarse" matching up of chromosomal areas approximately of the dimensions of bands or of chromomeres and, second, a more precise pairing at the molecular level.

The forces leading to synapsis (or somatic pairing, for that matter) are unknown. If it could be assumed that homologous loci on a chromosome engaged in similar functions tend to carry out these activities at a common site in the nucleus, possibly because of availability of substrate, etc., a congression of homologs could result, followed by the close juxtaposition of a few active chromosomal loci to serve as the starting points of synapsis. Other forces would have to be invoked for the maintenance of the synaptic state. But, once the relatively coarse alignment of homologous loci had occurred, the probability is greatly increased that homologous DNA molecules in those sites could find each other and become juxtaposed to permit crossing-over.

Among the mechanisms that have been proposed for recombination at the molecular level, at least in microorganisms, are "copy-choice" (Lederberg, 1954; Pritchard, 1960) and breakage and rejoining (Whitehouse, 1963). Both would seem to depend on DNA replication, the former occurring as a new polynucleotide strand is formed partly along one and partly along the other of two alternative template strands. The latter mechanism would require a localized and restricted replication (see, for example, Taylor *et al.*, 1962; Whitehouse, 1963) to repair the break. This kind of replication could occur at any time and might not be detectable by cytological (i.e., autoradiographic) means, in contrast to the copy-choice type of recombination which could be expected to occur during the normal period of replication. Most evidence points to crossing-over occurring during synapsis at the four-strand stage, and since with a few exceptions cytological analysis has shown that the DNA replication period is complete by this time, mechanisms involving exchange at the time of chromosomal DNA replication have been rejected. There have been some suggestions, however, that DNA replication may indeed extend into zygotene (in *Tradescantia*, Moses and Taylor, 1955) or even later (Sparrow *et al.*, 1952) base on cytophotometric estimations of DNA content. Recently, moreover, Wimber and Prensky (1963) employed pulse labeling with H^3-TDN to show clearly in *Triturus* that some replication occurs at selected sites along the pachytene chromosome. If this can be shown to be a general phenomenon, then, as they suggest, replication may well operate in crossing-over. The morphological basis of this process cannot be discerned in the light microscope. There is some suggestion, however, of a structure observed in the electron microscope that may play an important role in the process.

Bivalent chromosomes of meiotic prophases in gametocytes of animals and plants alike possess a well-defined and characteristic axial structure.

It was first described in spermatocytes of crayfish (Moses, 1956), pigeon, cat, and man (Fawcett, 1956) and has since been observed in such a wide variety of species and genera (see Moses, 1964b for summary) that it may be assumed to be a regular concomitant of synapsis (with certain exceptions to be mentioned). For this reason, and because of its filamentous appearance, it was named "synaptinemal complex." From transverse and longitudinal sections it can be reconstructed as a complex of three dense parallel elements lying in one plane and coaxial to the bivalent. The two outermost dense elements are separated by a consistent center to center spacing of 120–150 mμ (Fig. 14) and in some forms appear to be duplex when viewed in the plane of the ribbon (Fig. 15A). The central element varies in size and density from species to species and from one stage of prophase to another, and may be completely absent in some forms. The complex occupies large segments of the length of the chromosome and possibly the entire chromosome, the length involved probably varying with the stage.

The bulk of the chromatin is arranged in two masses, each associated with a main axial element; the masses are occasionally seen to flow together and appear to surround the complex completely (Moses, 1960). In longitudinal sections, where chromatin can be distinguished from interchromatin material, variations in size and shape of the chromatin masses occur along the chromosome (Fig. 14): these are usually bilaterally symmetrical and probably correspond to the chromomeres seen after acid fixation and in squash preparations.

The chromatin is mainly composed of irregular kinked fibrils ranging from roughly 70–150 Å in thickness, fine particles of the same order of magnitude, some of which are undoubtedly cross sections of fibrils as can be seen in stereomicrographs of sections, and larger granules about 300–400 mμ in diameter which may correspond to the perichromatin granules of Watson (1962b). Microfibrils are most clearly defined near the axial elements from which they emerge radially. The axial elements themselves appear to be composed of tightly packed microfibrils that are continuous with the chromatin masses (Figs. 15 and 16). After double fixation with formaldehyde and permanganate, the microfibrils are accentuated, probably because of extraction of some components, and their relationship to the complex is very apparent (Fig. 16 A,B). Whether the microfibrils are free-ending extensions from the axial elements or loops (Moses, 1960; Nebel and Coulon, 1962) has not been properly determined because of the limitations of observations in sections and the fact that the kinked fibrils may become coated and associated with

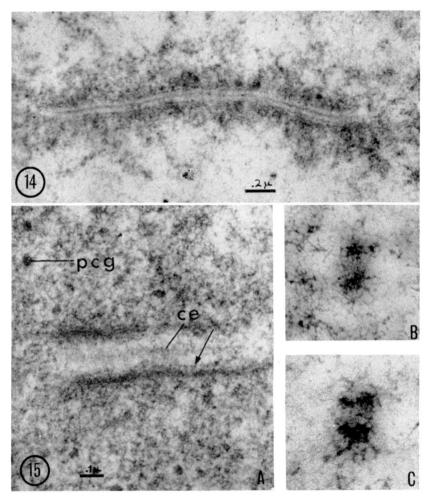

Fig. 14.   A longitudinal section of a bivalent chromosome from a primary spermatocyte prophase of *Procambarus clarki*. Tufted fibrillar chromosomal material is
massed on either side of a relatively clear area through the center of which passes a
pronounced dense line. In cross section, the entire structure is seen to be axial to the
chromosome. Fixation, osmium with sucrose.

Fig. 15.   A: Portion of a synaptinemal complex from a rat primary spermatocyte
prophase. The two dense main elements are seen to be composed of fibrillar material
and each consists of a dense outer portion with a less dense inner portion (arrow). A
tenuous central element (ce) is made up of very fine filaments of the sort that traverse
the space between the dense elements. Embedded in the chromatin microfibrils are
dense granules (pcg) 300–400 Å in diameter. Formaldehyde and osmium fixation;
stained with saturated uranyl acetate.

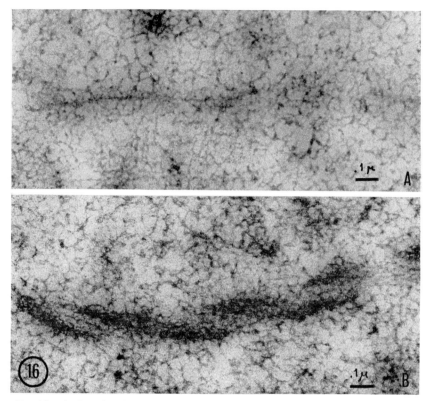

FIG. 16. A: Longitudinal section of a single axial element of a rat primary spermatocyte. This is a region of the nucleus where the chromosome is presumably unpaired. Note the kinked microfibrils that radiate from the thin axis. Fixation in
$KMnO_4$ and formaldehyde; stained with uranyl acetate. From Moses (1963).

B: Preparation similar to that in Fig. 16A. The bipartite complex twists along the
axis of a bivalent (synapsed) chromosome. The axial elements have thickened, but
radiating microfibrils are still quite apparent. The central pairing line is not prominent. Fixation in $KMnO_4$ and formaldehyde; stained with saturated uranyl acetate.
From Moses (1963).

B: Transverse section of the synaptinemal complex from a rat spermatocyte. The
fixation in $KMnO_4$–formaldehyde emphasizes the fibrils that radiate from the dense
axial elements. The central element is not apparent, but fine fibrils are visible crossing
the space between the two main elements. Stained with uranyl acetate.

C: Synaptinemal complex from another area of the same section as Fig. 15B. Each
main element can be seen to be double.

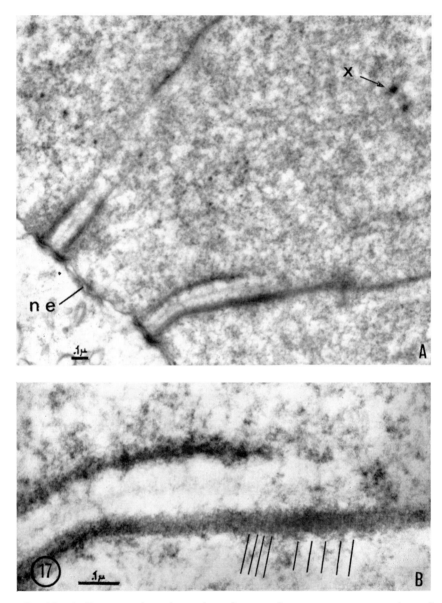

Fig. 17. A: Two synaptinemal complexes from a primary spermatocyte prophase of rat seen in longitudinal section and one shown in transverse section (x). The characteristic termination of the chromosomes against the nuclear envelope (ne) is shown. Dense thickenings of the two membranes of the envelope occur at the end of each

accessory material and cannot be followed easily. Occasionally, in a region where the complex in unformed (Fig. 19A), structures that could be interpreted as loops are apparent. Periodic spacings are sometimes seen along the axial elements (Fig. 17B), and the microfibrils appear to be spaced regularly (e.g., Guénin and Gautier, 1960), but as yet, no consistent pattern has emerged.

The central clear space between the lateral axial elements is frequently traversed by fine microfibrils 70 Å or less in thickness (Moses, 1960). These appear in many cases to tangle in some way and to make up the central element.

That the synaptinemal complex is axial to a bivalent, and not to a single homolog was demonstrated by comparing adjacent thick and thin sections of salamander spermatocytes (Moses, 1958, 1960). In forms with small chromosomes the complex is clearly part of a bivalent (Fig. 14). This has been questioned by Sotelo and Trujillo-Cenóz (1960), however, on the basis of comparisons of the spacing between pachytene chromosomes in squash preparations and those of the complex in sections of OsO_4-fixed material. Such comparisons are equivocal because of the obvious distortions produced by acid fixation and the difficulty of ascertaining and matching stages. Furthermore, additional evidence for the bivalent hypothesis comes from observations of single elements (as determined in both cross and longitudinal sections) at early stages of synapsis (Moses, 1958, 1960; Nebel, 1959) when pairing is assumed to be incomplete (see also Fig. 16A). The frequency of such structures decreases as pairing continues, and the frequency of the complex increases (Nebel, 1959).

Finally, if it is to be assumed that the main axial element is integral with the axis of the chromosome, then the doubleness of the chromosome, i.e., the fact that it is replicated and composed of two chromatids, should be manifest. While the usual appearance of an axial element in trans-

---

axial element. The boundaries of the chromatin are not easily distinguishable from the dense interchromatin substance, except at the terminal of the uppermost complex. In the transverse section, each element can be seen to be single and the central element is visible. Fixation in formaldehyde and OsO_4; stained with saturated uranyl acetate.

B: Higher magnification of an area of the lower chromosome seen in Fig. 17A. Lateral fibrillar extensions emerge from the dense axial elements. Fine fibrils traverse the area between the dense fibrils. A repeating pattern of lines nearly transverse to the direction of the dense axial element and with the spacing of approximately 170 Å can be seen in this area.

verse section is that of a dense dot (Figs. 15B and 17A) or a densely packed mass, in some nuclei it appears as a bipartite structure (Fig. 15C) (Moses, 1963). It may be that the physical doubleness of the axis does not manifest itself in the complex until some later stage of the prophase cycle of the complex, at which time it is not apt to be seen easily because the entire structure loses its organization and becomes dispersed.

It has thus been proposed that the main elements are each axial to a homolog and that when two homologous chromosomes pair, the elements pair, moving toward the central axis of the bivalent. The central element is supposed to be formed as a consequence of pairing (Moses, 1960). A

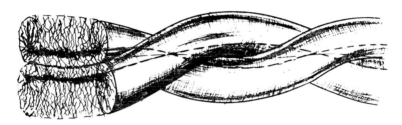

FIG. 18. Schematic diagram to illustrate the postulated relationship between the synaptinemal complex and a bivalent chromosome. The dense longitudinal elements from which microfibrils radiate are thought to be axial to the homologs, but displaced toward the pairing surfaces. The central linear element lies at the junction of the two chromosomes. The diagram leaves the question open as to whether the microfibrils are free-ending or loops.

schematic sketch indicating the relationship of the complex to the bivalent is shown in Fig. 18.

Although there are minor variations in structure from species to species, the essential organization of the complex is consistent and restricted mainly to synaptic chromosomes. Neither the complex nor anything even closely resembling it has been seen in somatic chromosomes. In several important cases, however, the complex does not occur in synaptic chromosomes. In *Drosophila* primary spermatocytes, crossing-over does not occur, although homologous chromosomes have been shown to pair (Cooper, 1949). In its classic definition, synapsis does not imply crossing-over, only pairing in meiotic prophase. Meyer (1961) has examined spermatocytes of *Drosophila* males and has failed to find synaptinemal complexes, although they are abundant in oocytes where clear-cut synapsis and crossing-over do occur. In males of *Steatococcus tuberculatus,* which are haploid and therefore do not undergo synapsis or reduction division, we have observed that complexes are not found in spermatocyte prophases. Meyer has shown further (1964) in triploid *Drosophila* females, where synapsis occurs between pairs and leaves one member unpaired, that the synaptinemal complex occurs in the paired and not in the unpaired members. This observation constitutes confirmation of the hypothesis that the complex is axial to a bivalent and not to a homolog and that it is thus truly a synaptinemal complex. One more observation by Meyer is important. In *Tipula oleracea* and *Phryne fenestralis* which are achiasmate, complexes are not found, whereas in another species of *Tipula* both chiasmata and complexes occur. Finally, in a *Drosophila* mutant in which synapsis and crossing-over are suppressed, axial complexes cannot be found in oocytes. Such observations strongly suggest that the presence of the complex is more closely allied with the process of crossing-over, presumably a consequence of synapsis, than with the mere event of synapsis itself.

Pursuing this argument further, it follows that the mechanism of pairing in meiosis may be independent of the structural refinements that constitute the complex. This kind of pairing could represent the first order or coarse pairing common to both meiotic and mitotic chromatin discussed above. The synaptinemal complex could then operate at the second or "effective" level of pairing leading to crossing-over. It could very well serve as the device by which homologous DNA molecules are paired and aligned. For example, the fine strands observed crossing the space between the two axial elements and appearing to unite in the central element could contain the selected molecules of DNA that are involved in crossing-over.

The key to such a hypothesis resides in knowing where DNA and related proteins are localized in the axial complex. In our laboratory, we have undertaken the cytochemical localization of these components employing the electron microscope (Coleman, 1964).

Rooster testis was selected as the source of meiotic chromosomes mainly because of its abundance. Tissue was fixed either in formaldehyde (Holt and Hicks, 1961) or in glutaraldehyde (Sabatini *et al.,* 1963). The characteristic morphology of the synaptinemal complex was evident in material postfixed with OsO_4 or stained with uranyl acetate (Fig. 19A,B). Blocks of aldehyde-fixed tissue were then digested with deoxyribonuclease (DNase) until spermatocytes in squashes of test samples were Feulgen-negative. Thin sections cut from epoxy-embedded pieces

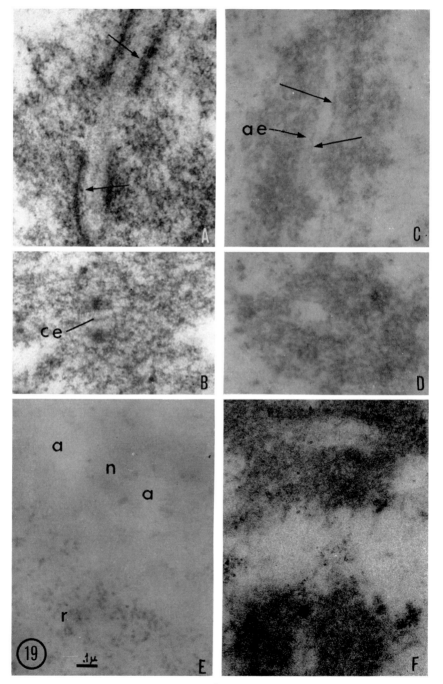

of the digested blocks were stained with uranyl acetate in various concentrations. Thick sections (1–2 μ) of the same material were Feulgen-negative and showed loss of nuclear absorption at 2,600 Å, in contrast to controls. There could be no doubt that DNA had been removed. Yet, even after uranyl staining, no significant difference in structure of the chromosomal complex could be observed with the electron microscope (Coleman and Moses, 1964; cf. Nebel and Coulon, 1962).

This anomaly was resolved by applying the $InCl_3$ method for nucleic acid. In the first place, the appearance of the $InCl_3$-stained chromosomes in control sections is strikingly different from the usual structure after OsO_4 or uranyl acetate (Fig. 19C,D). The main microfibrillar regions stain strongly, but the two ordinarily dense axial elements bind very little indium, except for their innermost bands which are more heavily stained. Structure and stain are conspicuously absent in the central area. Post-staining such sections with uranyl acetate again produces the usual

---

Fig. 19. A: Portion of a longitudinal section of a synaptinemal complex from primary spermatocyte of rooster. The dense lateral elements are seen to be composed of two parts; a dense fine inner segment (arrows) and a dense thicker outer segment. The central element is visible. Note that the continuity of the axial elements is interrupted and that in this region the chromosome puffs out in what appears to be a loop. Fixation in glutaraldehyde-OsO_4, stained with saturated uranyl acetate.

B: Transverse section of the synaptinemal complex from the same section as Fig. 19A. The main axial elements appear single; material crosses the space between them. The central element appears as a line (ce).

C: Longitudinal section of a rooster primary spermatocyte chromosome fixed with glutaraldehyde and stained with the $InCl_3$ method of Watson and Aldridge. The chromatin masses and the thin inner segment of the axial complex (arrows) stain heavily. The main elements themselves (ae) are less dense than the chromatin material in sharp contrast to their density as shown in Fig. 19A.

D: Transverse section of primary spermatocyte chromosome fixed with glutaraldehyde and stained with the indium method. The distribution of density is in striking contrast to that in Fig. 19B, which is a comparable area.

E: Portion of a rooster primary spermatocyte nucleus (n) fixed with glutaraldehyde, digested with DNase until adjacent preparations were Fuelgen-negative and decreased in absorption at 2600 Å in the ultraviolet, and then stained with the $InCl_3$ method. What are presumed to be the chromosomal axes (a) are seen as areas of slightly lighter density than the surrounding nucleoplasm. The periphery of the nucleus is shown and the adjacent cytoplasmic ribosomes which still stain with indium (r) are apparent.

F: DNase-treated preparation similar to that shown in Fig. 19E, except that the section has been stained with saturated uranyl acetate. Again the structure of the chromosome has been made visible. Axial complexes and chromosomal material are stained.

picture (Fig. 19F), though perhaps less intensely stained than after glutaraldehyde alone. Such an observation raises strong caution about making the unqualified assumption that uranyl acetate is selective for nucleic acid. It must be assumed that in this case, uranyl is binding significantly to other anionic sites, such as protein carboxyl, as well as to nucleic acid.

This was again borne out by observations on DNase-digested material. Here all significant InCl$_3$ staining was abolished from spermatocyte

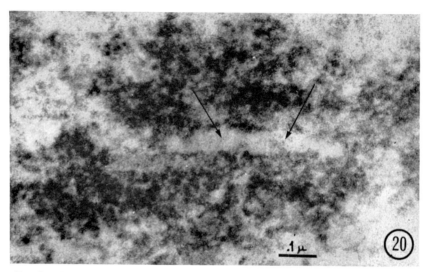

FIG. 20. Same section of InCl$_3$-stained chrosome shown in Fig. 19B. This print has been made from a copy negative prepared to amplify contrast. Suggestions of very fine strands (of the order of 50 Å or less) crossing the otherwise empty appearing space are just discernible (arrows).

nuclear structures that had stained previously, except for ribosomes and other entities that could be assumed to contain RNA (Fig. 19E). The loss of staining was now consistent with the light microscope Feulgen and ultraviolet results. Remarkably, however, when such negative sections were stained with uranyl acetate, the original structure reappeared, dense elements and all (Fig. 19F). There can now be little doubt that uranyl acetate, at least as we have used it, appreciably stains nonnucleic acid substances, presumably protein, and should be regarded as selective only with great caution and proper controls. Interestingly enough, sections of digested material also show the same typical pattern after postfixation with osmium or staining with alkaline lead (Karnovsky, 1961).

Thus, although DNA has been removed, the entire structural integrity remains, presumably through stabilization of protein by the aldehyde, indicating that none of the visible structure is due to DNA alone. One important question, however, is left unanswered. Do the 30–50 Å strands seen in uranyl-stained sections traversing the central area, together with the central element, contain DNA? The fact that the central area appears empty following $InCl_3$ suggests that they do not. But, when efforts are taken to amplify contrast (Fig. 20), occasional faint strands can be discerned (arrows) with difficulty. A quick calculation of the range of density required for normal contrast in a 1000 Å thick section of stained chromatin will indicate that the density of a 20 or 50 Å fiber is apt to be too low to be seen.

We consider it likely, therefore, that these microfibrils, and the central element as well, contain DNA associated with protein.

The fact that DNase-digested chromosomes may be stained with Karnovsky's lead complex at pH 12 raises the question of whether the lead is binding to the same component as the uranyl ion. To answer this, sections were digested with trypsin, either with or without previous digestion with DNase and then stained with lead or uranyl salts. Brief trypsin digestion almost completely abolished lead staining (Fig. 21A,B), but had only a small effect on uranyl staining (Fig. 21E), thus indicating that at least some of the binding sites are indeed different. Since trypsin apparently attacks peptide bonds involving either lysine or arginine, the possibility that histone was involved in lead staining became apparent.

Alkaline fast green (AFG) [Alfert and Geschwind's (1953) stain that is selective for histone] can be used to stain small blocks of DNase-digested material. This staining is visible in 1–2 μ sections in the light microscope and is abolished by brief tryptic digestion, as is lead staining. That lead is indeed bound to such a basic protein is further adduced from the observation that staining of tissue blocks with AFG inhibits subsequent staining of thin sections of the tissue with lead, but not with uranyl (Fig. 21F). The possibility that the lead complex at pH 12 stains as an anion, possibly $Pb(OH)_2$, and is thus analogous to AFG is not unreasonable (Karnovsky, 1961; cf. Reynolds, 1963). Preliminary observations on the ion-exchange properties and electrophoretic characteristics of the stain indicate that it behaves as an unstable anionic species. The binding of lead to histone after the $InCl_3$ method suggests further that mainly arginine groups are being stained, since the preparations are acetylated and lysine ε-amino groups are blocked, in contrast to the guanidino groups of arginine.

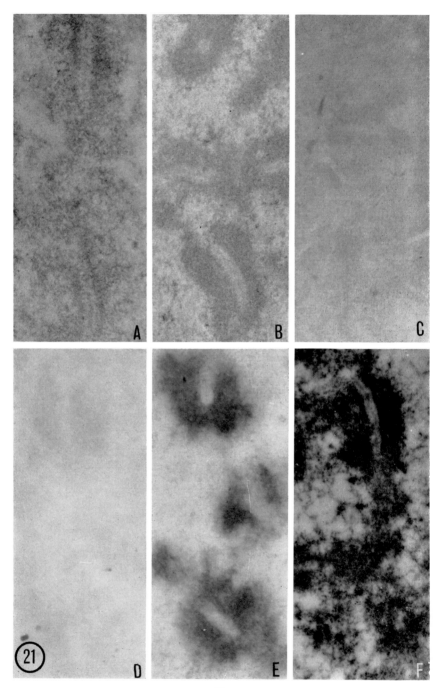

We may now draw some further conclusion about the composition of the synaptinemal complex. The distribution of DNA has already been noted. The same areas also contain a basic arginine-containing protein, probably histone. Its distribution differs from DNA in that it is a main component of the dense axial elements. Finally, if the staining by uranyl acetate following DNase can be attributed to protein carboxyl, a non-histone protein occupies the same areas, but also is more concentrated in the two main elements of the complex. There is some evidence that the histone of the dense axial and central elements differs in some way from that of the microfibrils in that trypsin sequentially abolishes lead binding, first in the former, then in the latter. If this can be substantiated, then functional significance of this difference can be sought.

It is now worth speculating briefly on the way in which the synaptinemal complex may function in synapsis and crossing-over. As has been pointed out, while this complex is unlikely to be involved with the force that leads to chromosome pairing, it could be responsible for "effective pairing," i.e., for holding the synaptic alignment firm for a protracted period and to enable or at least provide the opportunity for certain DNA strands to meet and pair in the central area, where crossing-over could occur. If true, it is not unreasonable to expect to detect occasional incorporation of H^3-TDN in this area during synapsis.

Exactly how the complex forms is not known, and it has not yet been settled whether at least some component (possibly the protein of the axial elements) is laid down first with the microfibrils collecting and associating with it later (Sotelo and Trujillo-Cenóz, 1960) or whether it is the product of the chromosome *in situ*. In any case, the tendency for reminiscent structures to form may be inherent in other nucleoplasms of germinal epithelium. Sotelo and Trujillo-Cenóz (1960) have reported, and we have observed in other species occasional stacks of parallel arrays,

FIG. 21.   All material shown is rooster testis fixed in glutaraldehyde and posttreated as indicated. A: Stained with Karnovsky's lead complex for 20 minutes. B: Digested with DNase in the block and then stained with lead after sectioning. C: Stained with alkaline fast green in the block and then with lead after embedding and sectioning. Only at low magnifications was it possible to discern structure in micrographs of this tissue. Contrast in this case seems to be due to the inherent density to electrons of the tissue. D: Digested with trypsin for ten minutes in the block and then with lead for 15 minutes after embedding and sectioning. E: Digested with trypsin for 15 minutes in the block and then stained with uranyl acetate after embedding and sectioning. F: Stained with alkaline fast green in the block and then with uranyl acetate. All magnifications 36,000 ×, except C, which is 15,000 ×.

each pair of which bears a superficial resemblance to the axial complex in spermatids. These structures are not associated with formed chromosomes. There may well be a tendency in the nucleoplasm of gametogenic cells for chromatin and other accessory materials to form periodic repeating structures under the proper conditions, and in synaptic chromosomes, these may be involved with the synaptinemal complex. For example, a closely packed periodicity of about 150 Å has been observed in rare instances along the axial elements (Fig. 17B).

Discussion and Summary

In seeking the morphological common denominator of the chromosome, we have been led to a microfibril of indeterminate length and of the order of 100 Å (ranging from 30–200 Å in thickness) as the structural unit (e.g., Ris and Chandler, 1963). Whether one 100 Å microfibril is composed of two 40 Å fibrils of nucleohistone as proposed by Ris (1962) or whether the larger fibrils consist of a protein matrix in which is embedded a fine filament that may be inferred to be DNA (Gall, 1962) remains to be confirmed. And whether the chromosome is a single long chain of DNA double helices or a multiple-stranded rope, involve open questions that will not be debated here.

As a point of departure, however, let us examine the model of the chromosome that emerges from the studies of Gall and Beermann on lampbrush and polytene chromosomes, respectively. Here the basic linear element, or chromonema, is a single strand that maintains the linear genetic sequence; it is probably composed of one long DNA double helix (either a single molecule or a chain of molecules). It follows that the configurations observed during the transcriber stages are the consequence of foldings, coilings, loopings, and the addition of accessory materials. It is not a difficult topological problem to envision the relatively simple rearrangements required to produce the various forms of the chromosome during its different functional states. We do not yet have enough information to confirm the hypothesized configurations, and such evidence seems more likely to come primarily from the perfection of methods for examining whole, unraveled chromosomes, such as that of spreading on an air-water interface (Kleinschmidt and Lang, 1962; Gall, 1963) than from reconstructions from thin sections in the electron microscope alone.

Of the three chromosomal configurations that have been examined, only one exposes the chromosome sufficiently to allow an attempt to

fit it to the general schemes of Gall and Beermann. During DNA replication at interphase the chromosome is too unfolded to see except in
segments, but we are led to the impression that microfibrillar elements
are opened out and reduced to their essential constituents in the areas
of replication. The sequestering and protection of the genetic material

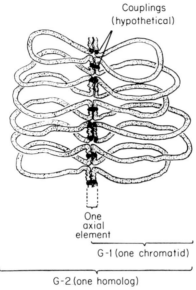

Couplings
(hypothetical)

One
axial
element

G-1 (one chromatid)

G-2 (one homolog)

Fig. 22.   Hypothetical scheme by which microfibrils could form a meiotic chromosome (single homolog) giving the kind of images seen in the electron microscope. It is
assumed that the microfibrils emanating from the axis are actually loops. A segment
of one (unpaired) chromosome is shown. Because it is replicated, it consists of two
chromatids, each composed of a chain of microfibrils joined by hypothetical linkers
(possibly protein) and looped out laterally. Note resemblance to organization of lampbrush chromosomes. While it is not known how many DNA double helices may be
contained in a microfibril, the model would be consistent with Taylor's (1963) and
Gall's (1962) if it contained one DNA molecule (plus associated protein, as in the
lampbrush loops). From Moses (1963).

in the sperm also involves reduction of microfibrillar elements, but a
more precise definition of the final packaging that ensues will depend
on further cytochemical studies with the electron microscope. Nevertheless, enough has been observed of the fine structure of chromosomes
in meiosis to say, conservatively, that it is not inconsistent with the
lampbrush hypothesis and may well be essentially such a structure
(Fig. 22).

In the course of this exploration, we have attempted to extend our understanding of the cytological manifestations of chromosome functions and to reveal by morphological and cytochemical examination with the electron microscope, clues to the common underlying pattern of organization. The pattern itself is still elusive, but it may be expected to yield to further exploitation of the methods employed and the systems studied here.

ACKNOWLEDGMENTS

The authors wish to recognize, with gratitude, the helpful cooperation of all the members of their laboratory in contributing to various aspects of the work reported. Our thanks go especially to Mrs. Marion Wilson, Mrs. Marlene Johnson, Messrs. Hayes Brown and Charles Knox for their very tangible assistance. This work has been generously supported by research grants from the American Cancer Society (E-213) and the United States Public Health Service (National Institutes of Health, GM-06753). One of us (J.R.C.) has been supported by a National Science Foundation Graduate Fellowship. Part of the work reported is included in his thesis, presented in partial fulfillment of the requirements for the Ph.D. degree at Duke University, 1964.

REFERENCES

ALFERT, M., AND GESCHWIND, I. I. (1953). A selective staining method for the basic proteins of cell nuclei. *Proc. Natl. Acad. Sci. U. S.* **39**, 991-999.

BEERMANN, W. (1959). Chromosomal differentiation in insects. *In* "Developmental Cytology," Growth Symposium No. 16 (D. Rudnick, ed.), pp. 83-103. Ronald Press, New York.

BEERMANN, W. (1963). Cytological aspects of information transfer in cellular differentiation. *Am. Zoologist* **3**, 23-32.

CARO, L. G. (1962). High resolution autoradiography. II. The problem of resolution. *J. Cell Biol.* **16**, 189-199.

CARO, L. G., AND VAN TUBERGEN, R. P. (1962). High resolution autoradiography I. Methods. *J. Cell Biol.* **15**, 173-188.

CASPERSSON, T. (1940). Nukleinsaure und Genvermehrung. *Chromosoma* **1**, 605-619.

COLEMAN, J. R. (1964). Fine structure and cytochemistry of the meiotic chromosome of the domestic rooster, *Gallus domesticus.* Ph.D. Thesis, Dept. of Zoology, Duke University, Durham, North Carolina.

COLEMAN, J. R., AND MOSES, M. J. (1964). DNA and the fine structure of synaptic Chromosomes in the domestic rooster (*Gallus domesticus*). *J. Cell Biol.* **23**, 63-78.

COOPER, K. W. (1949). The cytogenetics of meiosis in *Drosophila. J. Morphol.* **84**, 81-122.

CRICK, F. H. C. (1958). On protein synthesis. *Symp. Soc. Exptl. Biol.* **12**, 138-163.

DALES, S. (1960). A study of the fine structure of mammalian somatic chromosomes. *Exptl. Cell Res.* **19**, 577-590.

DASS, C. M. S., AND RIS, H. (1958). Submicroscopic organization of the nucleus during spermiogenesis in the grasshopper. *J. Biophys. Biochem. Cytol.* **4**, 129-132.

FAURÉ-FREMIET, E., ROUILLER, C., AND GAUCHERY, M. (1957). La réorganisation macronucléaire chez les euplotes. *Exptl. Cell Res.* **12**, 135-144.

FAWCETT, D. W. (1956). The fine structure of chromosomes in the meiotic prophase of vertebrate spermatocytes. *J. Biophys. Biochem. Cytol.* **2**, 403-406.

FREESE, E. (1958). The arrangement of DNA in the chromosome. *Cold Spring Harbor Symp. Quant. Biol.* 23, 13-18.

GALL, J. G. (1959). Macronuclear duplication in the ciliated protozoon *Euplotes*. *J. Biophys. Biochem. Cytol.* 5, 295-308.

GALL, J. G. (1962). Chromosome fibers from an interphase nucleus. *Science* 139, 120-121.

GALL, J. G. (1963). Chromosomes and cytodifferentiation. In "Cytodifferentiation and Macromolecular Synthesis," Growth Symposium No. 21 (M. Locke, ed.), pp. 119-143. Academic Press, New York.

GALL, J. G., AND BJORK, L. B. (1958). The spermatid nucleus in two species of grasshopper. *J. Biophys. Biochem. Cytol.* 4, 479-484.

GIBBONS, I. R., AND BRADFIELD, J. R. G. (1957). The fine structure of nuclei during sperm maturation in the locust. *J. Biophys. Biochem. Cytol.* 3, 133-140.

GRASSÉ, P., CARASSO, N., AND FAVARD, P. (1956). Les ultrastructures cellulaires au cours de la spermiogénèse de l'escargot. *Ann. Sci. Nat. Zool.* 18, 339-380.

GUÉNIN, H. A., AND GAUTIER, A. (1960). Observations sur la structure submicroscopique des chromosomes du *Blaps mucronata* Latr. *Rev. Suisse Zool.* 67, 210-216.

HAY, E. D., AND REVEL, J. P. (1963). The fine structure of the DNP component of the nucleus. An electron microscopic study utilizing autoradiography to localize DNA synthesis. *J. Cell Biol.* 16, 29-51.

HOLT, S. J., AND HICKS, M. (1961). Studies on formalin fixation for electron microscopy and for cytochemical staining purposes. *J. Biophys. Biochem. Cytol.* 11, 31-46.

HUGHES-SCHRADER, S. (1946). A new type of spermiogenesis in iceryine coccids—with linear alignment of chromosomes in the sperm. *J. Morphol.* 78, 43-84.

INOUÉ, S., AND SATO, H. (1962). Arrangement of DNA in living sperm: a biophysical analysis. *Science* 136, 1122-1124.

KARNOVSKY, M. (1961). Simple methods for staining with lead at high pH in electron microscopy. *J. Cell Biol.* 11, 729-732.

KAYE, J. S. (1962). Acrosome formation in the house cricket. *J. Cell Biol.* 12, 411-431.

KLEINSCHMIDT, A. K., AND LANG, D. (1962). Intrazelluläre desoxyribonucleinsäure von bakterien. In "Fifth International Congress for Electron Microscopy" (S. S. Breese, ed.), Vol. 2, 0-8. Academic Press, New York.

LA COUR, L. F., AND PELC, S. R. (1958). Effect of colchicine on the utilization of labelled thymidine during chromosomal reproduction. *Nature* 182, 506-509.

LAFONTAINE, J. G., AND CHOUINARD, L. A. (1963). A correlated light and electron microscope study of the nucleolar material during mitosis in *Vicia fabia. J. Cell Biol.* 17, 167-201.

LEDERBERG, J. (1954). Recombination mechanisms in bacteria. *J. Cellular Comp. Physiol.* 45, Suppl. 2, 75-107.

LIMA-DE-FARIA, A. (1959). Differential uptake of tritiated thymidine into hetero- and euchromatin in *Melanoplus* and *Secale. J. Biophys. Biochem. Cytol.* 6, 457-466.

LIMA-DE-FARIA, A. (1962). Progress in tritium autoradiography. *Progr. Biophys. Biophys. Chem.* 12, 281-317.

MEYER, G. (1961). Fine structure of spermatocyte nuclei of *Drosophila melanogaster. Proc. European Regional Conf. Electron Microscopy, Delft, 1960* 2, 951-954.

MEYER, G. (1964). A possible correlation between the submicroscopic structure of meiotic chromosomes and crossing-over. *Proc. Third European Regional Conf. Electron Microscopy, Prague, 1964,* pp. 461-462. Publishing House of the Czechoslovak Academy of Sciences, Prague.

Moses, M. J. (1956). Chromosomal structures in crayfish spermatocytes. *J. Biophys. Biochem. Cytol.* **2**, 215-218.

Moses, M. J. (1958). The relation between the axial complex of meiotic prophase chromosomes and chromosome pairing in a salamander *(Plethodon cinereus). J. Biophys. Biochem. Cytol.* **4**, 633-638.

Moses, M. J. (1960). Patterns of organization in the fine structure of chromosomes *Intern. Konf. Elektronenmikroskopie, 4th, Berlin, 1958* Vol. 2, pp. 199-211. Springer, Berlin.

Moses, M. J. (1961). Spermiogenesis in the crayfish *(Procambarus clarkii).* I. Structural characterization of the mature sperm. *J. Biophys. Biochem. Cytol.* **9**, 222-228.

Moses, M. J. (1963). Comments on chromosome structure. *In* "Radiation-Induced Chromosome Aberrations" (S. Wolff, ed.), pp. 155-164. Columbia Univ. Press, New York.

Moses, M. J. (1964a). Application of autoradiography to electron microscopy. *J. Histochem. Cytochem.* **12**, 115-130.

Moses, M. J. (1964b). The nucleus and chromosomes: a cytological perspective. *In* "Cytology and Cell Physiology" (G. Bourne, ed.), 3rd ed., pp. 423-558. Academic Press, New York.

Moses, M. J., and Lafontaine, J. G. (1961). Structural components of the nucleus at interphase and during division. *Recent Advan. Botany* **19**, 1053-1059.

Moses, M. J., and Taylor, J. H. (1955). Deoxypentase nucleic acid synthesis during microsporogenesis in *Tradescantia. Exptl. Cell Res.* **9**, 474-488.

Moses, M. J., Meek, G. A., and Price, J. M. (1962). Light and electron microscope studies of tritiated thymidine incorporation. *In* "Fifth International Congress for Electron Microscopy" (S. S. Breese, ed.), Vol. 2, XX-5. Academic Press, New York.

Nebel, B. R. (1957). Chromosomal and cytoplasmic microfibrillae in sperm of an iceryine coccid. *J. Heredity* **48**, 51-56.

Nebel, B. R. (1959). Observations on mammalian chromosome fine structure and replication with special reference to mouse testis after ionizing radiation. *Radiation Res.* Suppl. 1, 431-452.

Nebel, B. R., and Coulon, E. M. (1962). The fine structure of chromosomes in pigeon spermatocytes. *Chromosoma* **13**, 272-291.

Pontecorvo, G., and Käfer, E. (1958). Genetic analysis based on mitotic recombination. *Advan. Genet.* **9**, 71-104.

Prescott, D., and Bender, M. A. (1963). Autoradiographic study of chromatid distribution of labeled DNA in two types of mammalian cells *in vitro. Exptl. Cell Res.* **29**, 430-442.

Prescott, D. M., and Kimball, R. F. (1961). Relation between RNA, DNA and protein synthesis in the replicating nucleus of *Euplotes. Proc. Natl. Acad. Sci. U. S.* **47**, 686-693.

Pritchard, R. H. (1960). The bearing of recombination analysis at high resolution on genetic fine structure in *Aspergillus nidulans* and the mechanism of recombination in higher organisms. *Symp. Soc. Gen. Microbiol.* **10**, 155-180.

Rebhun, L. I. (1957). Nuclear changes during spermiogenesis in a pulmonate snail. *J. Biophys. Biochem. Cytol.* **3**, 509-524.

Revel, J. P., and Hay, E. D. (1961). Autoradiographic localization of DNA synthesis in a specific ultra-structural component of the interphase nucleus. *Exptl. Cell Res.* **25**, 474-480.

REYNOLDS, E. S. (1963). The use of lead citrate at high pH as an electron-opaque stain in electron microscopy. *J. Cell Biol.* **17**, 208-212.

RIS, H. (1962). Interpretation of ultrastructure in the cell nucleus. *In* "The Interpretation of Ultrastructure," *Symp. Intern. Soc. Cell Biol.* **1**, 69-86.

RIS, H., AND CHANDLER, B. L. (1963). The ultrastructure of genentic system in prokaryotes and eukaryotes. *Cold Spring Harbor Symp. Quant. Biol.* **28**, 1-8.

ROTH, L. E. (1957). An electron microscope study of the cytology of the protozoan *Euplotes patella. J. Biophys. Biochem. Cytol.* **3**, 985-1000.

SABATINI, D. D., BENSCH, K., AND BARRNETT, R. J. (1963). Cytochemistry and electron microscopy. The preservation of cellular ultrastructure and enzymatic activity by aldehyde fixation. *J. Cell Biol.* **17**, 19-58.

SOTELO, J. R., AND TRUJILLO-CENÓZ, O. (1960). Electron microscope study on spermatogenesis. Chromosome morphogenesis at the onset of meiosis (cyte I) and nuclear structure of early and late spermatids. *Z. Zellforsch. Mikroskop. Anat.* **51**, 243-277.

SPARROW, A. H., MOSES, M. J., AND STEELE, R. (1952). A cytological and cytochemical approach to an understanding of radiation damage in dividing cells. *Brit. J. Radiol.* **25**, 182-188.

STEFFENSEN, D. M. (1961). Chromosome structure with special reference to metal ions. *Intern. Rev. Cytol.* **10**, 163-197.

TAYLOR, J. H. (1958). The mode of chromosome duplication in *Crepis capillaris. Exptl. Cell Res.* **15**, 350-357.

TAYLOR, J. H. (1963). The replication and organization of DNA in chromosomes. *In* "Molecular Genetics" (J. H. Taylor, ed.), Pt. I, pp. 65-111. Academic Press, New York.

TAYLOR, J. H. (1964). The arrangement of chromosomes in the mature sperm of the grasshopper. *J. Cell Biol.* **21**, 286-289.

TAYLOR, J. H., HAUT, W. F., AND TUNG, J. (1962). Effects of fluorodeoxyuridine on DNA replication, chromosome breakage and reunion. *Proc. Natl. Acad. Sci. U.S.* **48**, 190-198.

WATSON, M. L. (1962a). Considerations of nucleic acid morphology in fixed tissues. *In* "Fifth International Congress for Electron Microscopy" (S. S. Breese, ed.), Vol. 2, O-5. Academic Press, New York.

WATSON, M. L. (1962b). Observations on a granule associated with chromatin in the nuclei of cells of rat and mouse. *J. Cell Biol.* **13**, 162-167.

WATSON, M. L., AND ALDRIDGE, W. G. (1961). Methods for the use of indium as an electron stain for nucleic acids. *J. Biophys. Biochem. Cytol.* **10**, 257-272.

WHITEHOUSE, H. L. K. (1963). A theory of crossing-over by means of hybrid deoxyribonucleic acid. *Nature* **199**, 1034-1040.

WIMBER, D. E., AND PRENSKY, W. (1963). Autoradiography with meiotic chromosomes of the male newt (*Triturus viridescens*) using H[3]-thymidine. *Genetics* **48**, 1731-1738.

WOODS, P. S., AND SCHAIRER, M. V. (1959). Distribution of newly synthesized deoxyribonucleic acid in dividing chromosomes. *Nature* **183**, 303-305.

Chromosomal Proteins

HARRIS BUSCH, WESLEY C. STARBUCK,
ERIC J. SINGH, AND TAE SUK RO

*Department of Pharmacology, Baylor University College of Medicine,
Houston, Texas*

Proteins and Chromosome Structure

The chromosomal proteins may be considered to be those proteins that are normally associated with deoxyribonucleic acid (DNA) in the interphase cell. They are generally divided into three groups: (1) the histones, (2) the acidic nuclear proteins, and (3) the aggregate enzyme systems. It is noteworthy that the types and number of proteins associated with metaphase chromosomes in their condensed and morphologically classifiable state have not yet been identified. In part this has resulted from the fact that biochemists are unable to deal satisfactorily with the limited amounts of material in preparations of isolated chromosomes obtained thus far. A satisfactory methodology for the isolation of metaphase chromosomes is required so that sufficient amounts and subtypes of chromosomes can be available for studies on questions concerning the specificity of association of proteins with chromosomal sites. Because the chromosomal preparations available at present are contaminated by whole nuclei, broken parts of nuclei, and adventitious extranuclear materials, analyses of the protein components are fruitless.

What is clear is that the chromosomes of the metaphase state must contain associated proteins since DNA alone could hardly provide the types of coiling and overlapping that characterize the electron micrographs of the chromosomes. The "information" that codes for chromosomal structure is of considerable interest in view of the fact that these structures are remarkably consistent in the cells of given individuals. The possibility that peptides or amino acids interspersed through DNA in ester linkages may have structural significance has been suggested recently by Bendich *et al.* (1963), who pointed out that a variety of amino acids were left in DNA obtained from bull sperm. These amino acids included aspartic acid, glutamic acid, valine, serine, and lesser amounts of other amino acids. The presence of serine prompted the authors to suggest that phosphoester bonds of phosphoserine might serve as a linkage point of peptide and nucleotide.

One of the possible functions of the histones has been suggested to be the gluing together of DNA components, but it is very doubtful that the histones are related to the structure of the metaphase chromosomes. In collaborative studies with Dr. Hsu, the systems that have been employed for fixing the chromosomes include 30–50% glacial acetic acid. This concentration of acetic acid has been found to extract histones quantitatively from the chromosomal preparations, i.e., the additional amount of histone extracted with 0.25 N HCl was negligible.

The Acidic Nuclear Proteins

Among the proteins that may be related to the structure of the chromosomes are the acidic nuclear proteins. These proteins have been grouped together because of the difficulty of carrying out studies on their structure or function. In view of their insolubility in media commonly employed for biochemical analysis, there has been little or no analysis of their role in cell function, despite the fact that they are present in large amounts in cell nuclei and that in nontumor tissues their turnover rate is considerably greater than that of the histones. The possible function of these proteins as structural proteins of the chromosomes was pointed out by Mirsky and Ris (1947–1948a,b, 1949, 1950–1951) and Stedman and Stedman (1943a,b, 1944) almost simultaneously. The former workers reported that these proteins were not extractable with acid from their "chromosin" preparation which was the deoxyribonucleoprotein extracted from tissues with 2 M NaCl, the reagent developed by Bensley (1942) and by Pollister and Mirsky (1946–1947) for this purpose. Stedman and Stedman (1943a,b, 1944) reported that "chromosomin," an alkali-soluble nuclear protein, was present in large amount in the nuclei and suggested that this group of proteins might have important genetic functions. Mazia and his colleagues (Mazia, 1954; Mazia and Dan, 1952) also found that the acidic nuclear proteins were associated with the chromosomes. Further characterization of these proteins was achieved only recently (Steele and Busch, 1963), but even in early studies it was found that these proteins had limited solubility in aqueous media unless these solutions were strongly alkaline. In addition, the acidic nuclear proteins differed from the histones in that they contained tryptophan. Because of the presence of tryptophan in these proteins, they were called Tr.Pr. by Mirsky and Ris (1947–1948a,b, 1950–1951).

The amino acid composition of the acidic proteins of many of the nuclear fractions including the nucleolus, nuclear sap, chromatin, and residual protein is extremely similar and closely resembles that of the ribosomal proteins (Table I). These proteins all contain 8–10% of aspartic and 11–14% glutamic acid as well as substantial amounts of leucine and glycine. What is notable is that the proteins of the microsomes have virtually the same amino acid composition as the nuclear globulins and

TABLE I
AVERAGE AMINO ACID ANALYSIS OF ACIDIC NUCLEAR PROTEINS[a]

Amino acid	Percentages of total moles
Alanine	7
Arginine	7
Aspartic acid	9
Cystine	Trace
Glutamic acid	12
Glycine	9
Histidine	2
Isoleucine	8
Leucine	9
Lysine	7
Methionine	2
Phenylalanine	4
Proline	6
Serine	7
Threonine	5
Tyrosine	3
Valine	5

[a] From Busch et al. (1963b).

the nuclear ribosomes (Busch, 1964). This fact may be related to the origin of the proteins of the microsomes, i.e., the nucleolus is probably related to the synthesis of the mass of proteins and nucleic acids of the ribosomes (Busch et al., 1963b). The most soluble proteins of the nuclear sap differed from those of the other fractions (Table II) in their relatively high content of alanine and histidine and the lower content of glutamic acid and arginine. Still, the composition of these proteins was very similar to that of other nuclear proteins including those extracted from the chromatin fractions. The latter had lower concentrations of alanine and somewhat more glutamic acid than the proteins of the nuclear sap. The NH$_2$-terminal amino acids of these proteins, however, were found to be remarkably similar in that glycine, serine, and alanine were found to be the chief members of this group of amino acids.

From these findings it would seem that the acidic nuclear proteins are a group of heterogeneous but related proteins in that they have similar solubilities, amino acid compositions, and NH_2-terminal amino acids. Their different locations suggest that they may subserve different functions, yet it is possible that these locations reflect more their sites

TABLE II

AMINO ACID COMPOSITION OF PROTEINS OF THE NUCLEAR SAP

Amino acid	Percentage of total moles
Alanine	9.4
Arginine	3.3
Aspartic acid	10.1
Cystine	0.7
Glutamic acid	10.0
Glycine	8.4
Histidine	3.8
Isoleucine	3.9
Leucine	9.5
Lysine	8.7
Methionine	1.3
Phenylalanine	4.1
Proline	5.5
Serine	6.3
Threonine	5.2
Tyrosine	2.1
Valine	7.4

of synthesis and utilization. For example, their presence in chromatin may reflect the synthesis of nucleolar precursors of ribosomes or the biosynthesis of ribonucleo-proteins in smaller amounts in structural entities that may be similar to the micronucleoli. The presence of the acidic proteins in the nucleoli is probably related to the biosynthesis of the ribosomal components in the nucleoli which are transported through the nuclear ribonucleoprotein network to the cytoplasm where they are joined to the endoplasmic reticulum (Busch *et al.*, 1963a; Smetana *et al.*, 1963; Smetana and Busch, 1963, 1964). The presence of these proteins in the nuclear sap is probably a reflection of the destruction of the nuclear ribonucleoprotein network and solubilization of its components with either tris buffer or dilute saline used for extraction of the nuclear sap.

The Acidic Proteins and Gene Modulation

The possible relationships between the histones and the other components of the genetic apparatus has been extensively discussed recently (Bonner, 1964; Busch et al., 1963b). The possible operon groups (polyoperons) involved in normal cell function, cell growth and multiplication, and abnormal cell growth are illustrated in Table III. Although the terminology is largely descriptive and the presence of such operon groups has not been established, it seems that most mammalian cells may share in common the components of Operon Group I which provides the basic elements necessary for the fundamental metabolism of the cell.

TABLE III
OPERON GROUPS (POLYOPERONS) AND GROWTH

I.	Basic cell metabolism. This operon group consists of genes controlling the basic carbohydrate and amino acid metabolism of cells and is designed to provide for fundamental cell function
II.	A specialized cell function. This operon group defines the individual characteristics of the particular cell based upon the specialized read-outs from the genome
III.	The operon group for cell growth. This operon group controls increases in cell size and increases in number of nuclei in cells, i.e., polyploidy
IV.	The operon group for cell division. This operon group initiates normal division as occurs in benign tumors
V.	The cancer operon group. This operon group codes for irregular cell division, chromosome breakage, metastases, invasiveness, uncontrolled growth, unequal cell division, multiple mitosis, as well as phenotypic repression

The mechanism of function of Operon Group II that may control cell specialization is clearly the subject of much discussion. Exactly why the genome of the liver cell should differ so remarkably in its expression from that of the rod cells of the retina or the many other specialized cells is not clear. As has been shown by Gurdon (1962), the potential totality of gene expression is not lost from the many phenotypically different cells of the adult organism, but rather the expression of the genes is blocked.

Interestingly, there are three types of cells in which there is total repression of the genome and they are the object of considerable individual study:

1. The nucleated red cell of birds. This cell cannot divide and apparently carries an inactive nucleus as manifested by its inability to biosynthesize ribonucleic acid (RNA), protein, or DNA (Allfrey and Mirsky, 1951; Cameron and Prescott, 1963).

2. The sperm. These highly specialized cells possess nuclear proteins of a special class, the protamines, which were discovered by Miescher (1897). Although the protamines are not present in all classes of sperm, they and the other nuclear proteins of the sperm serve to block metabolic functions of the spermatozoa completely.

3. The Mengo virus-infected cells. Franklin and Baltimore (1962) and, more recently, Franklin (1964) have shown that a basic protein which is coded for by the virus penetrates the nucleus of the host cell and totally blocks the metabolism of the nucleus of the host cell.

Operon Groups Involved in Growth

The development of information on the growth process has clarified the point that DNA synthesis is a rather late biochemical stage in the process. The synthesis of RNA (McArdle and Creaser, 1963) and histones (Holbrook et al., 1962) precedes the synthesis of DNA in regenerating liver as measured in this and other laboratories. From a cytochemical point of view the whole nucleus enlarges prior to the division of the cell. Under some circumstances this enlargement is as far as the growth process proceeds. In others the nucleus may undergo division without separation of the cytoplasm; as a result polyploid cells appear. These developments are regarded as individual types of changes and are suggested to be functions of Operon Group III. Operon Group IV is suggested to serve as the functional entity that is important in the replication of cells which are normal, as in the case of regenerating liver, the repair of wounds, hyperplasia, or hormone-controlled growth.

The characteristics of neoplastic growth are so remarkably different from those of the growth of other types of tissues that they are grouped together as a function of Operon Group V. Such highly individualistic characteristics as the development of metastases, multiplicity of division to form more than two daughter cells, invasiveness, aneuploidy of chromosomes, aneuploidy of nucleoli, etc., are altogether too bizarre to be included as part of the operon groups that are responsible for normal growth and division of cells. The suggestion has been made (Busch, 1961) that there is such an operon group in every cell of the adult mammal but that it is repressed until the cell is subjected to carcinogenic or oncogenic stimuli.

Interaction of Acidic Proteins and Histones

On the basis of turnover data, the concept has been presented that the histones are not rigidly bound to DNA and that they separate from

DNA at finite rates governed by equilibria and by the presence of molecules which compete with DNA for histones (Busch *et al.*, 1963b). One critical point that was lacking to support this suggestion was the apparent absence of soluble acidic proteins from the nucleus. As mentioned earlier, there are large concentrations of acidic proteins in a variety of nuclear and cytoplasmic structures, but for the most part these proteins are apparently unavailable for interaction with the histones because of their low solubility.

TABLE IV

AMINO ACID COMPOSITION OF GLUTAMIC-RICH ACIDIC NUCLEAR PROTEINS

Amino acid	Value[a]
Alanine	8.2
Arginine	4.4
Aspartic acid	11.7
Glutamic acid	20.8
Glycine	6.3
Histidine	1.6
Isoleucine	3.2
Leucine	9.7
Lysine	4.9
Methionine	0.1
Phenylalanine	2.4
Proline	3.8
Serine	8.5
Threonine	6.3
Tyrosine	1.3
Valine	5.8

[a] The values are moles per 100 moles of amino acids.

Recently, two new groups of proteins, the "glutamic acid-rich" nuclear proteins, have been found, one by Johns in London (1964) and the other in our laboratory. As shown in Table IV, these proteins have high concentrations of glutamic and aspartic acid. The proteins of Johns (1964) had very high concentrations of lysine and those found in our laboratory have very small amounts of basic amino acids. The precise isoelectric points of these proteins are not established, but from their amino acid compositions they could well be the most acidic proteins of mammalian nuclei. Until the glutamine and asparagine content of these proteins is ascertained, it is too early to consider them as very acidic rather than neutral or basic proteins. At pH 2 some migrate toward the cathode, but this is not surprising since ionization of the carboxyl groups is suppressed and the amines and guanidino groups should be protonated.

These proteins would appear to be better candidates than other acidic nuclear proteins for control of the equilibria mentioned previously, but a mechanism for such control is not yet apparent. It is conceivable that histones linked to DNA could be replaced by acidic proteins, be displaced by acidic proteins, or simply migrate off the surface of DNA and be "captured" by such acidic proteins in the same way that histones are bound to carboxymethyl cellulose columns which have been effective in their chromatographic analysis (Busch, 1965).

The Histones and Gene Modulation

Although the concept was originally proposed by Stedman and Stedman (1943b) and accepted by others (Busch, 1962), there was little evidence until recently that histones could be involved in control of the genome. The now classic experiments of Huang and Bonner (1962) served to show that not only was DNA-primed RNA labeling blocked by the histones but also that different histone fractions exerted different degrees of inhibition of labeling of RNA.

The experiments that have served to support this idea have not always agreed on the relative inhibition of RNA labeling by different histones and also have not agreed on the mechanism of the inhibition. For example, studies of Huang and Bonner (1962) showed that there was marked inhibition of labeling of RNA when very lysine-rich histones were added to the system, but the experiments of Allfrey et al. (1963) and of Hindley (1963) showed that there was little inhibition of RNA labeling by this group of the histones. Conversely, the experiments of Huang and Bonner showed that there was little inhibition of RNA labeling when "arginine-rich" histones were added to the medium, and both Allfrey et al. (1963) and Hindley (1963) reported an opposite result.

Effects of Histones on Labeling of RNA of Isolated Nucleoli

The development of methods for the isolation of nucleoli (Muramatsu et al., 1963; Desjardins et al., 1963) from tumors and other tissues has permitted the demonstration of RNA polymerase and DNA-primed RNA labeling in isolated nucleolar systems (Ro et al., 1964). These systems have the advantage of being representative of events in RNA synthesis in situ and of being satisfactory for the demonstration of reactions in vitro. The problem that has been very difficult in the studies on the effects of histones on DNA-primed RNA labeling has been that of the rapid precipitation of histone–DNA complexes from the saline solutions.

Crampton *et al.* (1954a, b) showed that deoxyribonucleoproteins are virtually insoluble in dilute salt solutions. Unfortunately, most of the studies made on the priming systems have been carried out in dilute saline solutions. Thus, the studies that have suggested that histones block the biosynthesis of RNA may be vitiated by the fact that DNA primers have simply been precipitated from solution.

In the systems in which tumor histones were either incubated with tumor nucleoli or with nucleoli of liver cells, there was some but not complete inhibition of DNA-primed labeling of RNA. As noted previously, both deoxyribonuclease (DNase) and actinomycin D completely blocked the labeling of RNA (Ro *et al.*, 1964), and hence the biosynthetic reactions were DNA dependent. The very lysine-rich histones of fraction 1 exerted no inhibitory effect on the activity of the system, and at low concentration some stimulation of the activity of the system was found, i.e., the RNA had a higher specific activity (Tables V and VI). Bonner (1964) has pointed out that this histone differs from the others in its greater solubility and greater number of proline residues. Since proline residues are related to angulation of the protein, the higher amount of proline in the very lysine-rich histones may reflect a greater degree of angulation. The most inhibitory histone fraction was fraction 3, the "arginine-rich" histone fraction, but this fraction only inhibited the activity of the system by 40–60% even in the presence of five times as much histone as DNA. A suggestion has been made that histones are sterically blocked from combining with DNA by the acidic proteins present.

These studies with isolated nucleoli have served to show that the inhibitory effect of the histones on the priming activity of DNA is not at all as marked as the inhibition that occurs in the systems with isolated DNA. Although steric factors may play a role in this lack of inhibition, it is more likely that the continued availability of DNA as a primer in suspension rather than in solution may have accounted for the greater priming activity manifested by the system. Although these studies do not rule out a role of histones in suppression of DNA labeling, they certainly suggest that there has been some overemphasis of this point and possibly that histones may facilitate RNA biosynthesis.

What is even more important is that new experiments can be suggested for testing the role of the histones. A number of procedures may markedly affect the activity of nucleoli or their size, including treatment of animals with thioacetamide, excision of portions of the liver to promote regeneration, and induction of neoplastic changes, either by chemical carcinogens or oncogenic viruses. It is now possible to learn whether the histone content or type changes in these nucleolar preparations. To obtain sufficient nucleoli and nucleolar histones for further analysis, studies have been made on mass isolation of the nucleoli. The original

TABLE V
EFFECT OF TUMOR HISTONES ON LABELING OF RNA OF ISOLATED LIVER NUCLEOLI

Histone	Addition (mg)	Average specific activity of RNA	Per cent inhibition or stimulation
Control		32,000	
Fraction 1	0.5	35,100	+10
Fraction 1	1.0	28,500	−12
Fraction 2a	0.5	22,700	−29
Fraction 2a	1.0	18,400	−42
Fraction 2b	0.5	21,300	−33
Fraction 2b	1.0	17,510	−45
Fraction 3	0.5	20,900	−35
Fraction 3	1.0	15,400	−52

TABLE VI
EFFECT OF TUMOR HISTONES ON LABELING OF RNA OF ISOLATED TUMOR NUCLEOLI

Histone	Addition (mg)	Average specific activity of RNA	Per cent inhibition or stimulation
Control		25,800	
Fraction 1	0.25	32,700	+27
Fraction 1	0.5	29,900	+17
Fraction 1	1.0	29,400	+14
Fraction 2a	0.5	21,700	−16
Fraction 2a	1.0	14,400	−44
Fraction 2b	0.25	22,600	−12
Fraction 2b	0.5	18,200	−29
Fraction 2b	1.0	13,700	−47
Fraction 3	0.25	28,200	−14
Fraction 3	0.5	16,800	−35
Fraction 3	1.0	15,600	−40

technique of sonic oscillation permitted isolation of only a few milligrams of nucleoli during 1 day; but recently both the amount of material that can be obtained by sonic oscillation has been increased and, in addition, it has been possible to develop a new apparatus for continuous compression and decompression of nuclei. Since the histochemical analysis of nucleoli and the surrounding "nucleolus-associated chromatin" has shown that there are only small amounts of DNA and histones associated with nucleoli (Busch *et al.*, 1963a), it is clear that the development of such mass isolation procedures is a necessary prelude to further fractionation procedures.

Structure of the *N*-Proline Histone

The development of theories of the mechanism of action or function of histones has been handicapped by lack of chemical characterization of any one or any group of histones. From the large amounts of arginine in protamines (Felix *et al.*, 1956) it naturally has been assumed that the protamines serve to neutralize the changes on DNA, and yet a precise relationship between positive charge on the protamines and the DNA of the sperm has not been demonstrated. Moreover, the recent findings of Bril-Peterson and Westenbrink (1963) have suggested that proteins other than protamines are associated with DNA in bull sperm, and these proteins are probably not basic proteins.

Following the finding of "arginine-rich" histones by Kossel and his colleagues (Kossel, 1921), it was assumed by many that histones were counterparts of the protamines that seemed to function as neutralizing substances for DNA. Continued experiments on the isolation of histones (Busch, 1965), however, have shown that there are a number of different histones and further that these differ markedly from one another in their contents of basic amino acids. In addition, they have some special properties. For example the "arginine-rich" histones have only about 12% of their total moles of amino acids accounted for as arginine residues, and as Phillips and Simson (1962) showed the spacing of the amino acids was such that there could be no precisely ordered neutralization of charges on the precisely regular alternating deoxyribose phosphates of DNA. Also, the "very lysine-rich" histones have the interesting feature that they are the most angulated and also most soluble of the various histone fractions.

Further evidence for the heterogeneity of the histones has been obtained in studies on the peptide composition of the histones. The histone fractions 2a and 2b largely contain the *N*-acetylalanine histone and the *N*-proline histone, respectively. When tryptic hydrolyzates of these two fractions were prepared, it was found that the peptide patterns were so different that completely different solvent systems were required for mapping the peptides (Busch *et al.*, 1963b). In addition, it was found that of the peptides studied for the elementary amino acid composition there were none that were identical in the two histone fractions. The obvious conclusion is that the *N*-acetylalanine histones and the *N*-proline histone are completely different proteins.

The improvement in techniques for the subfractionation of the histones finally has lead to the isolation of one highly purified histone

TABLE VII
AMINO ACID ANALYSIS OF *N*-PROLINE HISTONE

Amino acid	% Total moles	% Weight	Residues per mole protein
Alanine	10.1	7.1	20
Arginine	7.7	10.6	15
Aspartic Acid	5.5	5.7	11
Cysteine	—	—	—
Cystine	—	—	—
Glutamic acid	9.4	10.9	19
Glycine	6.3	3.7	13
Histidine	2.7	3.3	5
Isoleucine	4.4	4.5	9
Leucine	5.8	6.0	12
Lysine	14.8	17.3	30
Methionine	1.5	1.7	3
Phenylalanine	1.4	1.8	3
Proline	4.7	4.3	9
Serine	8.6	7.1	17
Threonine	6.3	5.9	13
Tyrosine	2.9	4.1	6
Valine	6.6	6.1	13
Tryptophan	<0.4	—	—
Total residues			198

fraction, the *N*-proline histone. As has been reported previously (Busch *et al.*, 1963b), this histone fraction contained moderately large amounts of lysine (Table VII) and smaller amounts of alanine, glutamic acid, and serine. Although the main fraction has been purified considerably, there is still some uncertainty about the final purity of the product in view of the fact that a small slow moving band appears on starch-gel electrophoresis as well as a small band that moves more rapidly than the main mass of the *N*-proline histone. In addition, Phillips (1963) has reported the possibility that proteins with blocked end groups are present in this fraction, and it may be surmised that these would not be detected by the analytical procedures employed.

Although a total of 46 peptides would be expected to be formed on tryptic hydrolysis of the *N*-proline histone, only 20 peptides have been isolated by means of chromatography of the tryptic hydrolyzate on Dowex 50-X2. In these studies, pyridine acetate in increasing concentration was utilized to elute the histones as shown in Fig. 1. When systems employing citrate buffers were utilized to elute the peptides from the resin, considerably more peptides were found, i.e., approximately 28–30 peptides were eluted. This number agrees better with the number of peptides found by peptide mapping (Hnilica *et al.*, 1963). The fact that

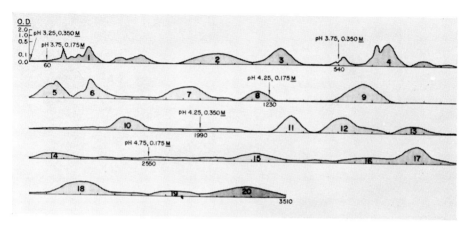

Fig. 1. The separation of twenty peptide peaks from a tryptic hydrolyzate of the *N*-proline histone. Pyridine acetate buffers were used to elute the peaks from a Dowex 50-X2 column 150 × 1.8 cm. The ordinate is optical density continually read at 570 mμ following the reaction with ninhydrin and the abscissa is milliliters of effluent volume.

approximately 29 peptides were found in a protein fraction that should produce about 50 has suggested the possibility that the *N*-proline histone may represent a dimer which has an over-all molecular weight of 22,000 and a molecular weight of 11,000 for each strand. The smaller value would agree with the subunit molecular weight for a histone fraction that was reported by Trautman and Crampton (1959).

The *elementary amino acid analysis* of the peptides of the *N*-proline histone is shown in Table VIII. Perhaps the most noteworthy of these analytical values is that for peptide 1 which is the largest of the peptide fractions and contains 16 amino acids. In addition, the NH$_2$-terminal amino acid of this peptide is proline, and this is the only terminal proline that has been found thus far. Although this peptide does not seem to be a mixture of peptides, further analytical studies are necessary before this point can be completely accepted.

A second point of interest is that the peptides isolated range in size from free lysine to the hexadecapeptide shown in peptide 1. The elementary amino acid analysis of these peptides accounts for approximately 59% of the total amino acid residues.

TABLE VIII

ELEMENTARY AMINO ACID COMPOSITION OF PEPTIDES OF THE N-PROLINE HISTONE

1. Ala_3, Asp_2, Glu_2, Gly_2, Phe_2, Pro, Ser, Thr, Val, Lys
2. Ala_2, Glu_2, Gly, Leu_2, Pro, Lys
3. Ala, Glu_2, Gly, Leu_3, Pro, Lys
4. Ala, Asp, Glu, Gly, His, Ser, Lys
5. Glu_2, Gly, Pro, Ser_4, Tyr_2, Val_2, Lys
6. Ala_2, Pro_2, Ser, Lys
7. Ala, Glu, Gly, Lys
8. Asp, Gly, Ser, Thr, Lys
9. Ala, Asp, Gly, Ser, Lys
10. Ala_2, Glu, Gly, Ileu, Ser, Arg
11. Ileu, Ser_2, Thr_2, Arg
12. Ala, Thr, Val, Lys
13. Ala, Val, Lys
14. Lys
15. Ala, Glu, Lys
16. Ser, Thr, Tyr, Lys
17. Asp, Lys

These data have led to a number of conclusions about the structure of the N-proline histone. The first of these is that there is no regularity of structure of this protein, i.e., it is not possible that the N-proline histone serves to neutralize the deoxyribose phosphates of DNA unless many unusual types of twists and bends occur in the molecule. The second is that the central peptide chain or the "core" of the protein is probably more basic than the peripheral parts of the protein.

To obtain further insight into the peptides of the N-proline histones,

TABLE IX

AMINO ACID SEQUENCES IN THE PEPTIDES OF THE N-PROLINE HISTONE

2. Leu-Pro-Ala-(Ala, Glu_2, Gly, Leu_2)-Lys
9. Asp-Ala-Ser-Gly-Lys
12. Ala-Val-Thr-Lys
13. Ala-Val-Lys
14. Lys
15. Ala-Glu-Lys
17. Asp-Lys

studies are in progress on the sequences of amino acids in the isolated peptides. At present, seven of the peptides have been analyzed as shown in Table IX. Further experiments are in progress to determine whether DNA binding sites can be established for the N-proline histone.

Mechanisms of Gene Modulation

In order to discuss logically the question of gene modulation, it is necessary to specify the point or stage being considered in the life of the individual as well as the specialized type of cell. Different types of gene modulation could be involved at different stages of development, such as early embryogenesis, tissue regeneration (liver, skin, and gastrointestinal tract), cell specialization (spermiogenesis), and in neoplasia. Some instances of total genome loss such as the nuclear extrusion phenomenon of red blood cells could be considered as an extreme type of modulation of the genome.

If one considers the totipotent cell of the zygote or the two-, four-, or eight-cell stage of embryogenesis, it would appear that these cells could produce any type of cell, including the whole organism. Nevertheless, they really are quite limited in their product. They neither produce a liver cell, cardiac fiber, or other cell type, but rather produce only a generalized kind of cell that remains totipotent. One can only ask the question whether in these cells the total genome is functional or is that segment of the genome functional that can produce an undifferentiated but totipotent cell.

At some point in embryogenesis the cells become predestined or specified with respect to specialization. The specification of functional and morphological characteristics apparently persists, since "omnia cellula e cellula ejusdem generis" (Thiersch, 1865). In regeneration, liver cells only give rise to liver cells, and no other cell types appear in the regenerating liver. The only types of cells that seem to have the ability to produce a variety of kinds of cells are those of teratomas. As an aside, one aspect of the problem of cell replacement that has connotations in other areas is that of inability of regeneration of specialized cells in a variety of tissues. This is a far more common phenomenon than is the regeneration of parenchyma as in the case of the regenerating liver.

Thus, it would appear that in the mammal, one form or type of gene modulation is a phenomenon related to the stage of development in the sense that the cells are totipotent only in the early embryonic stages and that later many are fully defined in terms of function or even in terms of their product when they are growing and dividing.

In neoplastic cells the cells produced represent either cells similar to the cells of origin or cells that simply are becoming less differentiated phenotypically, presumably by partial to complete blocks of Operon Group II (Table III). In spermatogenesis another type of change occurs in which the genome becomes blocked, apparently by specialized proteins.

Substances Involved in Gene Modulation

The choices of substances involved in these complex processes are not limited to proteins and nucleic acids, although it does not seem that either lipids or carbohydrates are directly involved in genomic control; however, it is clear that in many tissues Operon Groups III and IV are sensitive to growth hormone. In other tissues, these operon groups and Operon Group II are sensitive to steroids and other hormones.

From the experiments of Gurdon (1962) it seems clear that there is no alteration of DNA in the course of development, i.e., the master templates are not affected. What then can subserve the role of the controlling influence on cell function if the master templates are the same? In other terms, what types of substances have the broad range of specificity to affect the genome and stipulate whether one or another operon group (or polyoperon) regulates the phenotype of the cell.

One mechanism could involve proteins such as the *histones* and the *acidic nuclear proteins*. The number of types of these proteins, however, is quite limited, i.e., there are only about 10–15 types of histones, a few types of "very acidic" nuclear proteins, and a few types of relatively acidic nuclear proteins that have been found thus far. None of these would appear to have the degree of specificity necessary for influencing the genome. Nevertheless, special cases show that histones or other nuclear proteins are important to gene control. These include the nucleated red cell, the sperm head, and the nucleus in which activity is suppressed by the Mengo virus. In all of these, RNA synthesis is suppressed by proteins; RNA is not even found in the sperm head. The specificity required for gene control in embryogenesis would not seem to be found in the histones in the sense that the histones are few in types, although it is not possible to state yet the number of molecular species.

The studies of Ebisuzaki (1963) on the biological clock of the viruses have pointed toward proteins as gene repressors (Jacob and Wollman, 1961). It is conceivable that proteins adhere to DNA templates and block their activities, and it is not impossible, for example, that each cell makes one molecule of tryptophan pyrrolase or one molecule of its RNA template that adheres to the genome. If this were the case, release of the molecule through cytoplasmic demand could result in unblocking of the genome, and accumulation in the cytoplasm could result in gene repression.

Jacob and Monod (1961) suggested that *RNA* is the mechanism by which gene control occurs. Certainly there would be enough RNA molecules or potential molecular species, but as indicated above there is no RNA in some suppressed cells and it is difficult to envision that RNA complementary to the strand of its origin would also be complementary to the DNA which it is suppressing. Such a phenomenon is possible, but it is not likely. It has been suggested that the rapidly turning-over RNA of the nucleus is the key to this problem (Harris, 1964).

Functional State of the Genome

The qualitative control of the genome may well be related to the types of substances mentioned above, but it is difficult to understand at present how the genome is quantitatively controlled. For example, what determines the number of molecules of enzymes involved in the urea cycle that are present in the liver cell, or the size of the nucleolus and the number of nucleoli in such cells? Moreover, what determines the number of molecules of either β-galactosidase or tryptophan pyrrolase that are produced in response to the presence of inducers or hormones? These environmental influences may function in a way similar to the effect on the genome of cytoplasmic contact reported by Eagle (1964). The fibroblasts in cell culture continue to grow and divide until they touch adjacent cells and then they suddenly diminish their nuclear and cytoplasmic activity. This diminution of metabolic activity is associated with decreased biosynthesis of RNA in the nucleus.

It seems possible that some of the more mysterious effects on chromatin could be related to the release and repressive phenomena mentioned. Histone interaction with DNA, linkage of RNA or protein to the strands of DNA, derepression of RNA polymerases (Hurwitz, 1963; Chamberlin and Berg, 1962), hydrolysis of RNA by specifying RNase's, coiling and uncoiling of chromosomes, and geographical localization of genomic activity around nucleoli could all be involved in quantitative controls on gene activity.

At present, it is not possible to choose the likely candidates from these potential mechanisms of gene control. Some definitive experiments are being carried out with viruses and, hopefully, studies on nucleoli will permit some clarification of the mechanisms. To solve such important problems as neoplastic transformation, it is clearly important that such information be obtained.

Summary

In consideration of the problems involved in maintenance of the structure of the metaphase chromosomes and the function of the interphase chromosomes, the acidic nuclear proteins and the "very acidic" nuclear proteins generally seem to have been overlooked. The latter represents a recently described group of proteins that migrate slowly toward the cathode in electrophoresis, are eluted from carboxymethyl cellulose with 4 N formic acid, and contain 20% glutamic acid and 10–12% aspartic acid. The possible interactions between these proteins and the histones were discussed with respect to the release of gene segments for phenotypic modifications of cells and the release of the operon groups or polyoperons that relate to cell growth and cell division.

The effects of histones on the labeling of RNA in preparations containing isolated nucleoli were shown to be both stimulatory and inhibitory. The "very lysine-rich" histone fraction stimulated RNA labeling at low concentrations and inhibited RNA labeling at high concentrations. Although the most inhibitory histones were the "arginine-rich" histones, none were markedly inhibitory, i.e., maximal inhibitions of RNA labeling approached 40–60%. The nucleoli provide a system that is biologically of interest because they can be made to enlarge or diminish in size and function with the aid of such procedures as treatment of the whole animal with thioacetamide, actinomycin D, and 8-azaguanine. They are also enlarged in regenerating liver.

To learn more about the structure and function of the histones, one histone, the N-proline histone fraction, has been highly purified and subjected to tryptic hydrolysis and later amino acid analysis of the peptides. Although this work is not complete, it would appear that the peptide on the proline end of the molecule is a hexadecapeptide and that the "core" of the molecule is more basic than the periphery. Moreover, the variations in size of the peptides containing basic amino acids are such that the "neutralization" theory of the histone function is no longer tenable.

In consideration of the control of the function of the genome, it would appear that a number of molecular species could be involved, although specific mechanisms cannot be stated yet. The role of histones and other proteins in gene repression is now supported by several kinds of evidence. Quantitative modulation of the genome, however, in terms of definition of specific phenotype may be effected by different mechanisms than quantitative modulation of the genome in the phenotypically defined cell. The relationship of molecular modulation of the genome to coiling of chromosomes and geographical control by the development of nucleoli remains to be clarified.

ACKNOWLEDGMENTS

The authors wish to express their appreciation to Charles Taylor and Joe P. Arendell for their excellent technical assistance and to Drs. William J. Steele, Masami Muramatsu, and Hilmi Mavioglu for their helpful comments. The authors appreciate the preprint of the manuscript of Dr. E. W. Johns of the Chester Beatty Institute.

The original studies reported in this manuscript were supported in part by grants from the U. S. Public Health Service CA-05421 and CA-07201, the American Cancer Society, the Jane Coffin Childs Fund, and the National Science Foundation.

REFERENCES

ALLFREY, V. G., AND MIRSKY, A. E. (1951). The incorporation of N^{15}-glycine by avian erythrocytes and reticulocytes *in vitro*. *J. Gen. Physiol*. 35, 841-846.

ALLFREY, V. G., LITTAU, V. C., AND MIRSKY, A. E. (1963). On the role of histones in regulating ribonucleic acid synthesis in the cell nucleus. *Proc. Natl. Acad. Sci. U.S.* 49, 414-421.

BENDICH, A., BORENFREUND, E., KORNGOLD, G. C., KRIM, M., AND BALIS, M. E. (1963). Amino acids or small peptides as punctuation in the genetic code of DNA. *In* "Nucleic Acids and Their Role in Biology," Milan, 1963.

BENSLEY, R. R. (1942). Chemical structure of cytoplasm. *Science* 96, 389-393.

BONNER, J. (1964). *In* "The Nucleohistones" (J. Bonner and P. T'so, eds.), pp. 289-297. Holden-Day, San Francisco.

BRIL-PETERSEN, E., AND WESTENBRINIK, H. G. K. (1963). A structural basic protein as a counterpart of deoxyribonucleic acid in mammalian spermatozoa. *Biochim. Biophys. Acta* 76, 152-154.

BUSCH, H. (1961). Biochemistry of carcinogenesis: A theory. *Texas Rept. Biol. Med.* 19, 1-15.

BUSCH, H. (1962). "An Introduction to the Biochemistry of the Cancer Cell." Academic Press, New York.

BUSCH, H. (1964). "The Histones and Other Nuclear Proteins." Academic Press, New York. In press.

BUSCH, H., BYVOET, P., AND SMETANA, K. (1963a). The nucleolus of the cancer cell: a review. *Cancer Res*. 23, 313-339.

BUSCH, H., STEELE, W. J., HNILICA, L. S., TAYLOR, C. W., AND MAVIOGLU, H. (1963b). Biochemistry of histones and the cell cycle. *J. Cellular Comp. Physiol*. 62, Suppl. 1, 95-110.

CAMERON, I. L., AND PRESCOTT, D. M. (1963). RNA and protein metabolism in the maturation of the nucleated chicken erythrocyte. *Exptl. Cell Res*. 30, 609-612.

CHAMBERLIN, M., AND BERG, P. (1962). Deoxyribonucleic acid-directed synthesis of ribonucleic acid by an enzyme from *Escherichia coli*. *Proc. Natl. Acad. Sci. U.S.* **48**, 81-94.

CRAMPTON, C. F., LIPSHITZ, R., AND CHARGAFF, E. (1954b). Studies on nucleoproteins. I. Dissociation and reassociation of deoxyribonucleohistone of calf thymus. *J. Biol. Chem.* **206**, 499-510.

CRAMPTON, C. F., LIPSHITZ, R., AND CHARGAFF, E. (1954b). Studies on nucleoproteins. II. Fractionation of deoxyribonucleic acids through fractional dissociation of their complexes with basic protein. *J. Biol. Chem.* **211**, 125-142.

DESJARDINS, R., SMETANA, K., STEELE, W. J., AND BUSCH, H. (1963). Isolation of nucleoli of the Walker carcinosarcoma and liver of the rat following nuclear disruption in a French pressure cell. *Cancer Res.* **13**, 1819-1823.

EAGLE, H. (1964). Personal communication.

EBISUZAKI, K. (1963). On the regulation of the morphogenesis of bacteriophage T4. *J. Mol. Biol.* **7**, 379-387.

FELIX, K., FISCHER, H., AND KREKELS, A. (1956). Protamines and nucleoprotamines. *Progr. Biophys. Biophys. Chem.* **6**, 1-23.

FRANKLIN, R. M. (1964). Personal communication.

FRANKLIN, R. M., AND BALTIMORE, D. (1962). Patterns of macromolecular synthesis in normal and virus infected mammalian cells. *Cold Spring Harbor Symp. Quant. Biol.* **27**, 175-195.

GURDON, J. B. (1962). Adult frogs derived from the nuclei of single somatic cells. *Develop. Biol.* **4**, 256-273.

HARRIS, H. (1964). Function of the short-lived ribonucleic acid in the cell nucleus. *Nature* **201**, 863-867.

HINDLEY, J. (1963). The relative ability of reconstituted nucleohistones to allow DNA-dependent RNA synthesis. *Biochem. Biophys. Res. Commun.* **12**, 175-179.

HNILICA, L. S., TAYLOR, C. W., AND BUSCH, H. (1963). Analysis of peptides of the moderately lysine rich fraction, F2B, of the Walker tumor and other tissues. *Exptl. Cell Res.* Suppl. 9, 367-375.

HOLBROOK, D. J., JR., EVANS, J. H., AND IRVIN, J. L. (1962). Incorporation of labeled precursors into proteins and nucleic acids of nuclei of regenerating liver. *Exptl. Cell Res.* **28**, 120-125.

HUANG, R. C., AND BONNER, J. (1962). Histone, a suppressor of chromosomal RNA synthesis. *Proc. Natl. Acad. Sci. U. S.* **48**, 1216-1222.

HURWITZ, J. (1963). RNA polymerase. *In* "Methods in Enzymology" (S. P. Colowick and N. O. Kaplan, eds.), Vol. 6, pp. 23-27. Academic Press, New York.

JACOB, F., AND MONOD, J. (1961). Genetic regulatory mechanisms in the synthesis of proteins. *J. Mol. Biol.* **3**, 318-356.

JACOB, F., AND WOLLMAN, E. L. (1961). "Sexuality and the Genetics of Bacteria," p. 300. Academic Press, New York.

JOHNS, E. W. (1964). Studies on histones. 7. Preparative methods for histone fractions from calf thymus. *Biochem. J.* **92**, 55-59.

KOSSEL, A. (1921). "The Protamines and Histones." Longmans, Green, New York.

MCARDLE, A. H. (1963). Nucleoproteins in regenerating rat liver. II. A study of the rapidly labelled ribonucleic acid. *Biochim. Biophys. Acta* **68**, 569-577.

McArdle, A. H., and Creaser, E. H. (1963). Nucleoproteins in regenerating rat liver. I. Incorporation of $^{32}P_i$ into the ribonucleic acid of liver during the early stages of regeneration. *Biochim. Biophys. Acta* **68**, 561-568.

Mazia, D. (1954). The particulate organization of the chromosome. *Proc. Natl. Acad. Sci. U. S.* **40**, 521-527.

Mazia, D., and Dan, K. (1952). Isolation of mitotic apparatus of sea urchin egg. *Proc. Natl. Acad. Sci. U. S.* **38**, 826-838.

Miescher, F. (1897). "Die Histochemischen und Physiologischen Arbeiten." Vogel, Leipzig.

Mirsky, A. E., and Ris, H. (1947-1948a). Isolated chromosomes. *J. Gen. Physiol.* **31**, 1-6.

Mirsky, A. E., and Ris, H. (1947-1948b). The chemical composition of isolated chromosomes. *J. Gen. Physiol.* **31**, 7-18.

Mirsky, A. E., and Ris, H. (1949). Variable and constant components of chromosomes. *Nature* **163**, 666-667.

Mirsky, A. E., and Ris, H. (1950-1951). The composition and structure of isolated chromosomes. *J. Gen. Physiol.* **34**, 475-492.

Muramatsu, M., Smetana, K., and Busch, H. (1963). Quantitative aspects of isolation of nucleoli of the Walker carcinosarcoma and liver of the rat. *Cancer Res.* **23**, 510-518.

Phillips, D. M. P. (1963). The presence of acetyl groups in histones. *Biochem. J.* **87**, 258-263.

Phillips, D. M. P., and Simson, P. (1962). Identification of some peptides from an arginine-rich histone and their bearing on the structure of deoxyribonucleohistone. *Biochem. J.* **82**, 236-241.

Pollister, A. W., and Mirsky, A. E. (1946-1947). The nucleoprotamine of trout sperm. *J. Gen. Physiol.* **30**, 101-115.

Ro, T. S., Muramatsu, M., and Busch, H. (1964). Labeling of RNA of isolated nucleoli with UTP-14C. *Biochem. Biophys. Res. Commun.* **14**, 149-155.

Smetana, K., and Busch, H. (1963). On the ultrastructure of the Walker 256 carcinosarcoma. *Cancer Res.* **23**, 1600-1603.

Smetana, K., and Busch, H. (1964). Studies on the ultrastructure of the nucleoli of the Walker tumor and rat liver. *Cancer. Res.* **24**, 537-558.

Smetana, K., Steele, W. J., and Busch, H. (1963). A nuclear ribonucleoprotein network. *Exptl. Cell Res.* **31**, 198-202.

Stedman, E., and Stedman, E. (1943a). Chromosomin, a protein constituent of chromosomes. *Nature* **152**, 267.

Stedman, E., and Stedman, E. (1943b). Probable function of histone as a regulator of mitosis. *Nature* **152**, 556.

Stedman, E., and Stedman, E. (1944). "Chromosomin" and nucleic acids. *Nature* **153**, 500-502.

Steele, W. J., and Busch, H. (1963). Studies on acidic nuclear proteins of the Walker tumor and liver. *Cancer Res.* **23**, 1153-1163.

Thiersch, C. (1865). "Der Epithelial Krebs." Englemann, Leipzig.

Trautman, R., and Crampton, C. F. (1959). Application of the Archibald principle for the ultracentrifugal determination of the molecular weight in urea solutions of histone fractions from calf thymus. *J. Am. Chem. Soc.* **81**, 4036-4040.

Binding of Actinomycin
As a Model for the
Complex-Forming Capacity of DNA

EDWARD REICH

The Rockefeller Institute, New York, New York

The phenomenon of cellular differentiation—i.e., differing phenotypic character of cells possessing identical genotypes—has often been attributed to differential gene activity (Sonneborn, 1964). According to current theories the biochemical pathway of gene action involves the functioning in a complex sequence of (1) the gene itself (deoxyribonucleic acid, DNA), (2) the primary gene product (template ribonucleic acid, tRNA), and (3) the cellular equipment responsible for protein synthesis (ribosomes, aminoacyl-RNA, and amino acid-activating enzymes). Detailed knowledge of this series of reactions is still limited, and numerous biochemical steps probably remain to be discovered. However, the already known complexity of this process provides multiple potential points of control and implies that the unknown mechanisms that determine the qualitative and quantitative properties of a cellular phenotype may be affecting any and perhaps many of these reactions.

The most influential current working hypothesis proposes that the regulation of gene action operates at the genetic level, i.e., controls the functioning of DNA itself (Jacob and Monod, 1961). This hypothesis, which possesses many attractive features, is supported mainly by the results of genetic experiments performed with bacterial systems. Neither the structure of the "repressor" molecules, which are considered to control gene function, nor the characteristics of the postulated reaction with DNA is known. However, the possibility that molecular interactions involving DNA may have physiological significance justifies the study of model reactions. Such reactions between nucleic acids and small molecules of known structure may lead to greater understanding of the kinds of reaction mechanisms which might occur within the cell and of the reactive participating functional groups of DNA.

Numerous substances (partial list in Table I) including inorganic ions form reversible complexes with DNA, but very few of these interactions have been investigated systematically. In most reactions not involving only simple electrostatic forces, results of experiments have been inconclusive as regards the precise nature of the binding site, the basic mechanism of binding, and even the total number of sites. (Since the structure of helical nucleic acids has been elucidated in recent years, it may be ex-

TABLE I
Substances That Form Reversible Complexes with DNA

Class of compounds	Substance
Ions	Mg, Hg, Cu, Ag, Au, Mn
Dyes	Acridines (e.g., proflavine) and many of their derivatives
	Rosaniline, methylene blue, methyl green, safranine, neutral red
Antibiotics	Actinomycin, daunomycin, cinerubin, chromomycin, phleomycin
Peptides and proteins	Histones, protamines, albumin, ribonuclease, polylysine

pected that detailed understanding of many of these reactions will be achieved in the near future.) Because of their biological effects on intact systems, proflavine and actinomycin have been studied most extensively.

Actinomycin (Fig. 1) is a polypeptide antibiotic whose biological effects are noteworthy for their specificity and selectivity.

1. Actinomycin at low concentrations inhibits DNA-dependent RNA synthesis of intact mammalian and bacterial cells, but does not impair DNA replication (Reich *et al.*, 1961, 1962a; Goldberg and Rabinowitz, 1962; Hartmann and Coy, 1962; Hurwitz *et al.*, 1962). These effects of actinomycin are observed also under conditions *in vitro* when nucleic acid synthesis is catalyzed by purified enzymes (Goldberg and Rabinowitz, 1962; Hartmann and Coy, 1962; Hurwitz *et al.*, 1962). Thus, although a single template is involved in both reactions, actinomycin selectively inhibits only one of the polymerizations directed by DNA. It is important to note that the effect of actinomycin is due to its ability to complex with the DNA template and is not exerted on the enzyme protein or the other elements of the reaction. Since the DNA-dependent synthesis of RNA is considered to be the first step in gene action, the above facts mean that actinomycin is capable of blocking the expression of hereditary information while not interfering with genetic replication at all or interfering only very slightly.

2. The primary, direct toxicity of actinomycin appears to be restricted to those processes, such as nucleotide polymerizations, requiring the direct participation of DNA. This is suggested by the observations that the life cycles of numerous RNA viruses are unaffected by actinomycin, in both mammalian and bacterial systems (Reich *et al.*, 1961, 1962a; Haywood and Sinsheimer, 1963). These findings show that the large number of cellular functions required to sustain virus growth are

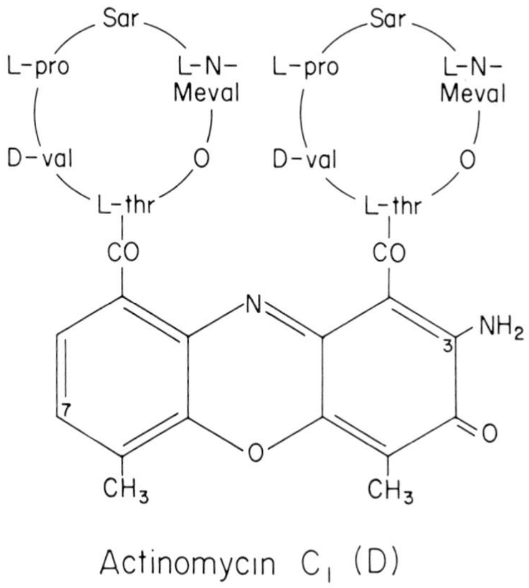

Actinomycin C₁ (D)

Fig. 1. Structure of Actinomycin C₁ (D) (Brockmann, 1960). thr, L-threonine; val, D-valine; pro, L-proline; sar, sarcosine; Meval, L-/N-methylvaline.

unimpaired by actinomycin, even when the host cell has been exposed to this antibiotic for 24 hours prior to infection.

3. Actinomycin forms reversible complexes with DNA, but not with other cellular components (Rauen *et al.*, 1960; Kirk, 1960; Kawamata and Imanishi, 1961; Reich, 1962). It would not be surprising if actinomycin were to bind to protein or even to some species of RNA, but so far all attempts to demonstrate such interactions have failed. Thus, within the limits of current knowledge actinomycin is a highly specific reagent for a single cellular constituent—DNA.

4. Several facts point to helical structure as an important determinant of the ability of DNA to bind actinomycin. For example, the maximal actinomycin-binding capacity of naturally occurring DNA's is reduced

by 15–20% following heating and rapid cooling (Goldberg *et al.*, 1962; Reich *et al.*, 1962b). The single-stranded DNA from bacteriophage ϕ-174 complexes less than half as much actinomycin as do DNA preparations of similar base composition. Finally, it has been observed that actinomycin remains bound to helical DNA throughout any temperature range in which the helical structure is preserved, whereas no complex formation is detectable under conditions which lead to strand separation (Reich, 1964).

For reasons which will not be discussed in detail here, it appears quite likely that the configuration of intracellular DNA is always helical and that this form, rather than single-stranded DNA, is the substrate for nucleic acid polymerases. Therefore, it is of interest that the specificity of actinomycin should be directed particularly toward helical DNA.

5. Of the four bases in DNA only guanine is indispensable for binding actinomycin (Goldberg *et al.*, 1962; Reich *et al.*, 1962b; Kahan *et al.*, 1963). Since actinomycin complexing occurs preferentially with helical DNA, the functional group(s) of guanine which interact with actinomycin must be accessible in this configuration. Only the edges of the base pairs are exposed in helical DNA, and the accessible functional groups of all bases are restricted to the two grooves on the surface of the DNA helix. Since actinomycin interacts in some way with guanine, at least a part of the bound actinomycin molecule must be located in one of the grooves. On the basis of considerations discussed in detail elsewhere (Hamilton *et al.*, 1963; Reich and Goldberg, 1964), it has been proposed that actinomycin is bound in the minor groove of helical DNA in the B conformation (Hamilton *et al.*, 1963). Under these conditions binding can be mediated by a series of hydrogen bonds which may be formed between actinomycin and DNA, and the specificity for guanine is determined by a hydrogen bond linking the amino group of guanine with the quinoidal oxygen of the actinomycin chromophore. This model is at present merely a working hypothesis which is in accord with all known facts of actinomycin action. It accounts satisfactorily for the role of the functional groups of actinomycin and the structures in DNA known to be required for complex formation, and it can be tested experimentally.

One prediction which follows from the model is that the elimination of the guanine amino group from the minor groove of DNA should be associated with loss of ability to bind actinomycin. The synthetic DNA polymer dIdC contains only hypoxanthine and cytosine; and its structure is identical with that of synthetic dGdC (containing only guanine and cytosine) (Kornberg, 1961) except that dIdC lacks an amino group in the minor groove. As seen in Fig. 2, the characteristic difference spectrum of actinomycin, which is observed on complexing with DNA, is not found in the presence of dAT or dIdC. A further prediction from the model is

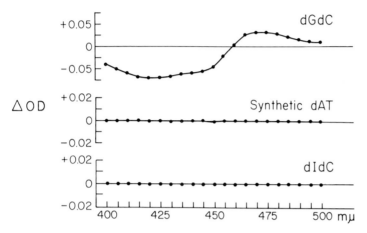

Fig. 2. Difference spectra of actinomycin in the presence of different synthetic DNA polymers. The data for dAT and dGdC taken from Goldberg *et al.* (1962).

that actinomycin should not interfere with the reaction between mustard gas and DNA, since it is known that mustard gas reacts with N-7 of guanine (Brookes and Lawley, 1960), which is located in the major groove of DNA. The data in Table II confirm this expectation. A corollary of the latter finding is that DNA containing guanine previously alkylated at

TABLE II
INCORPORATION OF S^{35}-MUSTARD GAS INTO DNA[a]

Sample	cpm
Control	7480
Actinomycin present	8360

[a] Native calf thymus DNA was dissolved (0.5 mg per milliliter) in phosphate buffer as described by Brookes and Lawley (1960) and maintained at 0°C. Radioactive mustard gas (labeled with S^{35}) was added at a molar ratio of one molecule of gas for two molecules of DNA-guanine. After 2 minutes a hundredfold excess of carrier mustard gas was added, and then the DNA was precipitated with streptomycin. The precipitate was washed with dilute buffer, hydrolyzed in perchloric acid, and the radioactivity measured in a scintillation counter. Actinomycin C_1 (D) was present at tenfold molar excess in relation to DNA-guanine.

N-7 should still be able to complex actinomycin; the data of Table III show that this is the case. A similar observation has been recorded by Troll (1964) and associates who used β-propiolactone rather than mustard gas as the alkylating agent. While these findings are reassuring, they

TABLE III
ACTINOMYCIN-BINDING CAPACITY OF DNA TREATED WITH MUSTARD GAS[a]

Sample	cpm/0.1 ml	Per cent remaining in solution
Control	7282	50.4
Mustard gas treated	7743	53.5

[a] Native calf thymus DNA (1 mg per milliliter) was incubated with mustard gas (eightfold molar excess in relation to DNA-guanine) at 37°C for 30 minutes in phosphate buffer (Brookes and Lawley, 1960); the control was incubated under identical conditions but without mustard gas. At the end of the incubation a twofold excess of radioactive actinomycin C (labeled with C[14]) was added, the DNA was precipitated with streptomycin. The actinomycin remaining in solution was measured by determining the radioactivity of aliquots of the supernatant after streptomycin precipitation.

are merely preliminary and in themselves do not prove the model. Nevertheless, a reasonable tentative conclusion from these experiments is that actinomycin binding to DNA is selective for a single base, guanine, for one of the grooves, the minor groove, and for a single functional group of guanine, the amino group.

On the assumption that gene action is regulated, at least in part, by physicochemical interactions occurring at the genetic level itself, it may be useful to speculate briefly about some properties of ideal regulator substances and the way in which they might react with DNA.

1. If cellular differentiation and its maintenance are considered to reflect differential activity of various segments of the cellular genome, the expression of these hereditary characteristics presumably would be mediated by the specification of different species of RNA molecules.

It would be reasonable to expect that molecules with regulator activity should affect DNA-dependent RNA synthesis selectively, and not interfere directly with gene replication (i.e., DNA synthesis). Moreover, the action of such regulators would have to be directed to specific regions of the DNA template and not to the RNA polymerase itself. In these respects the action of regulator molecules would resemble appreciably that of actinomycin.

2. Regulator molecules would be expected to combine with DNA, and particularly with helical DNA, since this is the normal configuration of the cellular DNA which is a substrate for RNA polymerase. A com-

bination with RNA or other cellular constituents would risk interfering with processes other than those occurring at the genetic level. These anticipated characteristics of regulators would also be similar to actinomycin.

3. In addition to specificity for DNA, and especially for helical DNA, regulators should be expected to demonstrate specificity for functional groups of DNA bases and/or base pairs. This would permit the recognition of bases (or base pairs) occurring in sequence or at defined intervals and thereby the polynucleotide specificity of different segments of the genome.

The ability to react with functional groups of bases (or base pairs) need not be the sole mechanism for the interaction of regulator molecules with DNA. For example, a nonspecific association might be formed between DNA and a basic polypeptide, the electrostatic component of which might be very weak under physiological conditions; however, the superimposition of several hydrogen bonds and hydrophobic interactions between suitably oriented amino acid side chains and bases of DNA could strengthen the binding in a specific manner. A model for this kind of interaction might be visualized by supposing a rather rigid protein to contain actinomycin molecules attached at intervals along the peptide chain.* An actinomycin moiety, properly oriented with respect to the DNA, would be capable of complexing with available guanines; suitably distributed basic residues in the polypeptide could simultaneously reinforce the binding by electrostatic interaction with DNA-phosphates. The strongest binding would occur with segments of DNA which permitted the most energetically favored combination of interactions. It is unlikely that there are intracellular polymers having prosthetic groups which resemble actinomycin or other small molecules now known to form complexes with DNA. Proteins and the side chains of their constituent amino acids, however, contain many different functional groups which are capable of participating in a variety of molecular interactions.

The binding of actinomycin to DNA, which is reversible, is thought to be mediated by a defined series of hydrogen bonds and to be stabilized by as yet undefined hydrophobic forces. A readily reversible inter-

* This could in fact be accomplished, e.g., by introduction of an amino group at position 7 of the chromphore (Müller, 1962), which would permit coupling of the actinomycin to protein carboxyl and still allow the attached actinomycin to complex with DNA. The presence of even large groups at position 7 of the actinomycin chromophore does not interfere with binding to DNA.

action with DNA, based on the same forces and not involving covalent bonds, would provide a sensitive and responsive mechanism for regulating gene action. The functional groups of actinomycin which govern its ability to react with DNA are the chromophore amino group, the quinoidal oxygen, and the lactones. Based on what is known of actinomycin chemistry (Brockmann, 1960), similar interactions could be mediated by protein amides, carboxyls, and peptide CO NH groups, respectively.

The biological actions of actinomycin and the characteristics of the actinomycin-DNA complex possess many of the essential characteristics which would be surmised for the interaction of hypothetical regulator molecules with the genetic material whose functions they are expected to control. Despite this, it is doubtful that any aspect of actinomycin action presents a really satisfactory model for visualizing basic mechanisms of genetic regulation. In this respect, perhaps its greatest value is the concrete demonstration that those elements of DNA structure and function that may be sites of regulatory activity do embody physicochemical properties that are recognizably unique among intracellular processes. It is reassuring that some of these unique, specific parameters can be a target for even a relatively simple molecule such as actinomycin—a small polypeptide derived from the same common intracellular metabolites which can be assembled to produce the exquisite specificity of proteins.

ACKNOWLEDGMENTS

It is a pleasure to acknowledge the support of E. L. Tatum, the Helen Hay Whitney Foundation, and the National Institute of Health (GM-10717-02).

REFERENCES

BROCKMANN, H. (1960). *Fortschr. Chem. Org. Naturstoffe* **18**, 1.

BROOKES, P., AND LAWLEY, P. D. (1961). *Biochem. J.* **80**, 496.

GOLDBERG, I. H., AND RABINOWITZ, M. (1962). **136**, 315.

GOLDBERG, I. H., RABINOWITZ, M., AND REICH, E. (1962). *Proc. Natl. Acad. Sci. U. S.* **48**, 2094.

HAMILTON, L., FULLER, W., AND REICH, E. (1963). *Nature* **198**, 538.

HARTMANN, G., AND COY, U. (1962). *Angew. Chem.* **74**, 501.

HAYWOOD, A. M., AND SINSHEIMER, R. L. (1963). *J. Mol. Biol.* **6**, 247.

HURWITZ, J., FURTH, J. J., MALAMY, M., AND ALEXANDER, M. (1962). *Proc. Natl. Acad. Sci. U. S.* **48**, 1222.

JACOB, F., AND MONOD, J. (1961). *J. Mol. Biol.* **3**, 318.

KAHAN, F., KAHAN, E., AND HURWITZ, J. (1963). *J. Biol. Chem.* **238**, 249.

KAWAMATA, J., AND IMANISHI, M. (1961). *Bikens's J.* **4**, 13.

KIRK, J. M. (1960). *Biochim. Biophys. Acta* **42**, 167.

KORNBERG, A. (1961). "Enzymatic Synthesis of DNA." Wiley, New York.

Müller, W. (1962). *Naturwissenschaften* **49**, 156.

Rauen, H. M., Kersten, H., and Kersten, W. (1960). *Z. Physiol. Chem.* **321**, 139.

Reich, E. (1962). Unpublished observations.

Reich, E. (1964). *Science* **143**, 684.

Reich, E., and Goldberg, I. H. (1964). *Prog. Nucleic Acid Res.* **3**. In press.

Reich, E., Franklin, R. M., Shatkin, A. J., and Tatum, E. L. (1961). *Science* **134**, 556.

Reich, E., Franklin, R. M., Shatkin, A. J., and Tatum, E. L. (1962a). *Proc. Natl. Acad. Sci. U. S.* **48**, 1238.

Reich, E., Goldberg, I. H., and Rabinowitz, M. (1962). *Nature* **196**, 743.

Sonneborn, T. M. (1964). *Proc. Natl. Acad. Sci. U. S.* **51**, 915.

Troll, W. (1964). Personal communication.

DNA Replication Sequences
in Higher Animals

T. C. HSU, WERNER SCHMID,*
AND ELTON STUBBLEFIELD

Department of Biology, The University of Texas M. D. Anderson Hospital and Tumor Institute, Houston, Texas

Introduction

During the past decade autoradiography has become one of the powerful methods in the study of cell biology. This success has been largely the result of the utilization of tritium which emits an extremely weak beta track and thereby gives excellent resolution. The successful synthesis of tritiated thymidine, which evoked great activity in experimental cell research, also stimulated the synthesis of more tritiated compounds with higher and higher specific activity. Tritiated thymidine, however, remains the most widely used tritiated compound, because thymidine is a precurser that is more specific for deoxyribonucleic acid (DNA) than others.

Autoradiographic studies with special reference to chromosomes began with Taylor *et al.* (1957). During the past few years numerous papers have appeared dealing with chromosome replication using labeled thymidine. One of the problems that has excited much interest is asynchronous DNA replication and its implications in gene activity. It is tempting, when discussing DNA replication sequences in higher animals, to elaborate and speculate on the relationships between heteropyknosis, gene inactivation, and DNA replication; however, in this brief review we hope to bring out the progress made to date with emphasis on the cytological aspects of the problem of DNA replication.

Materials and Methods

Any growing cell population (animal, plant, or microorganism) can be employed as experimental material. Investigators select their material according to their particular problem. Since each material has its unique-

---

* Present address: Kinderspital Zürich, Zürich, Switzerland.

ness, methods to be used should be suited to the particular system. In this review, special reference is made to animal cells grown in culture. Cell cultures minimize operational difficulties because the test material is directly exposed to the labeled precursor, and incorporation is therefore relatively uniform.

During the interphase of a growing cell, DNA synthetic activity is limited to a period known as the S phase. Autoradiographic data have shown that after the completion of DNA synthesis, a cell does not immediately enter mitosis. This "gap" period is known as the G_2 phase (for a detailed description of the cell cycle, cf. Stanners and Till, 1960).

In mammalian cells, the S phase generally lasts from 6 to 8 hours (Defendi and Manson, 1963), and the G_2 phase, from 2 to 4 hours. To study DNA replication with respect to chromosomes of a given species or a cell population, information concerning the time requirement for each phase is useful because it helps the investigators to determine when the samples should be taken.

Continuous Labeling

The continuous labeling method is more reliable for studying the terminal stages of DNA synthesis than is the conventional pulse labeling method because, in continuous labeling, tritiated thymidine is present in the test system all the time. With this method any chromosome segment showing no label at metaphase would mean that the chromosome had completed its DNA synthetic activity when the labeled precursor was introduced. Generally, colchicine or Colcemid is added to the culture medium or blood stream 1 or 2 hours prior to harvest to arrest mitotic divisions at metaphase. Samples are taken at various intervals after the introduction of tritiated thymidine, so that comparison of labeling patterns on metaphase chromosomes can be made; by this method, the DNA synthetic sequence that occurred during the previous interphase can be traced. Figure 1 diagrammatically illustrates the relationships between cell cycle, time of introduction of label, and eventual labeling pattern in metaphase. Considering a hypothetical population with an average G_2 period of 2 hours, introduction of label and harvest 3 hours later should give, in the metaphase figures, the labeling pattern during the last hour of S phase (Fig. 1a).

If a chromosome in the 3-hour sample is observed to be relatively free from label except a small segment (Fig. 1a), the segment with label must represent the region of this particular chromosome that is latest in

DNA replication activity. Examination of the labeling pattern of the same chromosome for samples with longer labeling times (e.g., 4 and 6 hours, Fig. 1b and c, respectively) should yield information concerning the termination stages of DNA synthesis of an entire complement as well as of every individual chromosome.

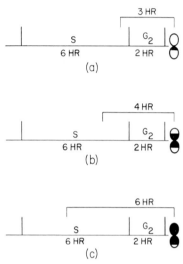

FIG. 1.   Diagrammatic representation of continuous H³-thymidine labeling method for revealing late DNA replicating regions.   (a) Labeling for 3 hours;   (b) labeling for 4 hours;   (c) labeling for 6 hours.

Pulse Labeling

In pulse labeling the precursor is added to the medium for a given time, after which it is washed off, and an excess of nonradioactive thymidine is added to the medium to stop further labeling. This method has many uses; for quantitative cell physiology studies it is perhaps the only sensible technique. In studying chromosomes the use of pulse labeling is excellent for cells in the early S phase, especially when used in combination with the method described below.

Cell Synchronization and Pulse Labeling

A difficulty intrinsic to the study of chromosome replication is that what takes place during the S phase must be deducted from the labeling patterns of the chromosomes in the ensuing metaphase. The method is further complicated by variation in the time requirement for each phase of the cell cycle existing in every cell population. The value obtained for any phase of the cell cycle by any method is an average one. For example, an S phase of 6 hours in a population may range from 5 to 7 or from 4 to 8 hours. This variation is not of great concern in studying the terminal stages of the S phase, since the individual stages can be determined by the presence or absence of label with the continuous labeling method. Detailed analysis of earlier periods of the S phase is more difficult because of the long duration between the commencement of DNA synthesis and mitosis; the variations in time requirements become exaggerated, thus causing ambiguous results in the analysis of the DNA-replication sequence.

The difficulty caused by the time variations can be partially resolved by synchronizing cell populations before labeling. Several agents are available to inhibit *de novo* DNA synthesis by blocking the conversion of deoxyuridylic acid to thymidylic acid, e.g., aminopterin, amethopterin, and 2-deoxy-5-fluorouridine (Ruechert and Mueller, 1960; Mueller *et al.*, 1962). When the population is treated with such an agent, cells originally in G_2, mitosis, and G_1 phases can be arrested at the entry of S phase. When thymidine is added to the medium, all cells resume DNA synthesis and proceed normally as long as thymidine is present. Following this relief, more cells reach mitosis at the same time, and a partial synchronization can be achieved. At any time during the relieved S phase and for any desired duration, pulse labeling can be performed by replacing nonradioactive thymidine with tritiated thymidine and later replacing the tritiated thymidine with nonradioactive thymidine. Stubblefield and Mueller (1962) demonstrated that the pulsing technique is reliable, inasmuch as the cells do not store appreciable quantities of thymidine in any reusable form. Thus the DNA synthetic pattern may be studied at its very beginning, during the first 45 minutes, for 10 minutes during the second hour, or at any period during this artificially created synchronized S phase. This method is most suitable for determining the beginning of DNA replication. The availability of tritiated thymidine with high specific activity makes it possible to label cells with an exposure of less than 5 minutes.

Techniques

Since Schmid (1964) described the detailed steps of the stripping film methods and Prescott (1964) presented a resume for the liquid emulsion techniques, we shall therefore omit repetition in describing the technical procedures in this discussion.

The Relationship between Heteropyknosis, Gene Inactivation, and DNA Replication

A number of workers, notably Ohno and associates (1959; Tjio and Ostergren 1958; Ohno and Hauschka, 1960) discovered that in female mammalian cells one of the two X chromosomes is heteropyknotic. This phenomenon was especially pronounced during prophase and prometaphase. Its cytological behavior is therefore similar to that of the heterochromatin in *Drosophila*. Genetically, the V-type position effect of sex-linked genes in the mouse (Russell, 1961) also resembled the behavior of genes of *Drosophila* involved in heterochromatin (Lewis, 1950). Lyon (1961) proposed that the mosaicism in phenotypic effect of sex-linked genes in heterozygous female mice is due to the inactivation of either of the X chromosomes. Hsu (1962) suggested that the inactivation may be a result of physical condensation of the chromatin which prevents the synthesis of messenger RNA.

In the Chinese hamster cells *in vitro* Taylor (1960a) found that the two X chromosomes in female cells behave differently with respect to the DNA-replication pattern. In relation to the entire complement, one of them is late replicating along its entire length, whereas the other is late replicating only on its long arm. In the male cells of this species, the single X chromosome also shows late replication on its long arm, but the Y chromosome is late replicating along its entire length.

Applying autoradiographic techniques to human material, Morishima et al. (1962) found that in female human leucocytes one of the X chromosomes is very late replicating along its entire length, whereas its homolog is not. This finding was confirmed in many other laboratories (German, 1962, 1964; Gilbert et al., 1962; Bader et al., 1963; Muldal et al., 1963; Schmid, 1963; Kikuchi and Sandberg, 1964). This behavior of out-of-phase replication of one X chromosome seemed to parallel its heteropyknotic appearance.

In human subjects with multiple X chromosomes such as XXX, XXXX, XXXXY, and XXXXX decisive proof has been established to demonstrate that extra X chromosomes are always late replicating (Grumbach et al., 1963; Rowley et al., 1963; Gianelli, 1963; Atkins et al., 1963). The number of late replicating X chromosomes is one fewer than that of the total X chromosomes present, exactly the same as in the case of sex chromatin. These findings led Hsu (1964a) and Taylor (1964) to hypothesize that out-of-phase replication is related to gene inactivation, mediated by the process of heteropyknosis. In other words, gene inactivation, heteropyknosis of the chromosomes (physical condensation), and delayed replication are somehow all related phenomena.

In a number of laboratories the late replicating X chromosome in female somatic cells is colloquially called the "hot X," implying that this X chromosome is particularly rich in radioactivity. This is a misnomer. Since all chromosomes of a cell must replicate once in every cell cycle, all chromosomes would take up tritiated thymidine (or become "hot") at some time during the S phase. The difference is therefore only a matter of timing. In fact, it has been demonstrated by several workers (Taylor, 1960a; Hsu, 1964b; Petersen, 1964) that the "hot X" is indeed "cold" at the beginning stage of the S phase. The proper term for the "hot X" should therefore be the "late replicating X" and that for the homologous X chromosome, "early replicating X."

It is also worth mentioning in this connection that sex chromatin has been found in females of the domestic fowl where only one Z chromosome exists (Kosin and Ishizahi, 1959). Autoradiographic analysis of bone marrow cells from both sexes of this species revealed that in male cells the two Z chromosomes replicate more or less synchronously and are not out of phase with the autosomes (Schmid, 1962). In the female cells the single Z chromosome is not delayed, but one of the large microchromosomes is late replicating (Fig. 2). It is possible that this chromosome is the W, for it bears morphological resemblance to the presumed W described by Frederic (1961).

Another interesting feature of DNA replication among chromosomes of the domestic fowl is the difference in timing between the macro- and the microchromosomes. Donnally and Newcomer (1963) and Schmid (1962) found that the microchromosomes are early replicating. Donnally and Newcomer called the microchromosomes "chromosomoids," a term without sound justification.

Although in the Chinese hamster and in man the relationship between heteropyknosis and delayed DNA replication seems positive, at least in the sex chromosomes, information concerning DNA replication is still wanting in such classic cases as the cat, where the first sex chromatin was found (Barr and Bertram, 1949), the mouse, where the first heteropyknotic X was described, and in *Drosophila,* where a tremendous amount of data are available on the genetics of heterochromatin. According to the very recent work of Galton and Holt (1964), a late replicating chromosome resembling the X has been detected in female embryonic mouse cells in culture. Our own data (Hsu and Witt, unpublished material) showed that this phenomenon is not clear-cut in all female mouse

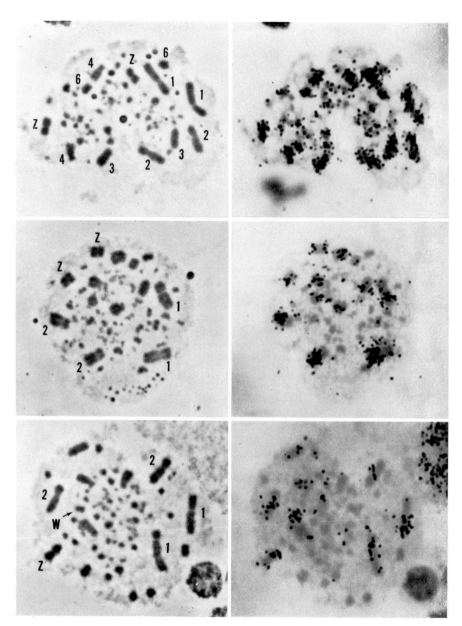

FIG. 2. Autoradiographs of cells from bone marrow of the domestic fowl showing late replicating regions. Left-hand side, cells before film exposure; right-hand side, autoradiographs of the same. *Top:* ♂, relatively early stages of S phase. *Middle:* ♂, late S phase; note the two Z chromosomes are synchronous. *Bottom:* ♀, late S phase; note heavy label on the presumed W chromosome.

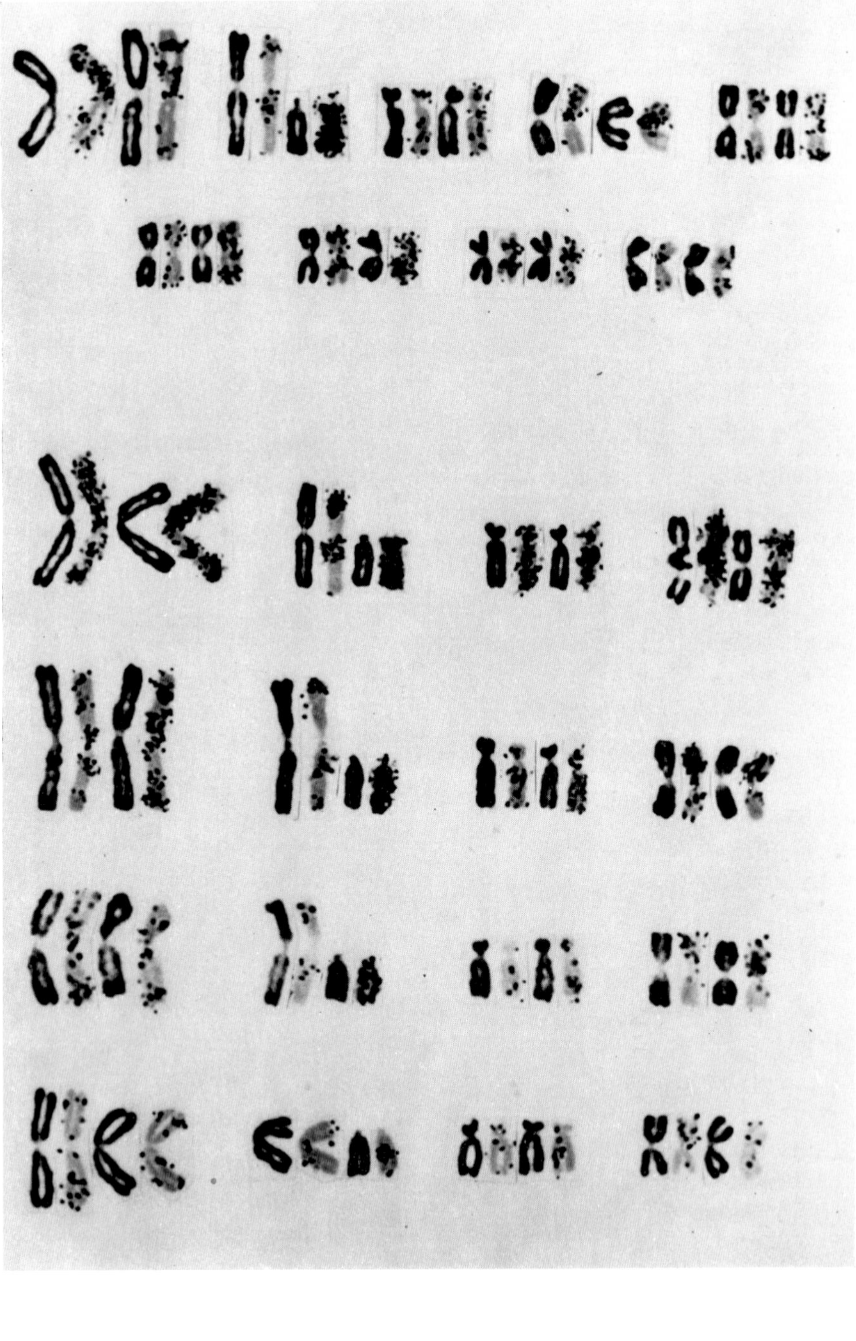

cells, although both teams could unequivocally identify the late replicating Y of the mouse.

Our studies on the chromosomes of the creeping vole *Microtus oregoni,* however, appear to contradict the generalization just outlined. The diploid number of *Microtus oregoni* was first reported by Matthey (1958) as 17. After detailed analysis, Ohno *et al.* (1963) discovered that the number varies according to sex as well as to tissue. Briefly, the following chromosome numbers exist in the same species:

> ♀ Somatic cells, 17 (XO)   Gonad, 18 (XX)
> ♂ Somatic cells, 18 (XY)   Gonad, 17 (OY)

Ohno *et al.* (1963) observed, in embryonic liver cells of *Microtus oregoni,* that the X chromosome, a submetacentric, has two long heteropyknotic segments, the distal three-fourths of the long arm and the proximal two-thirds of the short arm. Autoradiographs prepared in this laboratory from lung fibroblasts *in vitro,* however, revealed a pattern opposite from that expected, viz., the heteropyknotic segments were early replicating and the euchromatic segments, late replicating (Fig. 3). Thus it is possible that out-of-phase DNA replication is not necessarily a reflection of heteropyknosis. More data must be collected before a convincing generalization can be made.

The Terminal Stages of DNA Replication

As mentioned previously, the terminal stages of DNA replication are relatively easy to study because the continuous labeling method yields accurate information without technical difficulties. Several species have been investigated in considerable detail by this method. Schmid reported detailed analyses on chromosomes of the domestic fowl (1962) and of man (1963), and Hsu (1964b) presented data on those of the chinese hamster. More recently, several additional mammalian species, including *Microtus oregoni,* have been analyzed in this laboratory, but no data have been published. The results obtained from these various species

---

Fic. 3. Autoradiographs of cells of male *Microtus oregoni* showing late replicating regions. *Top* block, a complete cell; *bottom* block, selected chromosomes from four different cells showing termination process of DNA replication. Note the characteristic late replicating regions of the X chromosome and the heavy labeling of the Y chromosome. The late replicating regions of the X correspond to euchromatic segments observed by Ohno *et al.* (1963).

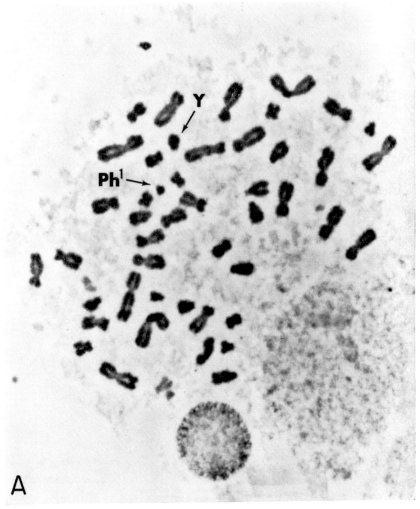

Fig. 4. Autoradiograph of a human cell from a blood culture of chronic myelogenous leukemia. (A) Cell before film exposure; (B) autoradiagraph of the same. Note heavy label over the Ph1 chromosome.

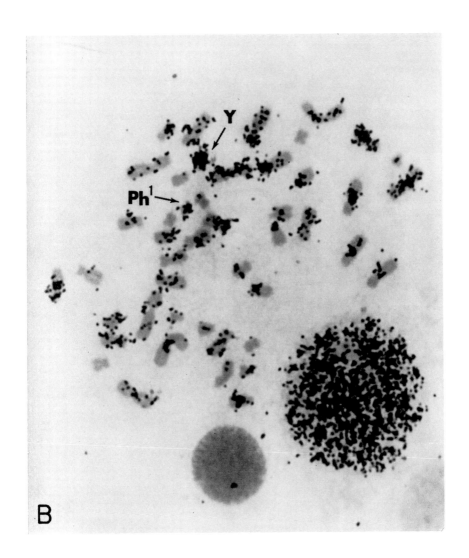

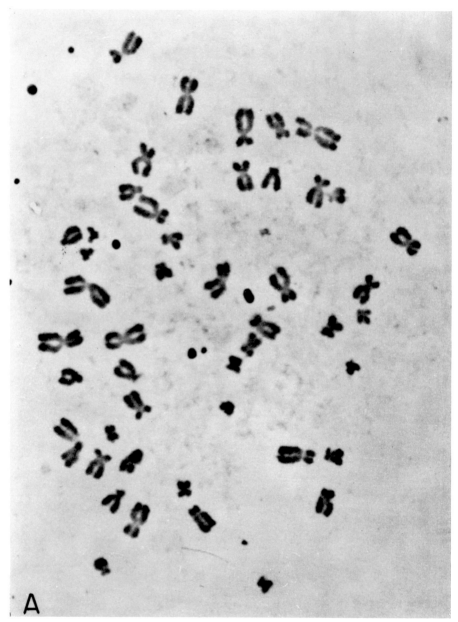

Fig. 5. Autoradiograph of a human fibroblast originated from a skin biopsy of a patient with trisomic 18. (A) Cell before film exposure; (B) autoradiograph of the

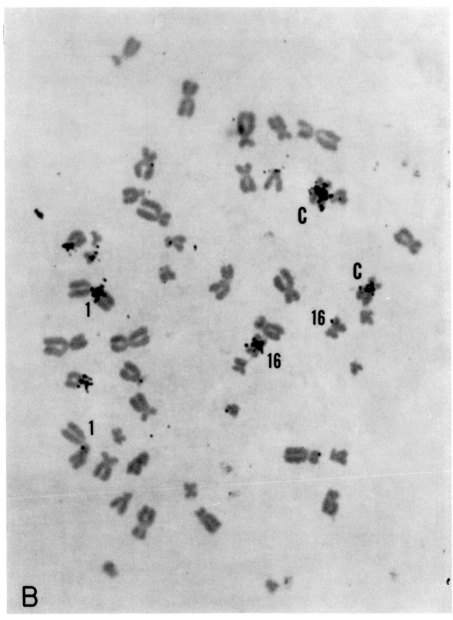

same. Note asynchrony in replication patterns between homologous chromosomes 1 and 16.

indicate that they have several common characteristics which may be summarized by the following paragraphs.

Differential Rate in Termination of DNA Replication among Chromosomes

Not all chromosomes within a complement terminate DNA replication simultaneously. This property can be utilized to distinguish chromosome pairs which are morphologically identical, e.g., chromosomes 21 and 22 of man. At one stage near the end of the S phase, two chromosomes belonging to the G group show little radioactivity, while two others still exhibit active incorporation of the precursor. Naturally, it is possible that within a pair one chromosome may be delayed more than the other; but other evidence appears to support the conclusion that generally homologous chromosomes possess similar replication patterns.

Several anomalies are known to occur in the G group of human chromosomes. The Down's syndrome, for example, is a trisomy of, and the Philadelphia chromosome, a deletion in one of the two pairs, numbers 21 and 22. Because of the morphological similarity between these two pairs, ascribing both anomalies to pair 21 is somewhat arbitrary. It would be of great interest to learn whether these abnormalities can be identified by the DNA-replication patterns. Schmid (1963) found in the leucocytes of patients with Down's syndrome three late and two early replicating small acrocentrics. Unless the extra chromosome behaves in a different manner from the regular pair, the Down's syndrome is therefore trisomic for the late replicating pair. Since there is no strong reason to break the traditional nomenclature, the late replicating pair of the G group is considered pair 21. Of particular interest is the replication pattern of the Philadelphia chromosome in the leucocytes of patients with chronic myelogenous leukemia. Schmid (1963) observed that in several cases the Philadelphia chromosome belonged to the late replicating pair. The Ph[1] chromosome, however, appeared to be especially late in DNA synthesis as compared with its presumed partner, the normal 21 (Fig. 4).

Specific Late Replicating Regions

Many chromosomes have distinct regions that are late replicating. This property can also be utilized to distinguish morphologically similar chromosome pairs. In the human karyotype, chromosomes 1 and 16 each possess a late replicating zone on the proximal portion of the long arm (Moorhead and Defendi, 1963; Schmid, 1963).

In the Chinese hamster karyotype, late replicating regions have been detected in a number of chromosomes (Hsu, 1964b). The two largest chromosomes each possess several such regions. In autoradiographs for the late S phase, these large chromosomes may assume a banded appearance. In *Microtus oregoni* (Fig. 3), the late replicating regions of the X chromosome are very characteristic.

Replication Patterns between Homologous Chromosomes

In general, homologous chromosomes have similar replication patterns. This conclusion was reached after comparing the specific late replication regions in morphologically distinct chromosomes, e.g., chromosomes 1 and 16 of man. Nevertheless, one well-known exception to this generalization exists, i.e., the X chromosomes of female mammals.

When one examines an autoradiograph, the number of silver grains over a particular region of a chromosome may vary owing to random disintegration of the isotope. Therefore, it is not possible to conclude from a few autoradiographs that there is a difference in DNA synthetic activity between two homologs showing a different grain count. German (1964) emphasized that continuous labeling will obliterate, whereas pulse labeling tends to reveal, such subtle differences. Conceivably, this is true. As amplified in Fig. 5, however, gross asynchrony can be detected occasionally even in a single autoradiograph from continuous labeling. When the resolutions of autoradiography is increased (to be discussed in a later section), asynchrony between homologous chromosomes becomes more obvious.

We may conclude tentatively that some chromosomes, or regions thereof, may complete replication earlier than others. The pattern appears to be consistent, at least within a cell population or a cell line.

Late Replication and Metaphase Chromosome Morphology

Sasaki and Makino (1963), using a calcium-free medium to treat human cell cultures prior to harvest for cytological preparation, observed consistent secondary constrictions in a number of metaphase chromosomes. Almost simultaneously, Saksela and Moorhead (1962) also found characteristic constriction patterns in human chromosomes after fixing the cells with a modified fixative formula. Interestingly, many of these constricted regions corresponded to the late replicating regions analyzed by Schmid (1963), who constructed a diagram for comparison of these characteristics (Fig. 6).

In chromosome cytology, secondary constriction has been a well-known morphological characteristic for decades. Many secondary constrictions are considered nucleolus organizers. In some plant material, secondary constrictions can be induced by cold treatment (Darlington and La Cour, 1940). According to Woodard and Swift (1964), these constricted regions do not represent abnormalities in DNA synthetic activities.

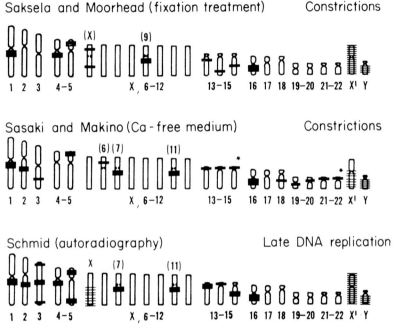

Fig. 6. Comparison of late replicating chromosome regions (Schmid, 1963) in human karyotype with secondary constrictions produced by the methods of Sasaki and Makino (1963) and Saksela and Moorhead (1962). After Schmid (1963).

Furthermore, these gaps do not form chromocenters in interphase nuclei as do the classic heteropyknotic chromosomes or segments. In human cells, secondary constrictions were noted before the invention of special treatments; however, because of their low frequency of incidence, they have not been used as effective markers. In the Chinese hamster cells Somers and Hsu (1962) and Somers et al. (1963) frequently noted constricted chromosomes, stretched chromosomes, and beaded chromosomes, but these workers offered no explanation.

The discovery of a possible correlation between late DNA replication

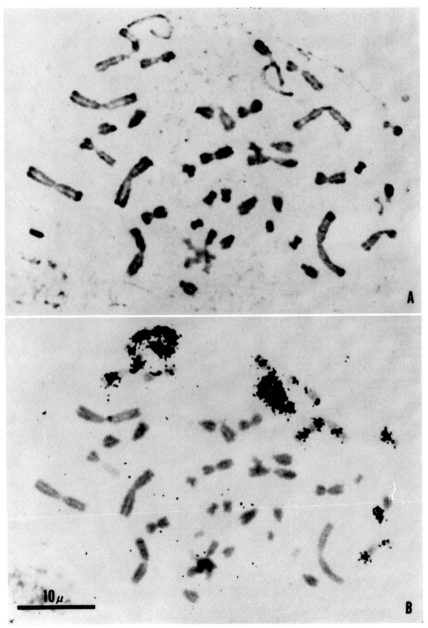

FIG. 7. (A) Metaphase of a tetraploid male Chinese hamster cell induced by prolonged treatment with Colcemid. Note stretched chromosomes and chromosome constrictions. (B) Autoradiography of the same, showing late replicating chromosomes and regions. Note heavy label on stretched chromosomes and constrictions.

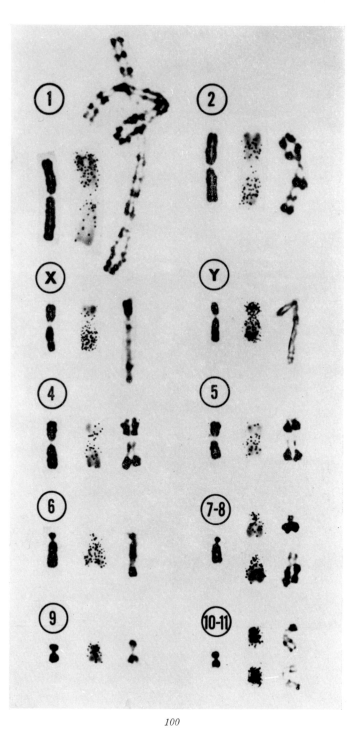

and secondary constriction seems to be a major step toward the understanding of chromosome morphology and physiology. The work of Stubblefield (1964a) is thus significant since it directly demonstrates the relationship just mentioned. When diploid male Chinese hamster cells *in vitro* were treated with Colcemid, the cells, after prolonged metaphase arrest, entered interphase without anaphase. This event is similar to the c-mitosis described in plant material. Because of the lack of anaphase, the daughter cell, now tetraploid, may contain numerous micronuclei instead of a single large nucleus. Other than requiring a longer generation time than the diploids, the micronucleated tetraploid cells were apparently able to grow and to replicate chromosomal components, as indicated by their tritiated thymidine (H^3-TdN) uptake. Interestingly, one may find asynchronous DNA replication among micronuclei of these cells, indicating that some micronuclei may complete replication before others. Using the continuous labeling method, Stubblefield found that some chromosomes showed heavy label, but others showed no label (Fig. 7). In such metaphases, distortion of chromosome morphology was found frequently among those replicating late, but never among those replicating early. The abnormality consisted of extended (uncoiled?) segments or gaps corresponding with those portions of each chromosome which synthesized last. It appeared that those nuclei which finished DNA synthesis early somehow interfered with the late S phase of the slower replicating nuclei, resulting in abnormal or incomplete chromosomal segments. Thus for each chromosome the characteristic late replicating pattern of labeled and unlabeled segments was converted into a morphological pattern of abnormal (extended) and normal segments (Fig. 8). Among the chromosomes 7 and 8, which are usually of identical morphology, two different extended forms were observed which may correspond to the two different chromosomes. This was also true of the smallest chromosomes, pairs 10 and 11. Corresponding autoradiograph patterns have also been found, and this will be considered more fully in the section in high-resolution autoradiography.

From a morphological standpoint, secondary constrictions and other abnormalities, when specific and consistent, are excellent karyological markers. Without an understanding of the molecular architecture of

---

FIG. 8. Karyotype of the Chinese hamster. Under each chromosome, *left,* metaphase morphology; *middle,* composite autoradiograph (cf. section VII) showing late replicating regions; *right,* distorted chromosomes from Colcemid-induced tetraploid cells. In each case the positions of centromeres are matched. Note the good agreement between late replicating regions and stretched chromosomes or gaps.

chromosomes, however, it is rather difficult to explain why a region of late DNA replication may be represented by a constriction occurring in metaphase. One can visualize that divalent cations such as Ca++ and Mg++ are necessary to bind DNA and histones; therefore, when divalent ions are replaced by monovalent ions, distortion of metaphase morphology could be expected (Somers *et al.*, 1963). It is still not clear, however, that the distortion caused by reduced Ca++ content should be related to the late synthetic activity (Sasaki and Makino, 1963), unless we assume that DNA of inactivated chromosomes binds with a certain species of histone which specifically requires divalent ions.

The Commencement of DNA Replication

Because of the long duration between the beginning of the S phase and mitosis, it is more difficult to study the commencement stage of DNA replication than the terminal stages. By applying agents to block the formation of thymidylic acid, however, large numbers of cells may be accumulated in a cell population to start DNA synthesis simultaneously. Pulse labeling with H³-thymidine for a desired duration may therefore be used for analysis of the early substages of the S phase. Stubblefield and Mueller (1962) introduced this method in studies on the localized synthesis of DNA in the chromosomes of HeLa cells. Petersen (1964) used aminopterin on human leucocyte cultures and found that one of the medium-sized metacentrics resembling the morphology of the X chromosome was not labeled, whereas other chromosomes were. This finding suggests that late replicating chromosomes either do not start replication immediately when the S phase is reached or else the initial rate of DNA synthesis is much less than in the other chromosomes.

Hsu (1964b) used deoxyfluorouridine to inhibit DNA synthesis of Chinese hamster cells and relieved the arrest for various periods of time with tritiated thymidine. The early phases of DNA replication appeared to be the exact reverse of the terminal phases, i.e., chromosomes showing late replicating activities were not active in early S phase. For example, in the male Chinese hamster, the Y chromosome and the long arm of the X exhibited little capacity for thymidine incorporation at the beginning of the S phase (Fig. 9). It is also of interest to note that many chromosomes, after a 5-minute pulse labeling, showed label along most of their lengths, indicating that DNA replication starts at multiple sites instead of at one point and spreading in a definite gradient.

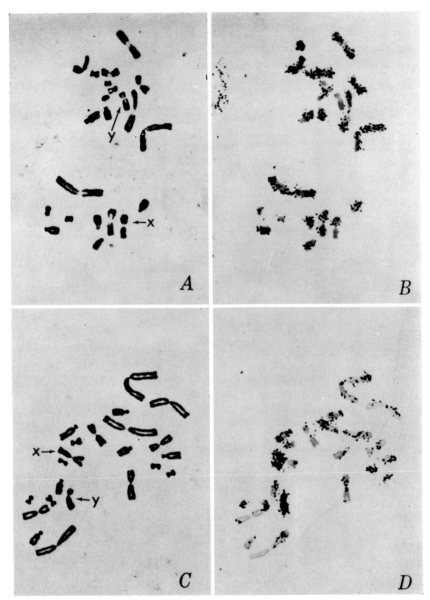

Fig. 9. DNA-replication patterns of the Chinese hamster. Left-hand side, cells before film exposure; right-hand side, autoradiographs of the same. (A and B) The beginning 5 minutes of the S phase; note unlabeled y and long arm of the X. (C and D) The last 45 minutes of S phase; note the reversed labeling pattern of early stages.

By relieving the block with tritiated thymidine mixed with nonradio-active thymidine for varying periods of time, we found that the Y chromosome and the long arm of the X of the Chinese hamster began to synthesize DNA very actively about 4 hours after the S phase had begun. Some factor or factors must have been operative to regulate the synthetic sequence of the entire complement.

Quantitative Autoradiography of Chromosomes

The observation of bands of radioactivity along chromosomes labeled at the end of the S period encouraged the development of techniques to quantitate the isotope distribution on such chromosomes. The usual grain counting techniques are not sufficient to reveal such distributions, except where gross differences exist, e.g., the distinct early and late labeling of the short and long arms, respectively, of the X chromosome of the Chinese hamster. The major problem is a statistical one: enough grains to give reliable data cannot be accumulated above a chromosome without coincidence and overlap which prohibits accurate quantitation. One solution to this problem is to add together the data from many morphologically similar chromosomes (Stubblefield and Mueller, 1962). This technique, however, assumes that all chromosomes that look alike are physiologically identical, and this may not be true. A more reason-able approach is to obtain many samples from a single set of chromo-somes by a process called *repeated autoradiography* (Stubblefield, 1964b). It should be mentioned that Bishop and Bishop (1963) also proposed a repeated autoradiography method which differs from the one described here in detail.

When a series of autoradiographs are made of a cell, it is necessary to protect the preparation from mechanical forces involved in the re-moval of the stripping film at the end of each sampling cycle. To this end, the cells are covered with a thin film of Formvar. This film is thin enough (ca. 150 mμ) to absorb very little radiation, but is strong enough to hold the cells firmly in place while the Kodak AR-10 stripping film is being removed. The stripping film is applied in the usual way directly over the Formvar film. After suitable exposure, the autoradiograph is developed and dried, and a cover glass mounted on it with glycerol. A photomicrograph is made of the pattern of silver grains in the autoradio-graph; all further analyses are made from this picture. After the photo-graphic record is completed, the cover slip and glycerol are removed in water; and the moist stripping film is peeled easily from the Formvar film. New stripping film can then be applied and the process repeated

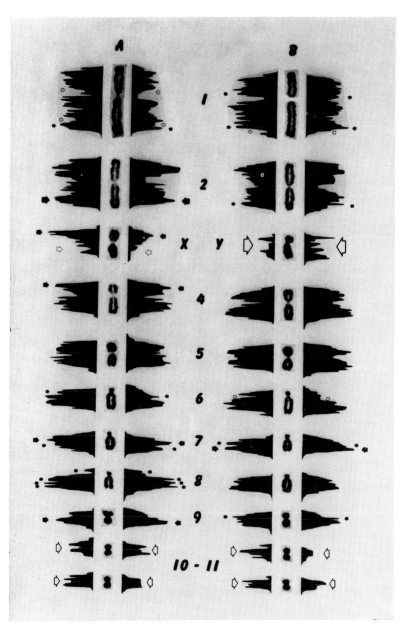

Fɪɢ. 10. The first 15 minutes of DNA synthesis in the Chinese hamster, analyzed by repeated autoradiography. Data from two cells are shown for each chromosome. Consistent differences between homologs are indicated (column A vs. column B). Black arrows, high synthetic activity; white arrows, low synthetic activity. The graphs to the left in both columns belong to the chromosomes depicted in the middle. White lines in each graph represent the position of the centromere.

indefinitely. In this fashion a series of samplings of the isotope distribution in chromosomes can be taken; each sample can be easily quantitated, and the sum of the samples is statistically reliable.

Since we were interested in not only the total amount of radioactivity per chromosome, but also the distribution of radioactivity along the chromosome axis, additional methods were developed to integrate the series of autoradiographs into a single, composite, high-resolution picture. The image of each silver grain on the photomicrographs was punched with a pin. This procedure converted grain images of various sizes and densities into uniform pinholes. All of the punched negatives could be superimposed to yield a composite autoradiograph (Fig. 8). For quantitative analysis, however, additional steps were required. Each punched photograph was placed in a projection device with a linear light source oriented at 90° to the axis of a particular chromosome. Each pinhole projected an image of the linear source onto photographic film; each grain was thus converted into a line at right angles to the chromosome axis, and the line density at any given locus accurately reflected the grain density of the autoradiograph. The entire series of autoradiographs was superimposed in this manner. The line densities along the chromosome were then put into graphical form with a recording microdensitometer.

Studies of early and late replicating patterns in the chromosomes of the Chinese hamster by the repeated autoradiography method have confirmed the findings of Hsu (1964b) described earlier in this review. The higher resolution of the method revealed, however, that although homologous chromosomes had similar replication patterns there were distinct differences between homologous chromosomes that could be used to identify the homologs in most cases. Figure 10 shows the pattern of DNA replication during the first 15 minutes of the S phase in two different cells. The consistent differences between homologous chromosomes are indicated by arrows. Among the chromosomes 7 and 8, four distinct early labeling patterns have been observed. One (8B) is usually less radioactive than the other three; 8A has distinct early replication in the short arm. Of the remaining two, 7B labels more heavily toward the distal end of the long arm. whereas 7A contains more isotope proximally on the long arm. The four chromosomes have been numbered arbitrarily in Fig. 10, as we have no way of knowing which pairs are actually homologs. The Y chromosome, the long arms of the X, and chromosomes 10 and 11 all contain less isotope than the others, as these are distinct late replicators. It should be noted, however, that all chromosomes have at least some capacity for DNA synthesis in the initial 15 minutes of the S phase. The amount of isotope in chromosomes 10 and 11 is not sufficient to distinguish any of the four. The problem is also made difficult by the small size of the chromosomes.

Discussion

In general, autoradiographic data collected by various investigators agree well. Nevertheless, discrepancies exist. For example, some conclusions on human chromosome duplication made by Schmid (1963) and by German (1964) are not in complete accord with those of Kikuchi and Sandberg (1964). Possibly the differences were the results of the methods (continuous labeling vs. pulse labeling) used. Pulse labeling is primarily designed for analysis of the rate of incorporation during a given interval at specific loci, whereas continuous labeling is more suitable for revealing the sequence of DNA replication at the terminal stages. Furthermore, in pulse labeling with suspension cultures (e.g., leucocytes), the necessity for centrifugation and chasing may easily upset the normal sequence of the cell cycle, especially when the chasing medium is not "conditioned" and when a very large quantity of nonradioactive thymidine is used. It should be remembered that thymidine at high concentrations inhibits DNA synthesis (Xeros, 1962).

It is well known that metaphase and anaphase chromosomes are incapable of synthesizing RNA (Taylor, 1960b; Prescott and Bender, 1962). Hsu (1962) demonstrated that heteropyknotic chromosomes appear to be inactive in conducting RNA synthesis during interphase. Metaphase chromosomes and interphase chromocenters have one property in common, i.e., both are cytologically condensed. Since recent evidence strongly suggests that histones may regulate the DNA molecules for their RNA (Huang and Bonner, 1962) and DNA synthetic activities (Lehnert, 1964; Billen and Hnilica, 1964), it is possible that this condensation is the result of DNA–histone association. Frenster *et al.* (1963) noted that the fraction of histone found predominantly in isolated heterochromatin from mammalian cells was lysine-rich; the same fraction showed the strongest binding capacity with DNA by melting point analysis (Huang *et al.*, 1964).

With more and more cases to document that viral and microbial DNA molecules are circular (Jacob and Wollman, 1961; Streisinger and Bruce, 1960; Fiers and Sinsheimer, 1962; Weil and Vinograd, 1963) and that the replication appears to proceed in one direction (Cairns, 1963;

Yoshikawa and Sueoka, 1963; Nagata, 1963), it is possible that DNA molecules of higher forms of life are likewise circular. The molecular weight of the DNA of *Escherichia coli* is approximately 0.5×10^9. Microscopically, the *E. coli* chromosome is almost invisible. It is not likely, therefore, that each chromosome of the higher forms, some of which may be 10μ in length, represents a single DNA molecule. The chromosomes of higher animals and plants are more likely to be composites of numerous DNA molecules arranged in definite patterns with each basic unit being similar to the DNA of a bacterium. Taylor (1963) proposed a chromosome model which would permit DNA replication at any place. The model is quite different from the "centipede" model proposed by Taylor (1959) a few years earlier. In either case, Taylor favors the view that a half-chromatid represents a DNA double helix, possibly interspersed with non-DNA linkages. Even though the problem of redundancy of DNA molecules in a chromosome is not solved, the question does not seriously affect the basic issue, i.e., whether the double helix stretches from one telomere to the other or whether there are numerous double helices linked in some way along a chromosome. According to Moses and Coleman (1964), electron micrographs of meiotic prophase reveals that structures containing DNA appear to locate at the periphery of the so-called synaptinemal complex in such a way that the chromosome resembles a bottle brush. In this respect, the original centipede model seems attractive if each "leg" were a circle, which in electron micrographs is represented by a strand because the circle has been cut by the microtome knife. If this were so, replication of any circle along the chromosome may start or end independently of any other circle. This may also explain the discontinuous H^3-thymidine uptake in polytene chromosomes (Ficq and Pavan, 1957; Plaut, 1963; Plaut and Nash, 1964) and in meiotic prophase (Wimber and Prensky, 1963).

The progress made during recent years concerning DNA replication of chromosomes in higher forms of life has been impressive. Although the data are still descriptive in nature, they constitute invaluable background knowledge for future experimentation, which should yield pertinent information regarding chromosome structure, chromosome behavior, and cell physiology.

ACKNOWLEDGMENTS

This work was supported in part by research grants No. GB-1867 from the National Science Foundation, No. DRG-269 from the Damon Runyon Memorial Fund for Cancer Research, and No. E-286 from the American Cancer Society.

REFERENCES

ATKINS, L., BOOK, J. A., GUSTAVSON, K.-H., HASSON, O., AND HJELM, M. (1963). A case of sex chromosome anomaly with autoradiographic studies. *Cytogenetics* **2**, 208-231.

BADER, S., MILLER, O. J., AND MUKHERJEE, B. B. (1963). Observations on chromosome duplication in cultured human leucocytes. *Exptl. Cell Res.* **31**, 100-112.

BARR, M. L., AND BERTRAM, E. G. (1949). A morphological distinction between neurons of the male and female, and the behavior of the nucleoprotein synthesis. *Nature* **163**, 676-677.

BILLEN, D., AND HNILICA, L. S. (1964). Inhibition of DNA synthesis *in vitro* by histones. In "The Nucleohistones" (J. Bonner and P. T'so, eds.), pp. 289-297. Holden-Day, San Francisco.

BISHOP, A., AND BISHOP, O. N. (1963). Analysis of tritium-labelled human chromosomes with sex chromatin. *Nature* **199**, 930-932.

CAIRNS, J. (1963). The bacterial chromosome and its manner of replication as seen by autoradiography. *J. Mol. Biol.* **6**, 208-213.

DARLINGTON, C. D., AND LA COUR, L. F. (1940). Nucleic acid starvation of the chromosomes in Trillium. *J. Genet.* **40**, 185-213.

DEFENDI, V., AND MANSON, L. A. (1963). Analysis of the life-cycle in mammalian cells. *Nature* **198**, 359-361.

DONNALLY, G. M., AND NEWCOMER, E. H. (1963). Autoradiographic patterns in cultured leucocytes of the domestic fowl. *Exptl. Cell Res.* **30**, 363-368.

FICQ, A., AND PAVAN, C. (1957). Autoradiography of polytene chromosomes of *Rhynchosciara angelae* at different stages of larval development. *Nature* **180**, 983-984.

FIERS, W., AND SINSHEIMER, R. L. (1962). The structure of the DNA of bacteriophage ϕX174. III. Ultracentrifugal evidence for a ring structure. *J. Mol. Biol.* **5**, 424-434.

FREDERIC, J. (1961). Contribution a l'etude du caryotype chez le poulet. *Arch. Biol.* **72**, 185-209.

FRENSTER, J. H., ALLFREY, V. G., AND MIRSKY, A. E. (1963). Repressed and active chromatin isolated from interphase lymphocytes. *Proc. Natl. Acad. Sci. U.S.* **50**, 1026-1032.

GALTON, M., AND HOLT, S. F. (1964). Asynchronous replication of the mouse sex chromosomes. *Exptl. Cell Res.* (in press).

GERMAN, J. L. (1962). DNA synthesis in human chromosomes. *Trans. N.Y. Acad. Sci.* **24**, 395-407.

GERMAN, J. L. (1964). The pattern of DNA synthesis in the chromosomes of human blood cells. *J. Cell Biol.* **20**, 37-55.

GIANELLI, F. (1963). The pattern of X-chromosome deoxyribonucleic acid synthesis in two women with abnormal sex-chromosome complements. *Lancet* **I**, 863-865.

GILBERT, C. W., MULDAL, S., LAJTHA, L. G., AND ROWLEY, J. (1962). Time sequence of human chromosome duplication. *Nature* **195**, 869-873.

GRUMBACH, M. M., MORISHIMA, A., AND TAYLOR, J. H. (1963). Human sex chromosome abnormalities in relation to DNA replication and heterochromatization. *Proc. Natl. Acad. Sci. U.S.* **49**, 581-589.

HSU, T. C. (1962). Differential rate of RNA synthesis between euchromatin and heterochromatin. *Exptl. Cell Res.* **27**, 332-334.

HSU, T. C. (1964a). Genetic cytology. In "Biology of Cells and Tissues in Culture" (E. N. Willmer, ed.), pp. 397-461. Academic Press, New York.

HSU, T. C. (1964b). Mammalian chromosomes *in vitro*. XVIII. DNA replication sequences in the Chinese hamster. *J. Cell Biol.* **23**, 53-62.

HUANG, R. C., AND BONNER, J. (1962). Histone, a suppressor of chromosomal RNA synthesis. *Proc. Natl. Acad. Sci. U. S.* **48**, 1216-1222.

HUANG, R. C., BONNER, J., AND MURRAY, K. (1964). Physical and Biological properties of soluble nucleohistones. *J. Mol. Biol.* **8**, 54-64.

JACOB, F., AND WOLLMAN, E. L. (1961). "Sexuality and the Genetics of Bacteria." Academic Press, New York.

KIKUCHI, Y., AND SANDBERG, A. A. (1964). Chronology and pattern of human chromosome replication. I. Blood leukocytes of normal subjects. *J. Natl. Cancer Inst.* **32**, 1109-1143.

KOSIN, I. L., AND ISHIZAKI, H. (1959). Incidence of sex chromatin in *Gallus domesticus*. *Science* **130**, 43-44.

LEHNERT, S. M. (1964). The inhibition of DNA synthesis by nuclear proteins. *Biochim. Biophys. Acta* **80**, 338-339.

LEWIS, E. B. (1950). The phenomenon of position effect. *Advan. Genet.* **3**, 75-115.

LYON, M. F. (1961). Gene action in the X-chromosome of the mouse (*Mus musculus* L.). *Nature* **190**, 372-373.

MATTHEY, R. (1958). Un nouveau type de determination chromosomique du sexe chez les mammiferes *Ellobuis lutescens* Th. et *Microtus* (*Chilotus*) *oregoni* Bachm. (Murides-Microtines). *Experientia* **7**, 240.

MOORHEAD, P. S., AND DEFENDI, V. (1963). Asynchrony of DNA synthesis in chromosomes of human diploid cells. *J. Cell Biol.* **16**, 202-209.

MORISHIMA, A., GRUMBACH, M. M., AND TAYLOR, J. H. (1962). Asynchronous duplication of human chromosomes and the origin of sex chromatin. *Proc. Natl. Acad. Sci. U. S.* **48**, 756-763.

MOSES, M. J., AND COLEMAN, J. R. (1964). Structural patterns and the functional organization of chromosomes. *In* "The Role of Chromosomes in Development" (M. Locke, ed.), pp. 11-49. Academic Press, New York.

MUELLER, G. C., KAJIWARA, K., STUBBLEFIELD, E., AND RUEKERT, R. R. (1962). Molecular events in the reproduction of animal cells. I. The effect of puromycin on the duplication of DNA. *Cancer Res.* **22**, 1084-1090.

MULDAL, S., GILBERT, C. W., LAJTHA, L. G., LINDSTEN, J., ROWLEY, J., AND FRACCARO, M. (1963). Tritiated thymidine incorporation in an isochromosome for the long arm of the X chromosome in man. *Lancet* **I**, 861-863.

NAGATA, T. (1963). The molecular synchrony and sequential replication of DNA in *Escherichia coli*. *Proc. Natl. Acad. Sci. U. S.* **49**, 551-559.

OHNO, S., AND HAUSCHKA, T. S. (1960). Allocycly of the X-chromosome in tumors and normal tissues. *Cancer Res.* **20**, 541-545.

OHNO, S., KAPLAN, W. D., AND KINOSITA, R. (1959). Formation of the sex chromatin by a single X-chromosome in liver cells of *Rattus norvegicus*. *Exptl. Cell Res.* **18**, 415-418.

OHNO, S., JAINCHILL, J., AND STENIUS, C. (1963). The creeping vole (*Microtus oregoni*) as a gonosomic mosaic. I. The OY/XY constitution of the male. *Cytogenetics* **2**, 232-239.

PETERSEN, A. J. (1964). DNA synthesis and chromosome asynchrony. Induced parasynchronous DNA synthesis in human leukocytes cultures and chromosomal asynchrony in the early S-phase. *J. Cell Biol.* (in press).

PLAUT, W. (1963). On the replication organization of DNA in the polytene chromosome of *Drosophila melanogaster*. *J. Mol. Biol.* **7**, 632-635.

PLAUT, W., AND NASH, D. (1964). Localized DNA synthesis in polytene chromosomes and its implications. In "The Role of Chromosomes in Development" (M. Locke, ed.), pp. 113-135. Academic Press, New York.

PRESCOTT, D. M. (1964). Autoradiography with liquid emulsion. In "Methods in Cell Physiology" (D. M. Prescott, ed.), Vol. 1, pp. 365-370. Academic Press, New York.

PRESCOTT, D. M., AND BENDER, M. A. (1962). Synthesis of RNA and protein during mitosis in mammalian tissue culture cells. *Exptl. Cell Res.* **26**, 260-268.

ROWLEY, J., MULDAL, S., GILBERT, C. W., LAJTHA, L. G., LINSTEN, J., FRACCARO, M., AND KAJSER, K. (1963). Synthesis of deoxyribonucleic acid on X-chromosomes of an XXXXY male. *Nature* **197**, 251-252.

RUECKERT, R. R., AND MUELLER, G. C. (1960). Studies on unbalanced growth in tissue culture. I. Induction and consequences of thymidine deficiency. *Cancer Res.* **20**. 1584-1591.

RUSSELL, L. B. (1961). Genetics of mammalian sex chromosomes. *Science* **133**, 1795-1803.

SAKSELA, E., AND MOORHEAD, P. S. (1962). Enhancement of secondary constrictions and the heterochromatic X in human cells. *Cytogenetics* **2**, 225-244.

SASAKI, M. S., AND MAKINO, S. (1963). The demonstration of secondary constrictions in human chromosomes by means of new techniques. *Am. J. Human Genet.* **15**, 24-33.

SCHMID, W. (1962). DNA replication patterns of the heterochromosomes in *Gallus domesticus*. *Cytogenetics* **1**, 344-352.

SCHMID, W. (1963). DNA replication patterns of human chromosomes. *Cytogenetics* **2**, 175-193.

SCHMID, W. (1964). Autoradiography of human chromosomes. In "Human Chromosome Methodology" (J. Yunis, ed.). Academic Press, New York. In press.

SOMERS, C. E., AND HSU, T. C. (1962). Chromosome damage induced by hydroxylamine in mammalian cells. *Proc. Natl. Acad. Sci. U.S.* **48**, 937-953.

SOMERS, C. E., HSU, T. C., AND COLE, A. (1963). Isolation of chromosomes. *Exptl. Cell Res.* Suppl. 9, 220-234.

STANNERS, C. P., AND TILL, J. E. (1960). DNA synthesis in individual L-strain mouse cells. *Biochim. Biophys. Acta* **37**, 406-419.

STREISINGER, G., AND BRUCE, V. (1960). Linkage of genetic markers in phage T_2 and T_4. *Genetics* **45**, 1289-1296.

STUBBLEFIELD, E. (1964a). DNA synthesis and chromosome morphology of Chinese hamster cells cultured in media containing N-desacetyl-N-methylcolchicine (Colcemid). In "Cytogenetics of Cells in Culture, including Radiation Studies" (R. J. C. Harris, ed.). Academic Press, New York. In press.

STUBBLEFIELD, E. (1964b). High resolution autoradiography of mammalian chromosomes: A method for repeated exposures to one cell. *Federation Proc.* **23**, 332.

STUBBLEFIELD, E., AND MUELLER, G. C. (1962). Molecular events in the reproduction of animal cells. II. The focalized synthesis of DNA in the chromosomes of HeLa cells. *Cancer Res.* **22**, 1091-1099.

TAYLOR, J. H. (1959). Autoradiographic studies of the organization and mode of duplication of chromosomes. *In* "Symposium on Molecular Biology" (R. E. Zirkle, ed.), pp. 304-320. Univ. Chicago Press, Chicago, Illinois.

TAYLOR, J. H. (1960a). Asynchronous duplication of chromosomes in cultured cells of Chinese hamster. *J. Biophys. Biochem. Cytol.* 7, 455-464.

TAYLOR, J. H. (1960b). Nucleic acid synthesis in relation to the cell division cycle. *Ann. N. Y. Acad. Sci.* 90, 409-421.

TAYLOR, J. H. (1963). The replication and organization of DNA in chromosomes. *In* "Molecular Genetics" (J. H. Taylor, ed.), Pt. 1, pp. 65-111. Academic Press, New York.

TAYLOR, J. H. (1964). Regulation of DNA replication and variegation-type position effects. *In* "Cytogenetics of Cells in Culture, including Radiation Studies" (R. J. C. Harris, ed.). Academic Press, New York. In press.

TAYLOR, J. H., WOODS, P. S., AND HUGHES, W. L. (1957). The organization and duplication of chromosomes as revealed by autoradiographic studies using tritium-labeled thymidine. *Proc. Natl. Acad. Sci. U. S.* 43, 122-128.

TJIO, J. H., AND OSTERGREN, G. (1958). The chromosome of primary mammary carcinomas in Mills virus strains of the mouse. *Hereditas* 44, 451-465.

WEIL, R., AND VINOGRAD, J. (1963). The cyclic helix and cyclic coil forms of polyoma viral DNA. *Proc. Natl. Acad. Sci. U. S.* 50, 730-738.

WIMBER, D. E., AND PRENSKY, W. (1963). Autoradiography with meiotic chromosomes of the male newt (*Triturus viridescens*) using H3-thymidine. *Genetics* 48, 1731-1738.

WOODARD, J., AND SWIFT, H. (1964). The DNA content of cold-treated chromosomes. *Exptl. Cell Res.* 34, 131-137.

XEROS, N. (1962). Deoxyriboside control and synchronization of mitosis. *Nature* 194, 682-683.

YOSHIKAWA, H., AND SUEOKA, N. (1963). Sequential replication of *Bacillus subtilis* chromosome. I. Comparison of marker frequencies in exponential and stationary growth phases. *Proc. Natl. Acad. Sci. U. S.* 49, 559-566.

Localized DNA Synthesis in Polytene Chromosomes and Its Implications

WALTER PLAUT AND DAVID NASH

Department of Zoology, University of Wisconsin, Madison, Wisconsin

The chromosomes of nonmicrobial cells were named, on the basis of their dye affinity, about 76 years ago. While massive cytochemical data have since made possible a reasonably precise description of the chemical basis of this characteristic, the chromosomes of cells other than bacteria and phages remain poorly understood. We have yet to obtain a picture of their structure that is adequate to explain their function in the regulation of cellular activities and their complex behavior in mitotic and meiotic divisions. Our present state of ignorance is exemplified by the fact that the latest structural models proposed lean heavily on the least understood chromosomal components, the proteins (see Taylor, 1963), and the continuing lack of agreement on the lateral multiplicity of the most intensely studied constituent, the DNA molecule (Peacock, 1963; Ris, 1961; Taylor, 1963). This paper is devoted to an examination of experimental data which are relevant to a simple question concerning the longitudinal arrangement of DNA molecules in chromosomes and their replication. No complete structural model of the chromosome will emerge from this examination. By deliberately refraining from trying to explain it all, however, we may gain enough imaginative freedom to see the next incisive experiment and, eventually, the chromosome.

The specific question under study is whether or not the individual DNA molecules extend through the entire chromosome of higher organisms. The demonstration by Cairns (1963) that the chromosome of *Escherichia coli* consists of but a single molecular element in length and that this element is very long, even by nonmicrobial standards, has focused attention on this question and has shown a fairly direct way to its experimental resolution. If one assumes that each DNA molecule will replicate at only one point at a time, then the number of separate points of simultaneous synthesis will provide a minimal estimate of the number of molecular ends along a structure where synthesis can be initiated. Among the more complex chromosomes, those undergoing meiotic prophase and the polytene chromosomes are sufficiently extended to permit an approach to their longitudinal fine structure by light microscopy. The polytene chromosomes offer the additional advantages of being visible in interphase, when DNA synthesis occurs and when they are even more fully extended than in meiotic prophase (Beermann, 1962), and of having much higher local DNA concentrations. These advantages are due to their unequivocally multistranded nature. This latter circumstance is also useful in that it precludes any temptation to visualize the DNA as a single molecule in the chromosomal cross section at any one point.

The salivary gland chromosomes of *Drosophila* have been subjected to relatively short incubations with the labeled DNA precursor, tritiated thymidine, in several laboratories including our own. The tracer is either injected into whole larvae or, more simply, the salivary glands are dissected, removed, and placed in a modified Ringer's solution (Ephrussi and Beadle, 1936) to which the isotope has been added. The glands are subsequently fixed, squashed on slides, and covered with an autoradiographic emulsion. After suitable exposure the preparations are developed photographically and examined with ordinary bright-field, dark-field, or phase optics. In a successful preparation, the presence of silver grains in the emulsion indicates the fact and location of precursor incorporated into an acid-insoluble cell constituent; if the precursor used was radioactively pure thymidine, this cell constituent is likely to be DNA. Final proof of location of the label in DNA can be obtained by ascertaining the sensitivity of the label to deoxyribonuclease and its insensitivity to incubation with buffer solutions or other enzymes. The results obtained by Rudkin and Woods (1959), Gay (1963), Uesu *et al.* (1963), Swift (1964), Ritossa (1963), and ourselves (Plaut, 1963) agree in several respects: Not all nuclei of *Drosophila* salivary glands incubated with tritiated thymidine for short periods are labeled; those which do incorporate thymidine into DNA show labeling either along the entire length of the chromosomes or in restricted regions of varying length, with more or less extensive unlabeled stretches between them (Figs. 1–4, 6–8). The latter labeling pattern, which we have designated as discontinuous or spot labeling, has also been observed in *Chironomus* by Sengün (1961) and to a degree by Keyl and Pelling (1963). This pattern occurs in our experiments with *Drosophila melanogaster* in the majority of labeled nuclei after 3- to 90-minute incubations, but possibly only in a minority in *D. virilis,* incubated for periods of 30 to 240 minutes (Swift, 1964). Whether this difference is real and attributable to variation between the two species or, as is more likely, to variations in scoring intermediate labeling patterns (such as illustrated in Fig. 3) is uncertain; the fact remains that discontinuous labeling has been observed in every appropriate experiment on polytene chromosomes. The maximum number of spots we have observed to date over a single chromosome is about fifty. Within any one labeled nucleus only a single pattern can be seen: all chromosomes are either continuously or discontinuously labeled. Neither in *Drosophila* nor *Chironomus* (Sengün, 1961) is there any evidence for the assumption that the various labeling patterns are related to the differentiative state of the organisms; all possible patterns can be found in a single gland or even a single lobe (see, e.g., Fig. 2). Nor is there any evidence in *Drosophila* or *Chironomus* that thymidine incorporation represents synthesis of "metabolic," unstable DNA associated with puffs as may be the case in *Rhynchosciara* (Ficq and Pavan, 1957; Ficq *et al.,* 1959). In the absence of any indications to the contrary, it appears most reasonable to suppose that all of the labeling patterns observed occur in conjunction with normal doubling of pre-existing DNA molecules in the course of the polytenization of salivary gland chromosomes.

We have previously interpreted the occurrence of discontinuous labeling as indicative of the existence of many growing points and, hence, many ends of DNA molecules along a chromosome. In other words, the polytene chromosome of *Drosophila* is dissimilar from the chromosome of *E. coli* in this respect (cf. Cairns, 1963). Gay (1963) arrived at a similar conclusion. Uesu *et al.* (1963), on the other hand, prefer to reconcile "multicentric" synthesis with a single DNA molecule running the length of the chromosome; they visualize this molecule as subdivided into "tandemly linked autocatalytic subunits" and define the subunit as the stretch between points that are cut at the beginning of replication.

The assumption underlying this interpretation of the molecular basis of discontinuous labeling is that any DNA molecule undergoing replication adds nucleotides at only one or, at most, very few points along its length. Cairns (1963) has shown that the most likely number of autoradiographically resolvable points at which tritiated thymidine is incorporated into *E. coli* DNA molecule at a given time is one [see Nagata (1963) and Yoshikawa and Sueoka (1963) for supporting genetic evidence]. The most intensely studied enzyme involved directly in the

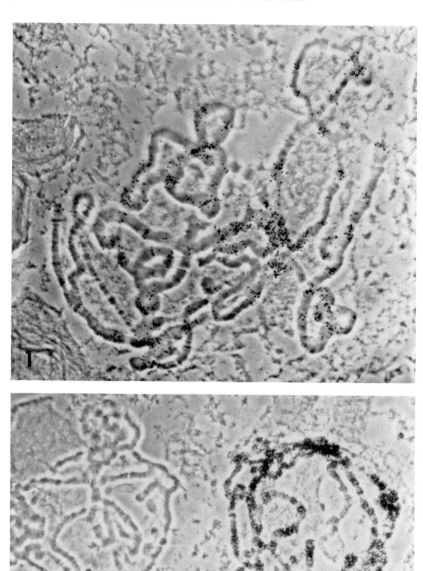

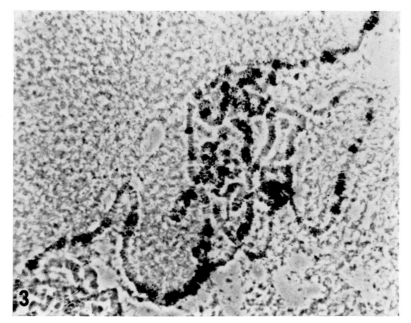

Fɪɢ. 3. Example of intermediate pattern; discontinuities are obvious, but each labeled spot appears extended. Ten-minute incubation with H³-thymidine (10 μC/ml, 6700 μC/μM); 14 days autoradiographic exposure; V-1042 emulsion. About 900 ×.

synthesis of DNA *in vitro*, the polymerase first isolated from *E. coli* by Kornberg (for review see Bessman, 1963), is now visualized as leading to the full replication of any available single-stranded primer molecule by starting at one end and working toward the other (Kornberg, 1964). Its mode of action is most simply reconciled with the notion that only one point along a DNA chain is being replicated at one time. Nonetheless, it should be recognized that the actual involvement of this polymerase in the discrete doubling characteristic of chromosomal DNA synthesis is problematical, particularly in view of its decided polarity preference. We are, therefore, making an assumption whose main

Fɪɢ. 1. Highly discontinuous labeling pattern. Ten-minute H³-thymidine incorporation (10 μC/ml, 6700 μC/μM); 14 days autoradiographic exposure; V-1042 emulsion. About 900 ×. From Plaut (1963).

Fɪɢ. 2. Example of distinctly different labeling patterns in two neighboring nuclei from one lobe of a gland. Ten-minute H³-thymidine incubation (10 μC/ml, 6700 μC/μM); 14 days autoradiographic exposure; V-1042 emulsion. About 400 ×.

strength is derived from its simplicity and the lack of contradictory evidence. Even the fact that it appears to be supported by studies on bacterial systems cannot be accepted without some reservations since we are dealing with a considerably more complex chromosome where the mechanics of DNA synthesis may differ under the influence of other structural components. It should also be pointed out that while the number of discrete sites of synthesis along a chromosome can be interpreted as an index of the minimal number of molecular ends, the ends may or may not exist as such between replication periods. The DNA molecule in the chromosome is thus operationally defined as that unit which replicates sequentially and once in a mitotic or endomitotic cycle; the mechanism which differentiates between one molecule and the next is not specified.

Before exploring further the implications of discontinuous DNA labeling with respect to the organization of chromosomal DNA and some of the behavioral characteristics of whole chromosomes, we must examine the possibility that a small spot of labeling represents (a) an artifact, (b) synthesis of DNA in only one of the large number of homologous DNA strands in a given polytene chromosome, and (c) equates with some analogous feature of replication in nonpolytene chromosomes.

The possibility that discontinuous labeling is a preparative artifact, attributable to the short range of tritium β-particles and uneven chromosomal preparations has been eliminated. Only continuous and uniform labeling is found when procedurally identical autoradiographic preparations are made from salivary glands derived from larvae fed with tritiated thymidine for several replication cycles (Plaut, 1963) (see Fig. 5). It is also conceivable, however, that spot labeling arises as a tritium effect, as the result of tritium decay. Two types of this radiation artifact might occur: The presence or frequency of thymidine incorporation sites could be affected by the tritium β-particle flux within a nucleus through the production of artificial DNA chain ends; alternatively, the decay of an already incorporated tritium atom might lead to further incorporation at a particular site by damaging the DNA molecule from within the chromosome. The former effect, if present in extreme form, would invalidate spot labeling as indicative of normal chromosomal behavior. This possibility has been ruled out by the results of an experiment in which tritiated thymidine was made available for incorporation to excised salivary glands for 10 minutes after prior incubations with either H³-uridine or unlabeled uridine at the same concentration. While over 95% of all nuclei showed substantial uridine

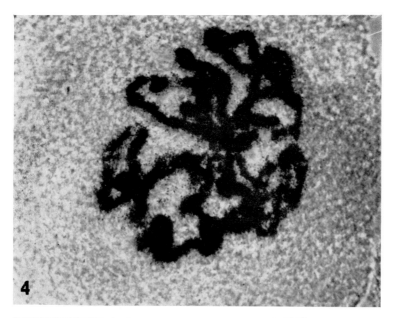

Fig. 4. Example of saturation labeling; no discontinuities evident. Eight- to 10-minute incubation with H³-thymidine (10 µC/ml, 6700 µC/µM); 14 days autoradiographic exposure; V-1042 emulsion. About 1000 ×. From Plaut (1963).

Fig. 5. Autoradiograph of squashed salivary gland nucleus from larva grown for 8 days in tritiated thymidine of reduced specific activity (67 µC/µM). Eleven days autoradiographic exposure; V-1042 emulsion. About 1000 ×. From Plaut (1963).

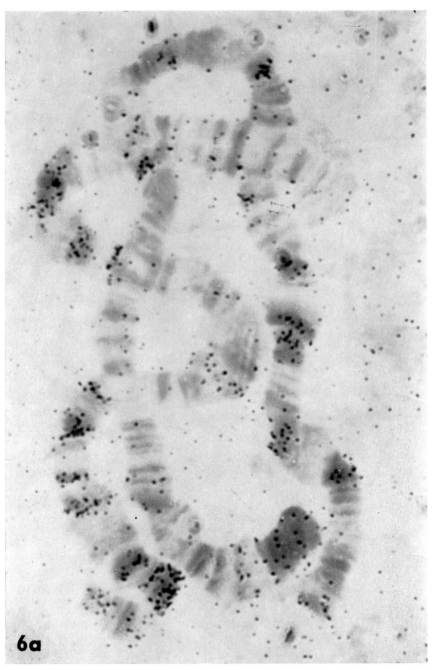

Fig. 6. (a) Autoradiograph of two chromosomes of squashed *Drosophila* salivary gland nucleus. Five- to 8-minute H³-thymidine incubation (15 μC/ml, 10000 μC/μM). (b) Phase contrast photograph of same field after light aceto-orcein staining; taken

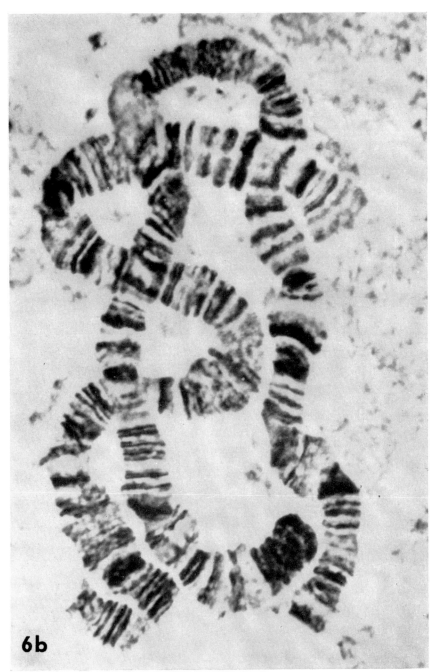

6b

before application of autoradiographic emulsion. Seventeen days autoradiographic exposure; AR-10 emulsion. About 1900 ×. Note lack of absolute correspondence between band density and presence or absence of label.

incorporation into RNA along the chromosomes, thymidine incorporation—examined on slides subjected to ribonuclease treatment—was comparable in the two sets of glands, those prelabeled with hot and those preincubated with cold uridine. In both sets about 30% of the nuclei showed no evidence of any DNA synthesis; in both, the various degrees of discontinuous thymidine incorporation could be observed. Clearly, spot labeling of DNA is not produced by tritium decay, even when tritium is present in RNA in physical contact with the chromosome.

The possibility remains that the second type of tritium effect, a stimulation of further incorporation by the decay of tritium already incorporated into DNA, may be operative. Preliminary results with H^3- and C^{14}-thymidine indicate that C^{14} incorporation may be detectably enhanced in salivary gland nuclei by the presence of H^3. A more complete study demonstrating such an effect has been made on root tip nuclei (Krause and Plaut, 1960). Consideration of the amount of decay taking place in a small spot of five or six grains during the critical incubation period of 10 minutes, for example, suggests that the probability of even a single decay in such a region is very small. Such a spot may thus be assumed to represent quantitatively normal incorporation and synthesis. Less quantitative reliance can be placed on more heavily labeled regions. In any event, while tritium decay may aid the detection of localized DNA synthesis by increasing thymidine incorporation at points where incorporation has already occurred, it does not cause it.

Discontinuous labeling of DNA along a polytene chromosome does not automatically imply a longitudinal sequence of several DNA molecules, even if we assume that replication can begin only at molecular ends. It is also conceivable that the many DNA strands, which make up a polytene chromosome by virtue of its failure to undergo mitotic segregation, each extend through the length of the chromosome or chromosome arm and replicate independently of each other. Thus, a series of labeling spots could be interpreted as representing the partial replication of many individual DNA molecules, each having begun the process at the chromosomal end or kinetochore at a different time. This interpretation was rejected previously (Plaut, 1963) on theoretical grounds and on the basis of quantitative estimates. It is now possible to replace these highly uncertain arguments with some direct experimental evidence. Thymidine incorporation at any point along the salivary gland chromosome involves more than a single DNA molecule; at least some of the various strands which make up the cross section of the polytene chromosome appear to be highly synchronized in their replication.

One of the stocks of *Drosophila melanogaster* (Oregon wild type) we have employed shows a relatively high frequency of unpaired chromosome sections, both interstitial and terminal, in squash preparations. Pulse-labeled glands of this stock were squashed, stained lightly with aceto-orcein, and examined *before* autoradiography for unpaired homologs with clearly evident homologous band patterns. Such chromosomes, when found, were photographed and their positions on the slides recorded. The slides were then covered with stripping film and exposed. After development the previously recorded chromosomes were analyzed for thymidine-incorporation patterns. While only a small proportion of the mapped unpaired homologs were suitably labeled so as to permit detailed comparative analysis, enough of these were found (about twenty) to leave little doubt that homologous loci, insofar as these can be identified by band patterns, synthesize DNA not only simultaneously but in equivalent amounts (see Figs. 7-9). A similar observation has been reported by Gay (1963). Among the unambiguously homologous regions, as judged *before* autoradiography, no deviations were found from this rule except in one case where three grains appeared over one homolog and none over the corresponding portion of the other homolog. We do not feel that this case is significant.

The degree of synchronization which can be ascertained is, of course, limited by the duration of the pulse, 10 minutes in most of the relevant experiments. The shortness of this pulse, relative to the total DNA synthesis time of nuclei in this tissue (8–14 hours, see later discussion), tempts us to conclude that the synchronization of DNA synthesis between homologs is absolute. It is also tempting to conclude that all the DNA strands making up each of the homologs are synchronized in their replication. The quantitative equivalence of label observed in the unpaired chromosomes offers some support for this conclusion, although a rigorous relationship between autoradiographic density and tritium decay is difficult to establish in view of the short range of the tritium β-particles relative to the thickness of the labeled structures. Estimates of the amount of DNA synthesis represented by a spot of five or six grains (after 15 days of autoradiographic exposure) suggest a minimum of 200 μ of new polynucleotide chain (4.5×10^8 molecular weight units). If such an amount of synthesis were attributable to the replication of but one of the several hundred basic units that make up the polytene chromosome, it would appear at first sight that there would not be sufficient volume in the chromosomal cross section to accommodate all of the DNA. Simple calculations show, however, that there is room for several thousand such

units, if one discounts the non-DNA constituents which may occupy the
same volume. Although RNA and protein are undoubtedly present, it
is unlikely that they would require 90% of the total space. A better,
although somewhat dangerous, argument arises from the conceptual
difficulty involved in visualizing a control mechanism for chromosomal

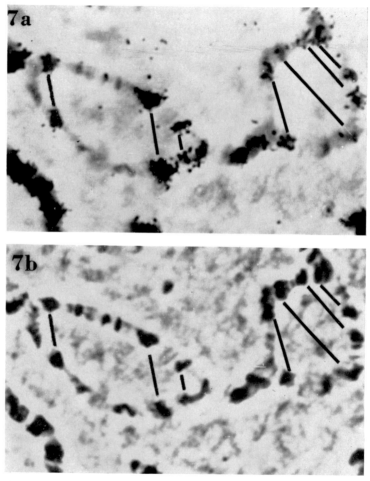

Fig. 7. (a) Autoradiograph of chromosome showing two unpaired regions. H3-thy-
midine incubation for 12 minutes (15 μC/ml, 10000 μC/μM). (b) Phase contrast photograph of same field before autoradiography. Preparation was lightly stained with
aceto-orcein. Seventeen days autoradiographic exposure; AR-10 emulsion. About 2000 ×.
The black lines connect points of homology on the two chromosomes.

DNA synthesis which produces a high level of synchrony between DNA strands in homologous chromosomes and is specific for equal numbers of individual strands in each without affecting all. The situation appears to justify the application of Occam's razor.

It may be asked whether homologous chromosomes which appear partly unpaired in squash preparations were, in fact, unpaired during the critical incubation period. Beermann (1962) argues against the possibility that lack of pairing in polytene chromosomes is ever a preparative artifact, primarily on the basis of the ineffectiveness of squashing in producing unpairing in normally paired chromosomes. An additional argument can be derived from Fig. 8; both homologs show massive and individual puffs which make it sterically unlikely that the chromosomes could have been tightly synapsed before fixation. Lastly, the significance of homologous labeling in the present context does not depend strictly on the synaptic relationship of the homologs unless we assume that spot labeling is brought about by localized tritium decay. This would be more likely to affect similarly those elements which are closely paired than those at some distance from each other. In addition to the already presented analysis of tritium effects, we would like to point to the geometry of low-level labeling as a further argument against this effect as the cause of the patterns. Most grain patterns consisting of 5–10 grains are not distributed at random, but extend laterally across the diameter (or surface) of the chromosome; if their presence were attributable to incorporation as a consequence of a radiation event, one would expect them to occupy random positions about the site of the event.

The conclusion of replicative synchrony between the DNA strands of the polytene chromosome, then, is not easily reconciled with spot labeling as a consequence of independent and asynchronous replication of individual DNA molecules beginning at chromosome ends or middles. It may be noted, in this context, that our data contradict the observations of Steffensen (1963) which, if correct, would lead to a much simpler demonstration of discontinuities in the longitudinal array of DNA molecules in *Drosophila* salivary gland chromosomes. On the basis of a lack of label in "interband" regions [defined by light microscopy; cf. Beermann and Bahr (1954) and Lowman (1956) for a discussion of "submicroscopic bands"] after incubation with H^3-thymidine, Steffensen concluded that DNA was restricted to the bands. Figure 9 shows clearly that H^3-thymidine can be incorporated in the interband area. Since incubation with deoxyribonuclease removes all chromosomal thymidine labeling in those preparations subjected to this control treatment, we

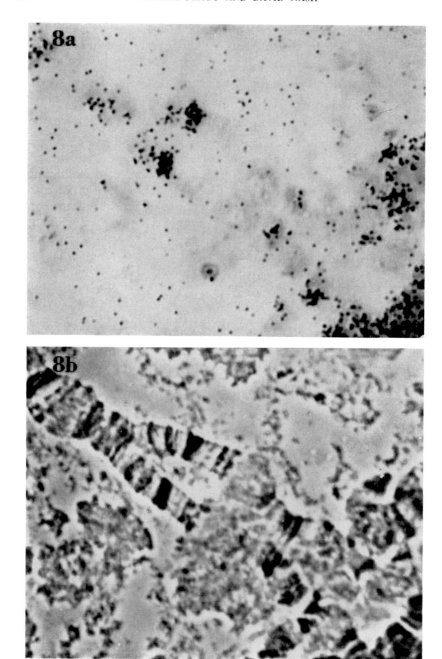

may assume that this incorporation represents DNA synthesis and, hence, that DNA is not restricted to bands. Longitudinal differences in DNA concentration do exist. In some interbands, particularly in well-squashed chromosomes, the concentration of DNA is, in fact, too low to be easily detected in Feulgen preparations. The use of the more sensitive fluorescent dyes, however, confirms the view that at the level of resolution offered by light microscope optics there are no discontinuities in DNA along the length of the salivary gland chromosomes of *Drosophila*.

Any conclusions which may be drawn from DNA-labeling patterns in polytene chromosomes are of general significance to the question of the architecture of chromosomal DNA only if it can be shown that these patterns bear some relationship to those observable in the more usual nonpolytene structures. Although there is general agreement that polytene chromosomes differ from normal interphase chromosomes only by their lateral complexity and should therefore have the same longitudinal structural characteristics (cf. Beermann, 1962), too little is known of this structure at the molecular level to regard this agreement as adequate justification for extrapolating from one to the other. The fact that nonpolytene chromosomes attain sufficient thickness—at the cost of length—for light microscope study only in prophase sharply reduces the resolvability of longitudinal detail. Moreover, their lower lateral complexity obviously reduces the amount of DNA at any one point. Thus, if we observe two groups of five grains each that are separated by 5 μ in the autoradiograph over a late third instar *Drosophila* salivary gland chromosome, this would correspond to two "labeled" spots of 0.01 grains each, about 0.05 μ apart on a somatic metaphase chromosome in the same organism; they could clearly be neither detected nor resolved. Nonetheless, spot or at least discontinuous labeling can be inferred from observations on a large variety of nonpolytene chromosomes after short incubations with tritiated thymidine (Taylor, 1960; Lima de Faria, 1961; Stubblefield and Mueller, 1962; Schmid, 1963; Moorhead and Defendi, 1963; German, 1964). Concerning the synchrony of localized replication between homologous chromosomes, the analysis of Schmid (1963) of labeling patterns in human chromosomes implies at least sufficient

FIG. 8. (a) Autoradiograph of unpaired chromosome region with a "puff." H^3-thymidine incubation for 12 minutes (15 μC/ml, 10000 μC/μM). (b) Phase contrast photograph of same field before autoradiography. Preparation was lightly stained with aceto-orcein; 17 days autoradiographic exposure; AR-10 emulsion. About 1800 ×. Note correspondence of label on the two homologous chromosome sections.

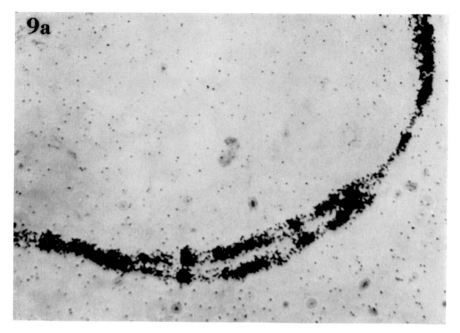

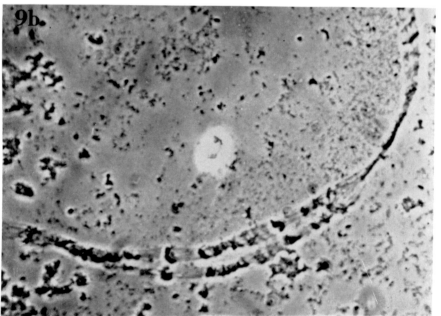

synchrony to permit distinction between either member of one pair of homologs and that of another. German (1964) finds limited asynchrony between autosomal homologs in human cells after 10-minute pulses; it is doubtful, however, whether all possibilities of autoradiographic artifact leading to occasional unequal labeling of corresponding sections of homologous chromosomes can be rigorously excluded in work with such small chromosomes. With the exception of the extreme asynchrony between the two X chromosomes in at least some tissues from several organisms (see, for example, Taylor, 1960; German, 1964), the limited evidence available does not favor a radical difference between nonpolytene and polytene chromosomes with respect to synchrony within a set of homologs. Whether nonpolytene autosomes show the same degree of synchronization as we observe in *Drosophila* salivary gland chromosomes and whether, in fact, this relationship is constant in cells of all tissue types, remain interesting but open questions.

One may also ask whether the timing of DNA synthesis and its quantitative consequences in nuclei with polytene chromosomes is similar to the pattern characteristic of other cells in which synthesis leads to a precise doubling of pre-existing DNA and usually occupies only a portion of the interphase period. Measurements by Rasch and Swift (see Alfert, 1954) have shown that quantitative DNA values in *Drosophila* salivary gland nuclei fall into a series of integral values suggestive of up to eight doublings of the original "nonpolytene" amount of DNA, with some nuclei falling between the various levels. This implies complete analogy to nonpolytene nuclei in that each synthetic phase leads to a doubling and is separated from the next period of DNA synthesis by a pause. Some simple estimates of the absolute time periods involved can be calculated. Since it takes about 1 week under normal culturing conditions for eggs to develop into late third instar larvae, the average time for each of the eight replication cycles is about 20 hours. After a 10- to 15-minute incubation of excised glands with tritiated thymidine we find from 40 to 70% of the nuclei labeled. (The percentage varies between experimental series owing to as yet undetermined causes.) It follows that

FIG. 9. (a) Autoradiograph of continuously labeled chromosome with unpaired section. H³-thymidine incubation for 12 minutes (15 μC/ml, 10000 μC/μM). (b) Phase contrast photograph of same field before autoradiography. Preparation was lightly stained with aceto-orcein; 17 days autoradiographic exposure; AR-10 emulsion. About 1300 ×. Note presence of label over interband regions and quantitative equivalence of label along the two homologs.

of the 20 hours, 8 to 14 hours are spent in DNA synthesis. Although this may appear to be a disproportionately long time when compared to other cells, it should be kept in mind that we are including in the labeled fraction large numbers of nuclei showing extremely light and discontinuous incorporation which would escape detection in nonpolytene cells. Moreover, the salivary gland nuclei do not undergo division and may thereby save several hours in total cycle time. In short, the over-all temporal and quantitative aspects of DNA synthesis do not appear to differ significantly between cells with normal and those with polytene chromosomes.

It has been suggested that highly localized spot labeling in *Drosophila* salivary gland chromosomes occurs toward the end of a DNA replication and that it occurs at heterochromatic loci (Keyl and Pelling, 1963). If this is correct, a further analogy between polytene and nonpolytene chromosomes could be drawn; among the latter there is considerable evidence for late replication of easily identified heterochromatic elements (see Schmid, 1963, for review). There is too little experimental information at present, however, for the definitive establishment of spot labeling as early, late, or in the middle of DNA replication in polytene chromosomes. Moreover, the concept of intercalary heterochromatin appears to be of limited usefulness when applied to short regions of polytene chromosomes, since every band could be designated as heterochromatic within the framework of the classic definition of heterochromatin as visibly distinct in the interphase nucleus. Until heterochromatin can be differentiated from euchromatin by some form of direct analysis, it is simpler and probably more useful to compare different chromosomal loci in terms of DNA density and ask whether spot labeling occurs preferentially at densely staining bands and may therefore be a simple concentration effect. There is little doubt that within any spot-labeled chromosome densely staining bands are more likely to show higher levels of labeling than less densely staining zones. There are sufficient exceptions to this pattern (see, e.g., Fig. 6) to make any simple relationship between the presence or absence of incorporated thymidine and DNA concentration highly unlikely as the primary cause of discontinuous labeling. An examination of Fig. 3 provides ample evidence that well-banded regions may still be entirely unlabeled when massive incorporation has taken place elsewhere (see also Swift, 1964).

We would like to suggest, as a simple hypothesis to explain the various labeling patterns observed in polytene chromosomes, that the chromosomal DNA is longitudinally subdivided into a series of independently replicating units. Within a given chromosome different numbers of these units are engaged in replicating at any one time and these are scattered more or less uniformly, though probably not randomly, along the chromosome. The maximum number of discrete labeled spots observable (about fifty so far) would represent a minimal estimate of the number of units. Whether the individual unit corresponds to a discrete DNA molecule, a longitudinally linked series of DNA molecules, or a predetermined piece of a DNA molecule that is established as such at the time of replication, cannot be resolved in the absence of any reliable data on the physical size of native *Drosophila* DNA; that it represents a single DNA molecule is the simplest and most attractive alternative. While the average molecular unit cannot extend for more than one-fiftieth the length of the longest *Drosophila* salivary gland chromosome—about 450 μ—it may be a good deal shorter than 9 μ in that direction. Our data are entirely consistent with the notion that the individual unit may be contained in less than 1-μ length of chromosome and may require only minutes for its replication. A comparison of labeling patterns after short and long incubation periods that is now in progress should provide some evidence with which to evaluate this length estimate. If the unit of replication extends for an appreciable distance along the chromosome axis, we should find an increase in the length of the average spot over well-stretched chromosomes. The data already available from this analysis (Emspak, 1964) satisfy one expectation of our hypothesis in that the average number of spots over a nucleus with discontinuously labeled chromosomes increases from about 16 after a 10-minute incorporation period to about 34 after 30 minutes of incubation. However, the degree to which labeling intensity effects this result has not been established.

This working hypothesis appears to conflict with conclusions drawn from some polarized light studies (Schmidt, 1941; Pfeiffer, 1941) on polytene chromosomes. The negative birefringence observed in bands suggested highly oriented DNA molecules, parallel to the chromosome axis. Caspersson (1940), using polarized ultraviolet, found little evidence for such orientation. Caspersson's conclusion was subsequently criticized by Schmidt (1941). The interpretation of these observations remains problematical since it is not at all clear to which level of structural organization the disputed birefringence should be attributed. No definite conclusions can or, for that matter, should be drawn about the physical arrangement of DNA molecules in either band or interband at this time, despite the temptation offered in that direction by the frequent occurrence of rows of single grains across the chromosome.

The idea that chromosomes are composed of a longitudinal array of DNA or nucleoprotein units is by no means original. Mazia (1954) as well as Rudkin *et al.* (1956), among others, have suggested this for salivary gland chromosomes on the basis of induced fragmentation in one case and photometric measurements in the other. It was suggested that such units reflect more or less precisely the functional genetic organization of the chromosome. In fact, Beermann (1962) considers the band as made up of one or several "units of genetic information" and tentatively equates each of these with a DNA molecule. In view of the fact that there are many possible units of genetic information, depending on the experimental operation used to define them, once one goes beyond the three base sequence which is presumed to specify a single amino acid of a protein, this equation of structural and functional units lacks real meaning for the present. The temptation to relate structural subunits of the chromosome to functional ones may be more productively relieved by considering the possibility that the DNA molecules—as operationally defined by spot-labeling patterns—correspond to those structural elements of the chromosome between which, but not within which, structural rearrangements can occur without producing lethal or seriously deleterious effects on the organism. Among such rearrangements one might consider, for example, inversions and translocations; either of these could lead to difficulties if their occurrence involved a break within a single genetically meaningful DNA molecule. Inversions might produce deletions (Hayashi *et al.,* 1963) if messenger RNA synthesis only involves one of the two DNA strands of a double helix in complex chromosomes; translocations might interrupt informational base sequences.

The close synchrony observed in the replication of DNA at homologous loci implies highly localized control of DNA synthesis, at least in the polytene chromosomes of *Drosophila melanogaster* salivary glands at an advanced stage of polytenization. Such control can be visualized either as a property of the locus itself or as a response to a signal which emanates from a given point on the chromosome and moves along its length so that all loci at the same distance from this point are made to replicate simultaneously. Although the latter possibility does not appear too likely in view of the wide variety of spot-labeling patterns observable in different nuclei, it is difficult to rule it out since more complex patterns might be explained by invoking a larger number of such remote control points. Fortunately, the alternative hypothesis, control by a quality of the locus itself, is subject to direct experimental verification in stocks with known structural anomalies. It predicts, for example, absolute correlation of labeling between duplicated loci, whether present in the same or translocated to a nonhomologous chromosome. Appropriate stocks are available and the experiments are in progress. The answer to this question on the origin or location of control will, unfortunately, not provide us with the mechanism, which promises to be a very complex problem indeed (see Lark, 1963, for a recent review). A final implication of close synchrony in DNA replication in homologs concerns the still open question of the mechanism of crossing-over, particularly in organisms with complex chromosomes. It represents the first experimental demonstration, as far as we can determine, that a copy-choice mechanism for recombination within a DNA molecule is at least possible.

It may be appropriate, in a symposium organized by the Growth Society, to close with an observation which may have some relevance to the problem of differentiation. As a test of our conclusion that homologous loci synthesize DNA simultaneously we have carefully mapped the bands of a single chromosome region (a portion of the X chromosome) in a large number of nuclei of H^3-thymidine-labeled salivary glands before autoradiography. Preliminary analysis of the labeled preparations (Fanning, 1964) shows the expected results—there is a high level of correlation between spot-labeled bands in different nuclei. In other words, the time at which a given locus replicates its DNA is not random but regulated; it bears a definite relationship to the schedule of other loci. The fact that *Drosophila* larvae have polytene chromosomes in a second tissue, the Malpighian tubules, will permit a direct investigation of the tissue specificity of the timing of DNA synthesis between loci. The polytene chromosomes may thus fulfill their promise as a cytogeneticist's ideal material at yet another level of analysis.*

ACKNOWLEDGMENTS

The original work reported in this paper was supported by a National Institutes of Health Research Grant (CA-03276) and by the Research Committee of the Graduate School from funds supplied by the Wisconsin Alumni Research Foundation.

* We have deliberately refrained from any reference to "links" between DNA elements along the length of the chromosome in this review. Their discussion might well be held in abeyance until convincing evidence for their existence is brought forth or until a need for them is demonstrated. It should be kept in mind that, even if our units of DNA replication are discrete DNA molecules rather than subdivisions which arise at the time of replication, they could be held in a permanent longitudinal sequence by the surrounding material without direct connections between their ends.

References

ALFERT, M. (1954). Composition and structure of giant chromosomes. *Intern. Rev. Cytol.* **3**, 131-176.

BEERMANN, W. (1962). Riesenchromosomen. "Protoplasmatologia" Vol. VI D, pp. 1-161.

BEERMANN, W., AND BAHR, G. F. (1954). The submicroscopic structure of the Balbiani-Ring. *Exptl. Cell Res.* **6**, 195-201.

BESSMAN, M. J. (1963). The replication of DNA in cell-free systems. *In* "Molecular Genetics" (J. H. Taylor, ed.), Pt. 1, pp. 1-64. Academic Press, New York.

CAIRNS, J. (1963). The bacterial chromosome and its manner of replication as seen by autoradiography. *J. Mol. Biol.* **6**, 208-213.

CASPERSSON, T. (1940). Nukleinsäureketten und Genvermehrung. *Chromosoma* **1**, 605-619.

EMSPAK, F. (1964). Unpublished data.

EPHRUSSI, B., AND BEADLE, G. W. (1936). A technique of transplantation for *Drosophila. Am. Naturalist* **70**, 218-225.

FANNING, T. G. (1964). Unpublished data.

FICQ, A., AND PAVAN, C. (1957). Autoradiography of polytene chromosomes of *Rhynchosciara angelae* at different stages of larval development. *Nature* **180**, 983-984.

FICQ, A., PAVAN, C., AND BRACHET, J. (1959). Metabolic processes in chromosomes. *Exptl. Cell Res.* Suppl. 6, 105-115.

GAY, H. (1963). Chromosome structure and function. *Carnegie Inst. Wash. Year Book* **62**, 503-510.

GERMAN, J. (1964). The pattern of DNA synthesis in the chromosomes of human blood cells. *J. Cell Biol.* **20**, 37-55.

HAYASHI, M., HAYASHI, M. N., AND SPIEGELMAN, S. (1963). Restriction of *in vivo* genetic transcription to one of the complementary strands of DNA. *Proc. Natl. Acad. Sci. U. S.* **50**, 664-672.

KEYL, H. G., AND PELLING, C. (1963). Differentielle DNS-Replikation in den Speicheldrüsenchromosomen von *Chironomus thummi. Chromosoma* **14**, 347-359.

KORNBERG, A. (1964). *Federation Proc.,* in press.

KRAUSE, M., AND PLAUT, W. (1960). An effect of tritiated thymidine on the incorporation of thymidine into chromosomal DNA. *Nature* **188**, 511-512.

LARK, K. G. (1963). Cellular control of DNA biosynthesis. *In* "Molecular Genetics" (J. H. Taylor, ed.), Pt. 1, pp. 153-206. Academic Press, New York.

LIMA DE FARIA, A. (1961). Initiation of DNA synthesis at specific segments in the meiotic chromosomes of *Melanoplus. Hereditas* **47**, 674-694.

LOWMAN, F. G. (1956). Electron microscope studies of *Drosophila* salivary gland chromosomes. *Chromosoma* **8**, 30-52.

MAZIA, D. (1954). The particulate organization of the chromosome. *Proc. Natl. Acad. Sci. U. S.* **40**, 521-527.

MOORHEAD, P. S., AND DEFENDI, V. (1963). Asynchrony of DNA synthesis in chromosomes of human diploid cells. *J. Cell Biol.* **16**, 202-209.

NAGATA, T. (1963). The molecular synchrony and sequential replication of DNA in *Escherichia coli. Proc. Natl. Acad. Sci. U. S.* **49**, 551-559.

PEACOCK, W. J. (1963). Chromosome duplication and structure as determined by autoradiography. *Proc. Natl. Acad. Sci. U. S.* **49**, 793-801.

PFEIFFER, H. H. (1941). Mikrurgisch-polarisationsoptische Beiträge zur submikroskopischen Morphologie larvaler Speicheldrüsenchromosomen von *Chironomus*. *Chromosoma* 2, 77-85.

PLAUT, W. (1963). On the replicative organization of DNA in the polytene chromosome of *Drosophila melanogaster*. *J. Mol. Biol.* 7, 632-635.

RIS, H. (1961). Ultrastructure and molecular organization of genetic systems. *Can. J. Genet. Cytol.* 3, 95-120.

RITOSSA, F. (1963). Personal communication.

RUDKIN, G. T., AND WOODS, P. S. (1959). Incorporation of H³ cytidine and H³ thymidine into giant chromosomes of *Drosophila* during puff formation. *Proc. Natl. Acad. Sci. U.S.* 45, 997-1003.

RUDKIN, G. T., CORLETTE, S. L., AND SCHULTZ, J. (1956). The relations of the nucleic acid content in salivary gland chromosome bands. *Genetics* 41, 657-658 (abstr.).

SCHMID, W. (1963). DNA replication patterns of human chromosomes. *Cytogenetics* 2, 175-193.

SCHMIDT, W. J. (1941). Einiges über optische Anisotropie und Feinbau von Chromatin und Chromosomen. *Chromosoma* 2, 86-110.

SENGÜN, A. (1961). Incorporation of tritiated thymidine into the giant chromosomes of larvae of *Chironomus*. *Pathol. Biol. Semaine Hop.* [N.S.] 9, 753-755.

STEFFENSEN, D. M. (1963). Evidence for the apparent absence of DNA in the interbands of *Drosophila* salivary chromosomes. *Genetics* 48, 1289-1301.

STUBBLEFIELD, E., AND MUELLER, G. C. (1962). Molecular events in the reproduction of animal cells. II. The focalized synthesis of DNA in the chromosomes of HeLa cells. *Cancer Res.* 22, 1091-1099.

SWIFT, H. (1964). The Histones of Polytene Chromosomes. In "The Nucleohistones" (J. Bonner and P. T'so, eds.), pp. 169-183. Holden-Day, San Francisco.

TAYLOR, J. H. (1960). Asynchronous duplication of chromosomes in cultured cells of Chinese hamster. *J. Biophys. Biochem. Cytol.* 7, 455-464.

TAYLOR, J. H. (1963). The replication and organization of DNA in chromosomes. In "Molecular Genetics" (J. H. Taylor, ed.), Pt. 1, pp. 65-111. Academic Press, New York.

UESU, M., KAKU, H., KOJIMA, A., AND FUJITA, S. (1963). Multicentric synthesis of DNA in the polytene chromosome of *Drosophila melanogaster*. *Kagaku (Tokyo)* 33, 596-597.

YOSHIKAWA, H., AND SUEOKA, N. (1963). Sequential replication of *Bacillus subtilis* chromosome I. Comparison of marker frequencies in exponential and stationary growth phases. *Proc. Natl. Acad. Sci. U.S.* 49, 559-566.

Chromosomal RNA and Other Nuclear RNA Fractions

JAN-ERIK EDSTRÖM

Department of Histology, University of Gothenburg, Gothenburg, Sweden

Chromosomal RNA

Data are now beginning to accumulate on ribonucleic acid (RNA) in the chromosomes and in chromatin (chRNA), but the role of this RNA, its nature and relation to other RNA components in the cell is far from clear. This is probably not only due to methodological difficulties in studies of nuclear fractions, but also to the variability of nuclear construction between and within species, and the heterogeneous nature of the RNA fractions in the nucleus.

Here chRNA is defined as nonnucleolar RNA physically connected to the interphase or prophase chromosomes or to the chromatin. The relation of mitotic chromosomes to RNA will not be treated.

Bulk isolation studies give an apparently simple and regular picture of the RNA which is associated to DNA and to the chromatin in animal and plant cells (Bonner *et al.*, 1961; Georgiev and Mantieva, 1962; Mead, 1964). RNA–DNA complexes have been recovered with the nucleic acids in defined ratios and an RNA that mimics DNA in composition. Complexes of this kind, whether they exist *in vivo* or not, are not representative of chRNA. This can be shown in instances where the morphology of the chromatin permits a study at a subnuclear level. The most illuminating example is provided by the giant polytene chromosomes. The majority of the bands contain little if any RNA (Rudkin, 1962; Pelling, 1964). Measurements of the contents of the two nucleic acids in isolated chromosomes (Edström and Beermann, 1962) show that for the first chromosome in *Chironomus tentans* there is about one-twentieth as much RNA as DNA. Within the chromosome a minority of the bands contain RNA and incorporate RNA precursors (Pelling, 1964). In the fourth chromosome the second Balbiani ring, which is a synthetically active band in an extreme degree of unfolding, contains about 20 μμg of RNA. The average DNA content per band of these bivalent chromosomes is about 1 μμg. The RNA/DNA quotient is consequently 400 times higher here than for the whole first chromosome (Table I). Such a heterogeneity is not restricted to polytene chromosomes, but can be observed also in lampbrush chromosomes from amphibian oocytes (Gall, 1958) and *Drosophila* spermatocytes (Meyer, 1963), as well as in somatic nuclei (Frenster *et al.*, 1963).

TABLE I

RNA/DNA Quotients in *Chironomus* Polytene Chromosomes[a]

Component	RNA/DNA
Whole set	1/7–1/8
Chromosome I	1/20
Chromosome IV	
Middle segment	1/3
Balbiani ring II	20

[a] From Edström and Beermann (1962).

A further manifestation of the heterogeneity of chRNA is provided by the differences in base composition of different chromosomes as revealed by microelectrophoresis (Edström, 1960a). In *Chironomus tentans* the base composition of RNA extracted from the first chromosome differs markedly and significantly from that of the fourth chromosome (Edström and Beermann, 1962). As expected there is also variation in composition within a chromosome, displayed by the three segments of the short fourth chromosome (Table II). Two of these segments are of particular interest since a large fraction of their RNA is derived from single Balbiani rings. The notable property of this RNA is its very high adenine content.

TABLE II

RNA Base Composition in Segments of the Fourth Chromosome
from *Chironomus*[a]

Chromosome	Adenine	Guanine	Cytosine	Uracil	Balbiani ring contribution (%)
Upper segment	35.7	20.6	23.2	20.8	75
Middle segment	38.0	20.5	24.5	17.1	85
Lower segment	31.2	22.0	26.4	20.2	—
Whole chromosome IV estimated average	36	21	24	19	—
Chromosome I	29.4	19.8	27.7	23.1	—

[a] After Edström and Beermann (1962).

The asymmetric RNA could either be representative of the composition of the DNA template or it could represent a product subjected to secondary changes. In the first case highly unrepresentative DNA molecules must have been synthetically active, in view of the great differences in contents of guanine plus cytosine between the bulk of DNA and the various kinds of chRNA investigated (Table III). It is, of course, not excluded that this is really the case, however, it does not seem likely in view of what is known about the relative uniformity of guanine plus

TABLE III

CONTENT OF GUANINE AND CYTOSINE IN RNA AND DNA OF *Chironomus*
POLYTENE CHROMOSOMES[a]

Chromosome	RNA	DNA
I	47.5	28.7
IV	45	30.3

[a] After Edström and Beermann (1962).

cytosine contents for DNA within a species (Sueoka, 1961). The results of Harris (1959; Harris and Watts, 1962; Harris, 1964a,b) suggesting that a large part of the nuclear RNA is broken down in the nucleus favors the second alternative, in particular since the nucleolar or ribosomal RNA does not seem to be the object of this degradation (Girard *et al.*, 1964). Furthermore, there is little nuclear sap in these nuclei, and an intranuclear breakdown of chRNA, if it occurs, probably has to take place on the chromosomes.

Brawerman (1963) observed RNA of an asymmetric composition and a high adenine content in extracts of the nuclear fraction of *Euglena* cells. These fractions were active in promoting amino acid incorporation (Eisenstadt and Brawerman, 1963). Adenine-rich nuclear fractions were also found in the nonnucleolar nuclear compartment of starfish oocytes (Edström *et al.*, 1961). A high adenine content and asymmetry, however, is not necessarily characteristic for chRNA. In analyses of isolated *Triturus viridiscens* and *T. cristatus* lampbrush chromosomes (Fig. 1) Edström and Gall (1963) found a rather good resemblance between chRNA and the bulk of DNA (Table IV). In particular the sums of the contents of guanine and cytosine agreed. In *Triturus* oocytes there is a large amount of nuclear sap and sap RNA. Consequently, if one accepts the idea of an intranuclear breakdown of a large part of the chRNA, it is not necessary that it should take place on the chromosomes.

A similarity with regard to RNA content between Balbiani rings and lampbrush chromosome loops is the high RNA/DNA quotient, which in

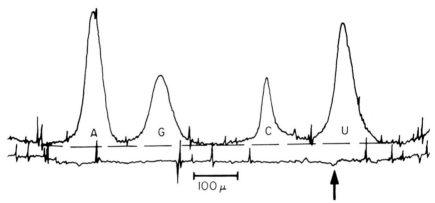

Fig. 1. A microelectrophoretic separation of RNA components from one set of lampbrush chromosomes used in the work of Edström and Gall (1963). A, G, C, and U stand for adenine, guanine, cytidylic acid, and uridylic acid, respectively. The origin is indicated by the arrow.

both cases makes a hybridization between DNA and the larger part of chRNA an impossibility. There is about ten times more RNA than DNA in a set of lampbrush chromosomes (Isawa *et al.,* 1963; Edström and Gall, 1963; 1964). Probably only about one-twentieth of the DNA, however, is located in the RNA-containing loops (Gall and Callan, 1962). The RNA/DNA quotient in the loops could consequently be about 200.

The possibility, which one cannot exclude at the present time, that the odd composition of the Balbiani ring RNA and other nuclear non-nucleolar RNA is due to degradation might at first seem unlikely on

TABLE IV

Base Composition of RNA from Individual Chromosome Sets from *Triturus* and of DNA Determined on Erythrocyte Nuclei[a]

Component	Adenine	Guanine	Cytosine	Uracil (thymine)
Triturus cristatus carnifex				
RNA	26.0	20.6	25.2	28.3
DNA	27.5	22.5	(22.5)	(27.5)
Triturus viridiscens				
RNA	26.6	20.4	23.8	29.3
DNA	27.3	22.7	(22.7)	(27.3)

[a] From Edström and Gall (1963). Values in parentheses assumed on the basis of complementary base composition.

genetic grounds. Beermann (1961) has shown that the appearance of a special kind of secretion in certain salivary gland cells is correlated to the presence of a special Balbiani ring in the fourth chromosome or at least a region comprising the Balbiani ring and a few unpuffed bands, i.e., bands showing no signs of RNA synthesis. The pattern of puffing, specific to tissue (Beermann, 1952) and developmental phase (Breuer and Pavan, 1955), also strongly suggests that puffing chromosomal loci are active in providing the cytoplasm with templates. Can this idea be reconciled with the view of Harris that practically all of the RNA synthesized on the chromosomes is broken down? The problem is related to the question of how much DNA there is in a chromomere and how this figure compares with the amount required to produce functioning structural templates.

In *Chironomus tentans* the amount of DNA in relation to the number of chromatid duplications has been determined by microelectrophoresis (Edström, 1964). The largest nuclei contain 3340 μμg DNA. These have duplicated the 2 C amount of DNA (double spermatid value) thirteen

TABLE V

DNA Content in Isolated Polytene Chromosomes from *Chironomus tentans* Salivary Gland Cells after 13 Chromatid Duplications[a]

Chromosome	DNA (μμg)	Number of C	μμg DNA/2 C	μμg DNA determined per somatic nucleus of smallest class
I	1044	—	0.13	—
II	1027	—	0.13	—
III	908	—	0.11	—
IV	361	—	0.044	—
Whole set	3340	16,384	0.41	0.5

[a] From Edström (1964). C = one chromatid set.

times and are 16,400 C (Table V). Beermann (1952) has obtained a value of 1900 for the number of bands by counting and extrapolation, and figures which are higher but of the same order have been calculated for *Drosophila* (quoted by Beermann, 1952). The probable number of bands lies in the range of 2000–5000 for *Chironomus,* which gives a DNA content of about 1 μμg per band and a value of 6×10^{-5} μμg per chromomere. This value is close to that of Rudkin and Schultz (1964) for the chromomere of average size in *Drosophila,* 3×10^{-5} μμg. Considering that the two values were obtained with completely different techniques, microelectrophoresis and microspectrophotometry respectively, the agreement is striking. The value 6×10^{-5} μμg represents 60,000 base pairs or a length of a DNA duplex in the unfolded state of about 18 μ. Active loop lengths of at least this size are certainly present in amphibian lampbrush chromosomes (Gall and Callan, 1962), but the amphibia are exceptional in containing large amounts of DNA. The unfolded lengths of bands in dipteran giant chromosomes may reach this order of length, but it is difficult to judge whether they are synthetically active in all parts. For pea embryo chromatin, removal of the histone results in a fivefold increase in templating activity for RNA synthesis (Huang and Bonner, 1962). In *Chironomus tentans* Pelling (1964) has shown that about 10% of the bands are active. If the order of magnitude observed for the pea chromatin is the same in *Chironomus*, this means that an appreciable part if not all of the band DNA is functioning synthetically. It must be admitted, however, that the question whether all the chromomeric DNA is used for synthesis in an active chromomere is an uncertain one, although the observations by Gall and Callan (1962) on lampbrush chromosomes suggest that this is quite likely. It is clear, however, that there is much more DNA in a band than is required to code a protein of average size. A 200 amino acid protein would require 600 base pairs which is about 1% of the DNA in an average chromomere from *Chironomus tentans* and which represents a length of a DNA duplex of a fraction of a micron. On genetic grounds one can disregard the possibility that the band contains repeating identical units producing a messenger with structural functions. An unlikely alternative is that the chromomere is occupied by a cistron complex consisting of such a large number of individual cistrons that it becomes necessary to engage all the DNA, producing functional messengers for cytoplasmic macromolecules involved in the same function. More probably only a small part of the chromomeric DNA produces messenger RNA for structural functions and for export to the cytoplasm.

In the light of this knowledge a transfer to the cytoplasm of only a small fraction of chRNA is not genetically unreasonable. The idea of an extensive intranuclear breakdown of chRNA need not contradict the notion that gene activation—as displayed by the puffing pattern of chromosomes—determines the cellular properties, even if it concerns each synthetically active band and the system is working with unstable messengers.

If the functional messenger is copied from only a minor part of DNA there is no obvious reason why it should resemble the bulk of DNA, irrespective of whether it is a single- or double-strand copy (Penman *et al.*, 1963). This part could be distributed over a wide density range in gradient centrifugation and not easily detected. For the rapidly labeled RNA in the nucleus other considerations apply. *A priori* it might be expected to hybridize with such a large fraction of DNA that it would mimic the composition of the bulk of DNA, at least with respect to content of guanine plus cytosine. If degradation takes place, however, there might be a preferential loss of certain bases during the initial stages and the hybridizing RNA would still not be representative for the DNA composition (Hoyer *et al.*, 1963).

Nucleolar RNA

Another prominent fraction of the nuclear RNA is the nucleolar RNA (nRNA). Vincent (1952) was a pioneer in the chemical investigation of nucleoli, which he made available to chemical study in bulk using starfish

TABLE VI

BASE COMPOSITION OF RNA IN NUCLEOLI AND CYTOPLASM OF MATURE STARFISH OOCYTES

Component	Adenine	Guanine	Cytosine	Uracil
Nucleoli[a]	21.8	36.2	26.2	14.7
Cytoplasm[a]	19.7	30.3	28.3	21.7
Nucleoli[b]				
Animal I	22.2	34.1	27.5	16.2
Animal II	24.3	33.9	24.1	17.7
Cytoplasm[b]				
Animal I	23.6	30.9	27.1	18.5
Animal II	24.9	31.7	24.9	18.5

[a] From Vincent (1952).
[b] Microelectrophoresis data from Edström (1964).

oocytes, with the aid of homogenization and centrifugation techniques. He demonstrated great differences in base composition between cytoplasmic, i.e., predominantly ribosomal RNA and nRNA. Nevertheless, it could not be excluded that losses or secondary changes during the isolations had not affected the results. After it became possible to study the base composition of individually collected cellular units (Edström, 1960a), Carnoy-fixed oocytes could be used in which *post mortem* changes are rapidly stopped by immersion in acidic ethanol. A study of mature or near-mature oocytes by microelectrophoresis gave results showing rather good agreement with the data of Vincent (Table VI). Thus at this stage nRNA did not appear to be much related to the bulk of cytoplasmic RNA. There is, however, one objection to such an interpretation. In fully grown oocytes the production of RNA has ceased. Whatever the origin of their ribosomal RNA, it is clear that the nucleolus, soon to disappear, cannot contribute significantly. If for some reason there are changes in the nRNA at the end of the life of the nucleolus, the cytoplasmic and nRNA might very well differ, even if the former derives from the latter. Microelectrophoretic investigations showed that the composition in young oocyte nucleoli differs from that of older stages, but now this composition agrees very well with that of the bulk of cytoplasmic RNA, which shows only slight changes during development (Table VII). The findings become more significant in view of the fact that the RNA of the combined chromosomal and sap fraction always differed markedly in base composition from the other two kinds of RNA.

TABLE VII
BASE COMPOSITION OF RNA IN NUCLEOLI AND CYTOPLASM OF YOUNG, GROWING STARFISH OOCYTES[a]

Component	Adenine	Guanine	Cytosine	Uracil
Nucleoli	22.7	31.5	25.7	20.0
Cytoplasm	23.4	31.1	25.3	20.3

[a] Average of four animals, determined by microelectrophoresis (Edström, 1964).

The correlation in compositional values has been observed in different species for guanine–cytosine-rich (Edström, 1960b; Edström *et al.*, 1961; Edström and Gall, 1963) as well as for adenine–uracil-rich RNA (Edström and Beermann, 1962). Sedimentation studies have revealed ribosomal nucleoprotein components in nucleoli (Birnstiel *et al.*, 1963) and similarities in the protein composition of ribosomes and nucleoli from pea seedlings (Birnstiel and Hyde, 1963). Finally, Chipchase and Birnstiel (1963) have found that ribosomal and nucleolar RNA form hybrids with identical DNA molecules. There can consequently be no doubt about the close chemical connection between ribosomes and at least a considerable part of the nucleolar material.

If the suggestion is accepted that all or at least a dominating part of cytoplasmic RNA is derived from the nucleus (Goldstein and Plaut, 1955), it is natural to give nRNA the role of a precursor to ribosomal RNA. It is now fairly clear that such a precursor relationship does in fact exist, since it has been shown that ribosomal RNA in the cytoplasm will no longer take up label during selective inhibition of nRNA synthesis (Perry, 1962). Ribosomal RNA which is labeled already leaves the nucleus and appears in the cytoplasm in the absence of all RNA synthesis during actinomycin treatment (Girard *et al.*, 1964). Finally, it has been demonstrated that the appearance of ribosomal RNA during embryonic development in *Xenopus* is dependent on the presence of the nucleolar organizer (Brown and Gurdon, 1964). It should be mentioned in this connection that several groups have shown that the ribosomal RNA first appears as larger pieces which then become depolymerized in the nucleus, probably in the nucleolus (Perry, 1962; Scherrer *et al.*, 1963; Girard *et al.*, 1964; Brown and Gurdon, 1964).

A role for the nucleolus as a station for ribosomal RNA may not be the only one. Sirlin *et al.* (1961) have obtained evidence that RNA with characteristics of transfer RNA is also located there. The suggestion was advanced several years ago by Caspersson (1950) that the formation of the nucleolus is dependent on heterochromatic areas in the chromosomes. It is an open question whether other RNA than ribosomal RNA and perhaps transfer RNA can engage in nucleolar formation.

The relation between the nucleolus and the genome was studied by Beermann (1960) using the two sibling species *Chironomus tentans* and *Ch. pallidivittatus* which have a different localization of the nucleolar organizers. Recombinant genotypes were obtained in hybrids containing from three homozygous organizers to none at all. Any one of the organizers could be absent without disturbing the development, but when all were lacking the embryos would die at an early stage. A single heterozygous organizer could support the development; even a partial organizer could do so. After X-ray-induced breaks and rearrangements both pieces could form nucleoli. These experiments demonstrate the functional equivalence of the nucleolar organizers and also show that a single organizer is composed of smaller parts, each of which contains a complete representation of the nucleolar function. This is in agreement with the results of hybrid experiments between ribosomal RNA and DNA for both microorganisms (Yankofsky and Spiegelman, 1962) and nucleated cells (Chipchase and Birnstiel, 1963). A multitude of cistrons are responsible for ribosomal RNA formation, forming an aggregate of repeating units in *Escherichia coli*. Beermann's experiments show that for animal cells also the identical units appear close together in the genome, which may be the reason for the primary appearance of ribosomal RNA as relatively large pieces.

Chironomus tentans offers a unique possibility for comparing the RNA from nucleoli formed at two different points of the genome. There are local formations of well-developed nucleoli by the nucleolar organizers on both the second and third chromosomes. By micromanipulation the

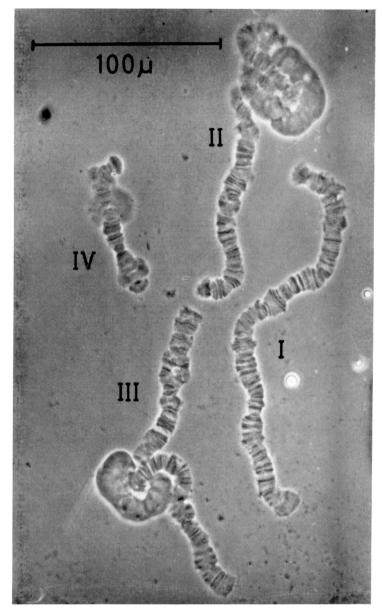

FIG. 2. Salivary gland polytene chromosomes from *Chironomus tentans* isolated by micromanipulation as seen in the oil chamber with phase-contrast illumination.

chromosomes can be isolated (Fig. 2) and the nucleoli removed from each chromosome. RNA extracts from nucleoli pooled from each of the two chromosomes have been analyzed by microelectrophoresis for base composition (Edström, 1964). The results show a very close agreement (Table VIII) and fit well with the notion of the equivalence of nucleolar organizers.

TABLE VIII

BASE COMPOSITION OF RNA FROM NUCLEOLI FORMED AT DIFFERENT CHROMOSOMES OF *Chironomus tentans*[a]

Nucleolus	Adenine	Guanine	Cytosine	Uracil
Chromosome II	31.0 ± 0.3	22.8 ± 0.2	18.5 ± 0.3	27.7 ± 0.4
Chromosome III	30.8 ± 0.4	22.2 ± 0.3	18.8 ± 0.6	28.3 ± 0.5

[a] Values given ± standard error mean. From Edström (1964).

The appearance of nucleoli is dependent on the presence of certain loci or nucleolar organizers, but opinions differ as to whether the organizer is in the first instance a producer of nucleolar substance (Sirlin, 1960; Pelling, 1964) or mainly a collector of it (Goldstein and Micou, 1959; Rho and Bonner, 1961). Both views could be combined, however, if cistron aggregates with a relatively large production of ribosomal RNA via their own nucleolar substance would attract ribosomal precursors produced in cistrons which spread over the genome in certain species. A tendency for nucleolar material to fuse in the cell can sometimes be observed. The results of Chipchase and Birnstiel (1963) on peas indicate that the cistrons for ribosomal RNA production are widespread in the genome and not only localized to DNA within the nucleolus. For *Chironomus tentans* Pelling's studies (1964) show clearly that nucleolar RNA is formed locally. The incorporation of tritiated uridine always begins in the central, chromosome-attached parts and proceeds outward, as has also been described for *Smittia* by Sirlin (1960). The label appears as fast in the center of the nucleolus as in other parts of the chromosome.

Chironomus is particularly interesting since it shows that the ribosomal RNA may be formed from a very small fraction of the genome, since even a part of a single heterozygous organizer can support normal development. It is possible that the nucleolar organizers contain more DNA than an average band, but probably the order of magnitude is the same, judging by their size and staining after regression of the nucleoli (Beermann, 1961). The average amount of DNA for a band in the chromosomes after 13 duplications is about 0.5 μμg for the unpaired chromosome. A cell of this size contains 70,000 μμg RNA (Edström, 1964) of which

50,000 µµg can be assumed to be ribosomal, and an amount of the order of half of this quantity can be assumed to have been synthesized during the previous week. It can be estimated that the DNA would have to produce half its own quantity in 10 seconds. Normally, when two homozygous loci are present, the time would be 40 seconds.

Finally, one is interested in knowing whether a band of average size really contains more DNA than required for a single cistron coding for the two ribosomal units. With a DNA content per homozygous band of 1 µµg the chromatid will contain 60,000 nucleotide pairs. The ribosomal complex requires about 4000 pairs. Evidently, there is enough DNA in a band of average size to permit the localization of several cistrons coding for the ribosomal RNA components.

Nuclear Sap RNA

The nonnucleolar, nonchromosomal nuclear RNA will be designated nuclear sap RNA. This RNA is probably more heterogeneous and variable from cell to cell than any other type of nuclear RNA. In certain cells nuclear ribosomes are present which carry out protein synthesis that also involves the participation of transfer RNA (Allfrey et al., 1960). This nuclear function, however, is probably not a general cell attribute since ribosomes may be absent from the nuclear sap compartment (Crawley and Harris, quoted by Harris, 1963). Furthermore, the sap is rather poorly developed in certain cell types like the salivary gland nuclei of *Chironomus.*

Large amounts of RNA may be present in the amphibian oocyte nuclear sap (Isawa et al., 1963), which contains RNA fractions having a base composition that varies from cell to cell, often highly asymmetric, with uracil as the dominating component (Edström and Gall, 1963). Fractions of this character have not been observed in other cellular compartments. The RNA base composition may also be very odd and asymmetric in the nonnucleolar nuclear compartment of starfish oocytes with adenine contents of up to 40% (Table IX). Since results of this kind appear after use of widely different procedures of preparation and in view of the fact that other nuclear components contain RNA of a constant composition after the same preparative procedures, it is unlikely that the compositions in the sap represent artifacts. The starfish oocytes are directly immersed in acidic ethanol and conditions for *post mortem* enzymatic degradation are never present. In starfish oocytes, furthermore, the amount of RNA in the nonnucleolar, nuclear compartment shows high variations from cell to cell (Edström *et al.*, 1961). This was originally interpreted as signs of rhythmic and varying gene activity, but the interpretation is not likely to be true, because Gall and Callan (1962) have shown that RNA synthesis occurs continuously in a great many sites during the growth of the primary oocyte. The idea is easier to reconcile with the view that a large part of chRNA is degraded in the nucleus. Such a process could easily lead to these great variations in base composition and RNA contents and would have no direct functional significance.

TABLE IX

BASE COMPOSITION OF RNA IN NUCLEAR SAP AND CHROMATIN FROM
POOLED STARFISH OOCYTES[a]

Adenine	Guanine	Cytosine	Uracil
27.1	22.3	24.6	25.9
31.6	24.4	18.0	26.0
28.5	22.0	26.9	22.6
28.3	25.6	22.2	23.8
35.7	24.8	16.5	23.0
38.8	21.4	20.2	19.6
39.9	17.9	17.6	24.6

[a] Each horizontal row the average of values from one separate animal (Edström, 1964).

There is at present no information available permitting conclusions about the general functions and characteristics of nonribosomal, nontransfer nuclear sap RNA. What is known about the variability in base composition and contents perhaps fits best the picture of the sap as a compartment for the breakdown of chRNA.

Summary

We have had to be selective and cover only a few aspects of nuclear RNA fractions in this review. Even so, it is clear that much elementary information is missing. One fact seems to be firmly established, however. At least part of the nRNA is transported to the cytoplasm as ribosomal RNA, and this RNA is coded by a small fraction of the genome consisting of repeating cistrons. It is possible that transfer RNA may follow a similar route, and it is advisable to continue to look for other functions for the nucleolus.

It cannot be excluded that only a small fraction of the chromomeric DNA may function as a template for messenger RNA with structural functions. RNA from other DNA in the same nonrepressed chromomere may be broken down in the nucleus, either on the chromosomes or in the sap. Such a hypothetical extra DNA could be involved in the regulation of gene activity or, perhaps more likely, it may act as a template source of evolutionary importance, necessary for genetic adaptation in organisms with long generation times.

ACKNOWLEDGMENTS

The original work by the author was supported by grants from the Swedish Cancer Society and the Swedish Medical Research Council.

REFERENCES

ALLFREY, V. G., HOPKINS, J. W., FRENSTER, J. H., AND MIRSKEY, A. E. (1960). Reactions governing incorporation of amino acids into the proteins of the isolated cell nucleus. *Ann. N. Y. Acad. Sci.* **88**, 722-740.

BEERMANN, W. (1952). Chromomerenkonstanz und spezifische Modifikationen der Chromosomenstruktur in der Entwicklung und Organdifferenzierung von *Chironomus tentans. Chromosoma* **5**, 139-198.

BEERMANN, W. (1960). Der Nukleolus als lebenswichtiger Bestandteil des Zellkernes. *Chromosoma* **11**, 263-296.

BEERMANN, W. (1961). Ein Balbiani-Ring als Locus einer Speicheldrüsenmutation. *Chromosoma* **12**, 1-25.

BIRNSTIEL, M. L., AND HYDE, B. B. (1963). Protein synthesis by isolated pea nucleoli. *J. Biophys. Biochem. Cytol.* **18**, 41-50.

BIRNSTIEL, M. L., CHIPCHASE, M. I. H., AND HYDE, B. B. (1963). The nucleolus, a source of ribosomes. *Biochim. Biophys. Acta* **76**, 454-462.

BONNER, J., HUANG, R. C., AND MAHESWARI, N. (1961). The physical state of newly synthesized RNA. *Proc. Natl. Acad. Sci. U. S.* **47**, 1548-1554.

BRAWERMAN, G. (1963). A procedure for the isolation of RNA fractions resembling DNA with respect to nucleotide composition. *Biochim. Biophys. Acta* **76**, 322-324.

BREUER, M. E., AND PAVAN, C. (1955). Behavior of polytene chromosomes of *Rhynchosciara angelae* at different stages of larval development. *Chromosoma* **7**, 371-386.

BROWN, D. D., AND GURDON, J. B. (1964). Absence of ribosomal RNA synthesis in the anucleolate mutant of *Xenopus laevis. Proc. Natl. Acad. Sci. U. S.* **51**, 139-146.

CASPERSSON, T. O. (1950). "Cell Growth and Cell Function." Norton, New York.

CHIPCHASE, M. I. H., AND BIRNSTIEL, M. L. (1963). On the nature of nucleolar RNA. *Proc. Natl. Acad. Sci. U. S.* **50**, 1101-1106.

EDSTRÖM, J.-E. (1960a). Extraction, hydrolysis and electrophoretic analysis of ribonucleic acid from microscopic tissue units (microphoresis). *J. Biophys. Biochem. Cytol.* **8**, 39-43.

EDSTRÖM, J.-E. (1960b). Composition of ribonucleic acid from various parts of the spider oocyte. *J. Biophys. Biochem. Cytol.* **8**, 47-51.

EDSTRÖM, J.-E. (1964). Unpublished material.

EDSTRÖM, J.-E., AND BEERMANN, W. (1962). The base composition of nucleic acids in chromosomes, puffs, nucleoli, and cystoplasm of *Chironomus* salivary gland cells. *J. Cell Biol.* **14**, 371-380.

EDSTRÖM, J.-E., AND GALL, J. G. (1963). The base composition of ribonucleic acid in lampbrush chromosomes, nucleoli, nuclear sap, and cytoplasm of *Triturus* oocytes. *J. Cell Biol.* **19**, 279-284.

EDSTRÖM, J.-E., AND GALL, J. G. (1964). Unpublished material.

EDSTRÖM, J.-E., GRAMPP, W., AND SCHOR, N. (1961). The intracellular distribution and heterogeneity of ribonucleic acid in starfish oocytes. *J. Biophys. Biochem. Cytol.* **11**, 549-558.

EISENSTADT, J., AND BRAWERMAN, G. (1963). The incorporation of amino acids into the protein of chloroplasts and chloroplast ribosomes of *Euglena gracilis. Biochim. Biophys. Acta* **76**, 319-321.

FRENSTER, J. H., ALLFREY, V. G., AND MIRSKY, A. E. (1963). Repressed and active chromatin isolated from interphase lymphocytes. *Proc. Natl. Acad. Sci. U.S.* **50**, 1026-1032.

GALL, J. G. (1958). Chromosomal differentiation. *In* "The Chemical Basis of Development" (W. D. McElroy and B. Glass, eds.), pp. 103-135. Johns Hopkins Press, Baltimore, Maryland.

GALL, J. G., AND CALLAN, H. G. (1962). H³ uridine incorporation in lampbrush chromosomes. *Proc. Natl. Acad. Sci. U.S.* **48**, 562-570.

GEORGIEV, G. P., AND MANTIEVA, V. E. (1962). The isolation of DNA-like RNA from the nucleolo-chromosomal apparatus of mammalian cells. *Biochim. Biophys. Acta* **61**, 153-154.

GIRARD, M., PENMAN, S., AND DARNELL, J. E. (1964). The effect of actinomycin on ribosome formation in HeLa cells. *Proc. Natl. Acad. Sci. U.S.* **51**, 205-211.

GOLDSTEIN, L., AND MICOU, J. (1959). On the primary site of nuclear RNA synthesis. *J. Biophys. Biochem. Cytol.* **6**, 301-303.

GOLDSTEIN, L., AND PLAUT, W. (1955). Direct evidence for nuclear synthesis of cytoplasmic ribose nucleic acid. *Proc. Natl. Acad. Sci. U.S.* **41**, 874-880.

HARRIS, H. (1959). Turnover of nuclear and cytoplasmic ribonucleic acid in two types of animal cell, with some further observations on the nucleolus. *Biochem. J.* **73**, 362-369.

HARRIS, H. (1963). Nuclear ribonucleic acid. *Progr. Nucleic Acid Res.* **2**, 19-59.

HARRIS, H. (1964a). Function of the short-lived ribonucleic acid in the cell nucleus. *Nature* **201**, 863-867.

HARRIS, H. (1964b). Transfer of radioactivity from nuclear to cytoplasmic ribonucleic acid. *Nature* **202**, 249-250.

HARRIS, H., AND WATTS, J. W. (1962). The relationship between nuclear and cytoplasmic ribonucleic acid. *Proc. Royal Soc.* **B156**, 109-121.

HOYER, B. H., McCARTHY, B. J., AND BOLTON, E. T. (1963). Complementary RNA in nucleus and cytoplasm of mouse liver cells. *Science* **140**, 1408-1412.

HUANG, R. C., AND BONNER, J. (1962). Histone, a suppressor of chromosomal RNA synthesis. *Proc. Natl. Acad. Sci. U.S.* **48**, 1216-1222.

ISAWA, M., ALLFREY, V. G., AND MIRSKY, A. E. (1963). Composition of the nucleus and chromosomes in the lampbrush stage of the newt oocyte. *Proc. Natl. Acad. Sci.* **50**, 811-817.

MEAD, C. (1964). A deoxyribonucleic-acid-associated ribonucleic acid from *Drosophila melanogaster. J. Biol. Chem.* **239**, 550-554.

MEYER, G. F. (1963). Die Funktionsstrukturen des Y-Chromosoms in den Spermatocytenkernen von *Drosophila hydei, D. neohydei, D. repleta* und einigen anderen *Drosophila*-Arten. *Chromosoma* **14**, 207-255.

PELLING, C. (1964). Ribonukleinsäure-Synthese der Riesenchromosomen, autoradiographische Untersuchungen an *Chironomus tentans. Chromosoma* **15**, 71-122.

PENMAN, S., SCHERRER, K., BECKER, Y., AND DARNELL, J. E. (1963). Polyribosomes in normal and polivirus-infected HeLa cells and their relationship to messenger RNA. *Proc. Natl. Acad. Sci. U. S.* **49**, 654-662.

PERRY, R. P. (1962). The cellular sites of synthesis of ribosomal and 4S RNA. *Proc. Natl. Acad. Sci. U. S.* **48**, 2179-2186.

RHO, J. A., AND BONNER, J. (1961). The site of ribonucleic acid synthesis in the isolated nucleus. *Proc. Natl. Acad. Sci. U. S.* **47**, 1611-1619.

RUDKIN, G. T. (1962). Nucleic acid metabolism in giant chromosomes of *Drosophila melanogaster. Ann. Histochim.* Suppl. 2, 77-84.

RUDKIN, G. T., AND SCHULTZ, J. (1964). Personal communication.

SCHERRER, K., LATHAM, H., AND DARNELL, J. E. (1963). Demonstration of an unstable RNA and of a precursor to ribosomal RNA in HeLa cells. *Proc. Natl. Acad. Sci. U. S.* **49**, 240-248.

SIRLIN, J. L. (1960). Cell sites of RNA and protein synthesis in the salivary gland of *Smittia (Chironomidae). Exptl. Cell Res.* **19**, 177-180.

SIRLIN, J. L., KATO, K., AND JONES, K. W. (1961). Synthesis of ribonucleic acid in the nucleolus. *Biochim. Biophys. Acta* **48**, 421-423.

SUEOKA, N. (1961). Variation and heterogeneity of base composition of deoxyribonucleic acids: a compilation of old and new data. *J. Mol. Biol.* **3**, 31-40.

VINCENT, W. S. (1952). The isolation and chemical properties of the nucleoli of starfish oocytes. *Proc. Natl. Acad. Sci. U. S.* **38**, 139-145.

YANKOFSKY, S. A., AND SPIEGELMAN, S. (1962). Saturation of and competitive interaction at the RNA cistron. *Proc. Natl. Acad. Sci. U. S.* **48**, 1466-1472.

Genetic and Functional Mosaicism in the Mouse

LIANE B. RUSSELL

Biology Division, Oak Ridge National Laboratory, Oak Ridge, Tennessee

In a sense, the whole process of differentiation is one of directed functional mosaicism. It is, however, the accidental or random juxtaposition in the same organism of cells having actually or effectively different genotypes that is generally thought of as true mosaicism. The study of this condition constitutes a perfect meeting place for the fields of genetics and developmental biology providing, as it does, interrelated information on mutability, cell lineage (including the special problems of cell lineage of the germ line), and the effect of genotype on part of the organism versus the whole. The discovery in recent years that most or all of one X chromosome of the normal mammalian female becomes randomly inactivated early in development—an event that leads to *functional* mosaicism—provides us with a great potential tool for the study of gene action.

The present paper will bring together results of diverse observations and experiments (many of them as yet unpublished) bearing on both genetic and functional mosaicism in the mouse. Although most of the mosaics to be discussed involve coat-color characters, this is only incidental to the circumstance that mosaic animals are usually detected by external observation; and coat color per se will not be a topic of discussion. Instead, attempts will be made to derive answers to (and, where this is not possible, to outline the problems involved in) general questions of mutability, cell lineage, and gene action.

I. Genetic Mosaicism

Three main types of genetic mosaicism will be considered. First, chimerism of two different genomes can result from polar-body retention or from the fusion of two zygotes or very early embryos (Section I, A). Second, changes in a single genome can have one of two main types of origin. Either, the zygote itself may already be mosaic as a result of a genetic event in one of the gametes, involving only one strand of a double-stranded chromosome (Section I, B); or, starting with a normal zygote, any of a number of genetic events may occur in subsequent cell multiplication, so that the finished organism contains cells of more than one genotype (Section I, C). Among such genetic events are some that produce only one new genotype (somatic mutation, deficiency, chromosome loss) and others that produce two reciprocal new ones (somatic crossover, nondisjunction).

A. Chimerism of Two Different Genomes

Of the various abnormalities of egg maturation and fertilization that have been described (Russell, 1962, Table 1, review), those involving "immediate cleavage" (Braden, 1957) can lead to mosaicism. "Immediate cleavage" is, essentially, the participation of one of the polar bodies in the formation of the embryo, and the resulting mosaics can be of the types $1n/2n$, $2n/2n$, $2n/3n$, etc. depending on the circumstances of fertilization.

Diploid-triploid mosaics have been found in man (Böök and Santesson, 1961; and others) and in the cat (Chu et al., 1964). The euploid $2n/2n$ type, however, cannot be detected unless an obvious gynandromorph has been formed (for a human case, see Gartler et al., 1962), or unless special genetic markers are present so that the mosaic can be shown to contain two meiotic products from at least one of the parents. A mosaic of this type was observed by us in a cross involving three alleles at one locus as well as closely linked markers (Woodiel and Russell, 1963; Russell and Woodiel, 1963).

The female, which came from a cross of

$$\frac{+\ A^y\ un\ we}{kr\ a^x\ +\ +}\ \female\ \times\ \frac{kr\ a}{kr\ a}\ \male$$

had yellow and black areas arranged roughly in transverse bands. She transmitted A^y, a^x, and a, and was presumed to be a mosaic of A^y/a or A^y/a^x (yellow patches) and a^x/a (black patches). The segregation of the linked markers, to be described in detail elsewhere, indicates that her actual constitution was

$$\frac{+\ A^y\ un\ we}{kr\ a\ +\ +}\ //\ \frac{kr\ a^x\ +\ +}{kr\ a\ +\ +},$$

which is compatible with two possible origins involving retention and fertilization of the first or second polar body, respectively (see Fig. 1). It should be noted that if the mosaic female had been formed by fusion of two originally independent zygotes or embryos, the results would be indistinguishable from those obtained. Two other modes of origin

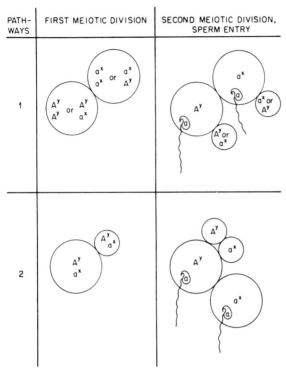

Fig. 1.   Possible modes of origin of the chimeric female described in Section I,A. Segregation at the *a* locus only is shown; for linked markers, see text. Pathways 1 and 2 show, respectively, retention of a fertilized first and second polar body. (Following our earlier usage, first and second polar bodies are shown to the upper and lower right of the vitellus, respectively.) A third possible pathway, not shown in the figure, is fusion of two normal zygotes.

which originally seemed possible can now be eliminated. One was retention of an *un*fertilized first polar body (i.e., yellow portions of A^y/a^x genotype), virtually ruled out by the breeding results. The other was mosaicism for trisomy-5, made unlikely by new cytological data obtained separately for yellow and black areas.

Gynandromorphism, which is rare in the mouse except possibly in certain inbred strains (Hollander *et al.,* 1956), can perhaps also be explained by chimerism resulting from polar-body retention or by fusion of independent zygotes. On the other hand, the gynandromorphs need not have been chimeras, but could merely have represented mosaicism for sex-chromosome anomalies, e.g., XY/XO or XYY/XO, resulting from somatic nondisjunction. (The cases reported were observed before adequate cytological techniques became available.) Recent work on sex-chromosome anomalies would, however, tend to indicate that at least certain sex-chromosome mosaics may be relatively rare in the mouse (Russell, 1961; Russell and Saylors, 1963).

B. *"Partial" Mutations in Gametes*

A genetic event occurring spontaneously in only one strand of a gamete chromosome cannot be distinguished in its end result from one occurring in the course of the first cleavage division; in each case one of the first two blastomeres is the bearer of the new genotype. The distinction becomes particularly meaningless in the case of maternal chromosomes since no separate female "gamete" stage exists in the mouse, the second meiotic division not being completed until after sperm entry.

It is, however, legitimate to ask whether genetic changes can be *induced* in only one strand of spermatozoal chromosomes. W. L. Russell (1964) has found that, whereas irradiation of spermatozoa causes a relatively high frequency of total-body mutations, the frequency of mosaics in the progeny is no greater than in the controls. The situation is similar in *Drosophila* (Altenburg and Browning, 1961).

At first glance, it may seem that the failure of radiation to induce mutations in a single strand argues against *spontaneous* genetic changes of this type and, therefore, that the spontaneous mouse mosaics that have been found are the result of mutation in early cleavage. Muller *et al.* (1961), however, have proposed that in *Drosophila* one of the two strands of the pre-existing gene *can* mutate spontaneously, whereas radiation to the spermatozoon alters *both* of the strands by "rotational substitution." Spontaneous half-and-half mosaics in the mouse will be discussed in Section I, C, 1.

C. *Mosaicism Arising after the Zygote Stage*

Any of a number of possible genetic changes occurring in the formation or maintenance of the organism can create at least a temporary state of mosaicism, but whether or not a mosaic organism actually persists depends on the survival of the newly formed cell type. Similarly, the finally observed proportion of mutant to original tissue need not give an accurate indication of the stage at which the genetic change occurred.

It should also be noted that the first cleavage division presents a special case in that certain events occurring then can lead to an organism consisting *wholly* of mutant tissue, either of a single type or of two reciprocal types. This has been diagrammatically outlined for loss and nondisjunction of sex chromosomes (Russell, 1961, Fig. 4). As discussed earlier (Russell, 1961), we believe that a relatively high proportion of spontaneous X monosomy in the mouse is the result of chromosome loss at the first cleavage; and radiation sensitivity of chromosomes has been found to be very high in the early pronuclear stage (Russell and Saylors, 1960, 1963; Russell, 1961).

There is no reason to believe that autosomes at these stages behave differently from the sex chromosomes (Russell and Saylors, 1963). Autosomal monosomy affecting the whole organism would very probably be lethal (Russell, 1962, pp. 243–244); but since autosomal trisomy in the mouse is, at least in some cases, compatible with viability (Cattanach, 1964), a trisomic/monosomic mosaic, such as would be formed from nondisjunction at the first cleavage, could perhaps survive—possibly as a pure trisomic.

Genetic events affecting single chromatids at the first cleavage would resemble those at all later divisions in that they potentially produce mosaics of the mutant and original genotypes. The remainder of this discussion will be devoted to mosaics of this type.

Since 1934, when Dunn reviewed twenty-one spontaneous rodent mosaics, about a dozen or more cases have been published. The whole array probably represents genetic mechanisms of various types, including mutations to dominants, recessives, and intermediate alleles. In less than one-fifth of all published cases of rodent mosaics could germinal involvement be demonstrated. Four of these were found in the mouse (Fisher, 1930; Dunn, 1934; Bhat, 1949; Carter, 1952).

The subsequent sections will summarize results on several hundred new mosaics in the mouse. Spontaneous somatic mutations of the wild-type alleles at standard coat-color loci, found in a very large heterozygous population, include over forty cases involving germinal tissue. In addition, several apparently unstable genes have now been found that revert to wild type with relatively high frequency. Radiation induction of somatic mutations has also been achieved.

1. Spontaneous Somatic Forward Mutations. In recent years, the opportunity for detection of somatic forward mutations has been very much increased by large-scale mutation-rate studies that use the specific-locus method (W. L. Russell, 1951, etc.). In this method, wild-type irradiated and nonirradiated mice are mated to animals homozygous for seven specific recessive mutations. Therefore, over the past several years, many thousands of F_1 mice have been observed that start life heterozygous for seven recessives, five of them affecting coat color (a = nonagouti; b = brown; c^{ch} = chinchilla; p = pink-eyed dilution; d = Maltese dilution). Two other features of this set-up aid in making it a good one for the detection of somatic mutations. First, of the five coat-color recessives in the cross, three have linked markers (c for p; p for c; se for d), so that it is possible to distinguish between mutations, deficiencies, or other events involving only part of a chromosome, on the one hand, and whole-chromosome losses on the other. Second, at two of the loci, the allele to which most mutations appear to occur is different from the recessive already present in the cross (c versus c^{ch}; d^l versus d).

Of 112 "mottled" and "questionably mottled" offspring in specific-locus experiments that have been analyzed to date (many experiments only partially analyzed are excluded), the distribution was as follows: At least 26, and probably as many as 40 were found to be somatic and germinal mosaics for one or another of the coat-color loci for which the population is heterozygous; in 13 others there were mutations to sex-linked genes that cause a "mosaic" phenotype; 4 carried X-autosome translocations involving one of the markers (Section II, C); 2 were heterozygous for new mottling alleles at one of the specific loci (Section II, B); and 2 had mutations to dominant spotting. In most of the remaining 51, tests ruled out mutation to a dominant or sex-linked factor, but were otherwise inadequate to discover a cause for the mottling. Adequate tests thus could have swelled the mosaic category even more. Results on only a small portion of the 51 are of a nature that could indicate somatic mosaicism without germinal involvement.

Of the 40 certain and probable specific-locus mosaics, 21 had one irradiated parent and 19 came from a contemporary control population of slightly smaller size. There is thus no evidence against all of them being of spontaneous origin, the more so since in 12 of the irradiated parents the germ-cell stage treated was spermatogonia (see also Section I, B).

The 40 can be subdivided into a group of 20 (Table I, group 1) in which germinal mosaics can be diagnosed with certainty because of close linkage or because the mutation is to a different allele; and another group of 20 (Table I, group 2) in which the evidence for germinal involvement comes from upset ratios only [probable repeat mutations, no close markers, e.g., mosaics of type $(+/b)//(b/b)$]. In group 2, there were only 6 in which the upset in ratio was large enough and/or the number

TABLE I

GONOSOMIC MOSAICS FOR MUTATION OR DELETION OF THE WILD-TYPE ALLELES AT FIVE STANDARD COAT-COLOR LOCI[a]

Group 1[b]			Group 2[c]			Group 3[d]		
Number of offspring[e]	% germinal tissue carrying mutation[f]	Locus	Number of offspring[e]	% germinal tissue carrying mutation[f]	Locus	Number of offspring[e]	% germinal tissue carrying mutation[f]	Locus
32	6.7	d	32	18.8	p	83	4.8	c
146	19.8	c	73	20.5	p	402	42.8	c
74	23.1	c	33	21.2	dse	807	51.5	d
96	23.3	c	68	23.5	c			
107	27.8	d	20	30.0	dse			
147	33.3	c	29	31.0	c			
112	34.9	d	33	39.4	b			
124	41.4	c	10	40.0	dse			
104	43.0	p	24	41.7	b			
39	44.4	p	26	46.2	c			
23	45.5	d	35	48.6	dse			
193	51.4	d	107	49.5	p			
56	52.4	c	41	51.2	b			
81	63.4	d	52	53.8	a			
50	65.5	c	34	58.8	b			
33	72.7	d	25	68.0	b			
66	73.0	c	14	71.4	$c^{ch}p$			
45	81.0	c	12	83.3	d			
92	89.9	p	83	92.8	p			
197	97.6	p	6	100.0	d			

[a] Ranked in order of percent of diploid germinal tissue estimated to be mutant.

[b] Group 1, original genotype heterozygous; mosaic coat and definitely mosaic gonad. Germinal involvement diagnosed with certainty because of close linkage or mutation to a new allele.

[c] Group 2, original genotype heterozygous; mosaic coat and probably mosaic gonad. Germinal involvement surmised from progeny ratios differing from 1:1 when presumed mosaic is tested for the recessive mutation indicated by the phenotype of mutant patches in the coat.

[d] Group 3, original genotype homozygous wild type; mosaic gonad (mosaicism in coat not detectable).

[e] Number classified in critical matings. Offspring from additional test-matings are not included.

[f] Cell-type proportions in diploid germinal tissue calculated by various methods, depending on the individual mutation and type of test-mating used.

of offspring classified was sufficient to indicate germinal mosaicism with a high degree of certainty. For groups 1 and 2, the distribution among loci involved was as follows: a, 1 certain; b, 3 certain and 2 questionable; c, 9 certain (6 c viable, 3 new viable alleles) and 3 questionable (c^{ch}); d, 7 certain (6 d^l, 1 d viable) and 2 questionable; p, 6 certain (1 p lethal, 3 p viable, 2 p untested) and 2 questionable; d se, 4 questionable; $c^{ch}p$, 1 questionable.

Loss of a chromosome is ruled out in the case of 29 of the mosaics (c, d, p loci). It is a possibility in 5 of the questionable cases (d se and $c^{ch}p$). Whole-chromosome losses could possibly survive somatically (see Section II, E on cell lethals) and even form gonadic mosaics. It is, however, unlikely that they would be transmitted to viable progeny, since there is evidence (Russell, 1962) that autosomal monosomy is lethal. Animals mosaic for such chromosome loss should then appear "partially sterile" since some of their progeny would die as embryos. One of the presumed d se mosaics indeed had a reduced litter size. The other 3 cases of d se and the presumed $c^{ch}p$ mosaic were, however, fully fertile. In addition, for most of the few mottleds that were clearly partially sterile in the unassigned group of 51, somatic chromosome loss could be ruled out.

Before making further calculations, it was necessary to determine whether there was any selection against the mutant type, either gametically or in the progeny. If the frequency of the gene that gave rise to the mutation (in our cases, the wild-type allele) is w, that of the new gene m, and that of the uninvolved homologous marker h, then, if there is no selection, the ratio $(m + w)/(m + w + h)$ should equal 0.50. Actually, for individual animals of group 1, it ranged from 0.38 to 0.58, the average being 0.50 (based on 1383 classified progeny).

The progeny ratios can therefore be used with confidence in calculating cell-type proportions in diploid germinal tissue. This was done by various different methods (to be described in detail elsewhere) depending on the individual mutation and the type of test-mating used. The proportion of heterozygous mutant cells in a mosaic gonad can also be calculated for another group of animals not yet mentioned. In addition to those somatic mutations that are detected by mosaic phenotype in the heterozygous F_1 population, others reveal themselves by the breeding results of the supposedly homozygous wild-type parent group. An occasional mouse in this group may produce, in the cross with the multiple recessive test stock, a cluster of like mutant progeny. Provided the animal has not had a radiation treatment that could account for this result (namely, depletion and repopulation of the testis encountered in measurements of spermatogonial mutation rates), one can assume that the supposedly homozygous wild-type mouse was actually a spontaneous gonadic mosaic. The fact that the animal was very probably also a mosaic in the coat cannot be detected, of course, since such mosaicism is covered by the wild-type allele in the homologous chromosome. Three such animals (group 3) are included in the distribution shown in Table I: two were gonosomic mosaic for *c* (viable) and one for *d* (prenatal lethal).

Many mutations at loci other than those used in specific-locus mutation-rate experiments have also originated somatically, e.g., a dominant spotting factor, the sex-linked mutation *spf*, and 7 of 8 independent sex-linked mottling factors (3 of these 7 first occurred in mosaic males, although they are male-lethal; see Section II, E). Because of problems of viability or penetrance, all of these have been excluded from calculations of proportion of mutant cells in mosaic gonads.

The distribution of mosaics with respect to per cent mutant cells in the gonad is shown in Table I. The average of individual percentages for all 43 animals (of groups 1, 2, and 3) is 48.3%, based on 3864 total progeny classified. If one restricts calculations to group 1 only, the average is 49.5 based on 1815 progeny. It is thus possible to interpret these results as showing that for the gonosomic mosaics listed in Table I about half the cells of the organism are mutant.

Four types of events might be considered as leading to a half-mutant state (Fig. 2): (1) mutation in one strand of a double-stranded gamete chromosome; (2) participation in the embryo of 2 meiotic products of the mother; (3) fusion of zygotes; and (4) mutation at the first cleavage or in 2-cell stage. Alternatives (2) and (3) can be ruled out for the cases considered here because the crosses that yielded the mosaics did not involve segregating alleles. Alternative (1) has been discussed above (Section I, B). Since no evidence comparable to that in *Drosophila* exists for the mouse, this alternative cannot be taken as any more probable than alternative (4).

Regardless of whether the event occurs in the postmeiotic germ cell or in the first cleavage, the results indicate that spontaneous mutation in one or both of these stages is considerably more frequent than it is in later cleavages. It may be recalled that of 112 "mottled" animals from specific-locus experiments analyzed to date, 40 were among the "half-mutants" discussed here, 21 had some other genetic explanation, and for 51 no cause of mottling was discovered (mostly as a result of inadequate tests). Even if *all* these 51 had been the result of mutations at later cleavages (a most unlikely assumption) this would constitute a grave deficiency on the hypothesis of equal mutability; for the frequency of mosaics should increase in proportion to the number of somatic cells available per embryo—at least to the limits of visibility, which would

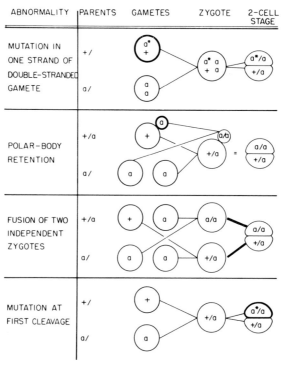

FIG. 2. Events that can lead to "half-and-half" mosaics (animals having about 50% mutant tissue). The generalized gene symbols + and *a* refer to wild type and recessive at any locus; *a** designates a mutation that may or may not differ from *a*. The origin of each abnormality is indicated by heavy lines.

not be reached until postcleavage stages. As will be shown later (Section I, C, 3) spontaneous somatic *reverse* events at the *pe* locus also showed evidence of much higher mutability at the first cleavage than at later ones. In the *pe* case, the mutation rate again increased at about day 10 postconception in pigment precursor cells (gonads not involved). The mutant spots produced by such late events are, however, small enough so that they might be easily missed in specific-locus experiments where the background color is wild type, although a few such may be included among the 51 animals for whom no answer was obtained.

The large class of half-mutant animals observed is useful for drawing certain conclusions concerning cell lineage of the gonads. First, it is abundantly clear (as had already been indicated by some of the early mammalian mosaics) that there is no such thing as purity of germ line, or even an early separation of cell lineages, in mammals; for if there were, one might expect either the germ line or the coat to be of uniform cell type. Actually, *both* are a mixture of cell types.

If the gonad primordium is set aside as a random assortment of n cells from a cell population that is half mutant and half nonmutant, then the distribution of animals with regard to proportion of gonad that is mutant should be described by the expansion of the binomial (0.5 mutant $+$ 0.5 nonmutant)^n. A glance at the observed distribution (Table I) will indicate that it is rather broad and presumably would be even broader if it were not slightly biased against detection of animals at the low end of the range (the chances of detecting a very small gonadic mosaic being relatively low and the zero-class being excluded by definition). If the gonad primordium is indeed set aside as a random assortment of n cells, the broad distribution indicates that n must be very small, perhaps around 5. Several of the individual mosaics, however, yielded progeny ratios that differ significantly from the discontinuous classes expected if the gonad comes from five random cells (e.g., an animal classified on the basis of 197 offspring as having 97.6% of its germinal cells mutant cannot be fitted into the expected 80% category). This could mean—if the idea of random assortment is retained—that n is not constant, but varies around a mean of 5, being perhaps considerably higher in some cases, or that the few primordial germ cells make uneven contributions to the adult gonad. Alternatively, it may mean that the idea of random assortment must be rejected and that there has been, instead, some segregation into cell lineages before the time the gonad primordium is set aside, the assortment being made from a cell population that is no longer half mutant. It is possible that, as breeding results of more mosaics become available and permit more accurate estimation of the true distribution, a decision between the various hypotheses will be possible. For *Drosophila* it has been concluded (Carlson and Southin, 1963) that the gonad primordium is set aside as a very small number of nuclei. Furthermore, mutant tissue tends to form an aggregate which remains together.

2. *Induced Somatic Forward Mutations.* The previous section dealt

in some detail with somatic mutations that occur very early. Information about later events comes from an experiment in which somatic mutations were induced by radiation (Russell and Major, 1957).

Embryos heterozygous for four coat-color genes (b = brown, c^{ch} = chinchilla, p = pink-eyed dilution, d = Maltese dilution) were produced by mating C57BL females (a/a, full color) to NB males (a/a; b/b; $c^{ch}p/c^{ch}p$; dse/dse). Some of these were irradiated $10\frac{1}{4}$ days postconception, and all were observed after reaching adulthood for spots of altered coat color on the normal black background. Parallel irradiated and non-irradiated groups from matings of C57BL females to C57BL males provided controls for radiation effects on pigment-cell killing or differentiation and for somatic dominant mutations. By making the proper allowance for these, it was possible to determine what spots were due to somatic expression of the recessives at the b, c, d, and p loci.

The mosaics found were not tested for gonadal involvement. For one thing, it was quite improbable that this could be detected, even if present. Moreover, it seemed unlikely from embryological facts that any cell of a $10\frac{1}{4}$-day mouse embryo would be ancestral both to germinal tissue and tissue involved in coat-color characteristics. This was borne out by independent results on spontaneous reverse mutations (Section I, C, 3). Since genetic tests were thus not available, the mechanisms by which the recessives in the mosaic spots came to reveal themselves could not be definitely ascertained. One spot was determined on the basis of histological analysis of pigment granules to be probably of genotype $+ \text{'}p\text{'}/c^{ch}p$, which would indicate that at least some of the cases were not the result of chromosome loss or somatic reduction. In addition to gene mutation, however, there remain the possibilities of deficiency, somatic crossover (Section I, C, 4), and rearrangements causing position effect.

Since it was considered unlikely that there would be selection against the cells in which the detectable change was observed, the frequency and size of spots could be used to make various calculations. One of these was the rate of induced genetic change per cell and per roentgen. Of more interest to the present paper is the calculation concerning modal number of prospective pigment cells in day $10\frac{1}{4}$ mouse embryos and the distribution about this mode. It was found that most embryos are rather narrowly distributed around a mode of 150–200, but that the extremes in the range of spot sizes differed by a factor of 2^6. This may indicate a very rapid cell-division rate at this stage (intermitotic interval ca. 4 hours). Alternatively, numbers of prospective pigment cells could vary widely in embryos at this developmental stage or cells of $10\frac{1}{4}$-day embryos which are ancestral to pigment cells could also contribute cell progeny to other tissue, the relative contribution to these two end products being quite variable.

The work of Rawles (1947) indicates that by day $10\frac{1}{4}$ some prospective pigment cells (probably from the neural crest) have already begun to spread laterally from the dorsal midline. Since the induced genetic change, in essence, gives a label to a cell lineage, the appearance of the mosaic areas provides some information on pigment-cell migration and multiplication. The spots, which, in general, appeared to be distributed randomly over the surface of the animal, were of diffuse outline; and within these areas there were varying degrees of mixture of mutant and apparently nonmutant hairs. Often, an animal might have two or more areas which were, however, close to each other with a few mutant hairs bridging the gap. A few, but by no means all, of the spots appeared to start at the dorsal midline; and some gave indication of being elongated roughly at right angles to the anterior-posterior axis of the animal.

All of these facts are consistent with the interpretations that the cell lineage from a given pigment precursor cell extends lateroventrally as well as anteriorly and posteriorly. Cell progeny may never be sent in a dorsal direction or, if it is, it probably does not cross the dorsal midline. Progeny from a given precursor cell rarely if ever populate the entire distance from dorsal to ventral midline. Thus, it is likely that the ventral and probably even lateral portions of the fur are populated by the progeny of cells that have migrated some distance before they reproduce. Finally, there appears to be a considerable degree of intermingling of the progenies of different precursor cells; and some of the progeny cells may also have appreciable migratory powers as evidenced by the occasional observation of two spots from the same mutational event.

Schaible and Gowen (1960) have used wild-type areas, presumed to result from somatic reverse mutations of Mi^{wh}, W^a, and Va, in a study of cell lineage. They deduce that there are six bilateral and two medial pigment areas and that melanocytes spread out from the centers of these areas during final stages of migration from the neural crest.

3. *Somatic Reverse Mutations.* A number of apparently unstable genes have now been observed in the mouse. These revert spontaneously to wild type with appreciable frequency. One case (Russell and Major, 1956) has been worked out in some detail and will be discussed first.

Animals homozygous for the coat-color-diluting mutation *pearl* (*pe*) occasionally have full-colored patches in their fur. The frequency of such individuals was 6% in about 800 A^y/a; pe/pe mice observed. (On the A^y/a; pe/pe background even small patches are detectable. The frequency appears less on other, less favorable backgrounds.) The frequency was not affected by whether one bred from mosaic or nonmosaic animals, indicating that the degree of instability was characteristic of the stock as a whole rather than being transmitted in sublines. Since germinal tissue was occasionally involved in the somatic event (see below), it was possible to subject the mosaics to genetic tests. In this manner it could be established that the event had occurred either at the pe locus itself or not more than 0.36 crossover units from it, and that it could, at least tentatively, be considered a reverse mutation of pe to pe^+ or to some gene resembling it. This gene proved to be fully viable, both in heterozygous and in homozygous condition, and is stable.

TABLE II

DISTRIBUTION OF MICE HAVING PRESUMED SOMATIC REVERSES OF *pearl*, *pe*

Estimated % of coat involved	Number observed	Number tested	Number with germinal tissue:		
			Not involved	Very slightly involved (or new events)	Heavily involved
0.1–1	39 + 15[a]	18 + 2[a]	19	1 (1/50)[b]	0
5	1	1	0	0	1 (6/33)
40–80	4	4	0	2 (1/27, 1/34)	2 (42/88, 17/39)
100	2	2	0	0	2 (10/26, 17/47)

[a] Animals with questionable spots. Diagnosis difficult either because of unfavorable background color ($A/$; pe/pe, a/a; pe/pe) or because of very small size of presumed spot.

[b] Fractions in parentheses show ratio of pe^+ to total classified progeny.

Of particular interest to the present discussion is the distribution of mosaic animals with respect to spot sizes. Of a total of 61 observed, six had from 50–100% of their coat full-colored, one had a full-color spot covering about 5% of the surface, and the remainder had much smaller spots (Table II). In other words, it appeared as though the reverse mutation could occur either very early or quite late. To estimate the amount of involvement, if any, of germinal tissue, one must multiply by two the proportion of pe^+ progeny, the presumed mosaic gonads being $(pe^+/pe)//(pe/pe)$. Since even a completely mutant gonad would produce only one-half full-colored offspring, it is difficult to decide whether the gonad is ever *fully* involved. For instance, are the two 100% full-colored animals the result of reverse mutation in the *previous* generation rather than somatic reverses? If so, they should produce 50% pe^+ progeny. Together they produced 37% (27 out of 73), which is significantly different from 50% at the 0.03 level and therefore suggests that both could have been mosaics. Another problem to resolve is whether single pe^+ animals in moderately large progenies of mosaics (1/50, 1/27, 1/34) indicate that a small part of the gonad is mutant or whether they represent new events.

In spite of these difficulties, the results are fairly clear on the following points. The spontaneous reverse mutations can occur either very early or moderately late in embryonic development. If they occur early, mutant cells participate both in the fur and in the gonad. If they occur late, they usually involve the fur but not the gonad or, in the event that the completely full-colored animals observed (see above) were the result of mutation in the previous generation, the gonad but not the fur. (Animals mosaic in other tissues would not be detected, of course.) One might guess from a comparison with the results of the induced somatic-mutation experiment discussed above (Section I, C, 2) that the late events scored as small spots in the fur occurred around 10 days postconception. Presumably, mutations occurring later would result in spot sizes too small to be visible. Animals that were heavily mottled with 40–80% of the fur involved can, by analogy with spontaneous somatic forward mutations discussed in Section I, C, 1 above, be assumed to have had a reverse mutation at the first cleavage or 2-cell stage. The tendency for the gonad to be either very heavily or very lightly involved is as apparent here as it was in the other cases. So far, there is only one animal in which a mutation could have occurred at a stage intermediate between days 1 and 10 postconception. This had about one-twentieth of the fur and more than one-third of the gonad involved, indicating that mutation occurred early. It is not impossible that this animal, too, traces back to 2-cell stage.

Rough calculations of the mutation rate per cell indicate that the frequency may be an order of magnitude higher in the first cleavage (or 2-cell stage) than it is in 10-day embryos. The difference is even greater if one includes the completely full-colored animals in the mosaic group. The frequency in intermediate stages is probably lower than that in 10-day embryos.

Since the time of the $pe \rightarrow pe^+$ reverse mutation study, several other genes also have been observed to give a relatively high spontaneous frequency of somatic reversions. One is at the p locus (Wolfe, 1963). Four are at the c locus: two appear identical to c in phenotypic effect (but one is homozygous lethal), and two are intermediate between c and c^e

(Russell, unpublished). All of these, either in the homozygous state or heterozygous with c, give a rather high frequency of animals with small dark (possibly full-colored) patches in the fur, and one has given a completely full-colored animal which transmits c^+. At the a locus, also, somatic "reverse mutations" of the type $a \rightarrow A^w$ (Bhat, 1949; Russell, unpublished) have been noted. Both of these involved gonadal tissue. Frequent full-colored spots in mice heterozygous for the dominants Mi^{wh}, W^a, of Va have been interpreted by Schaible and Gowen (1960) as due to somatic reverse mutation. No breeding results have been published for these animals.

It should be noted that the appearance of easily reversible alleles could, in effect, represent a different genetic situation, e.g., removal of a suppressor associated with wild type, such as the Ds situation in maize. Until there is evidence along these lines, however, it is easier to speak of "reverse mutation."

4. *Somatic Events That Produce Two New Genotypes.* Theoretically, some somatic events would produce two new cellular genotypes rather than one. These events are crossing-over, nondisjunction, and reduction to a haploid state. It has not been definitely established that any one of these occurs somatically in the mouse, but a number of cases have been observed that could be explained by one or the other mechanism.

One of these is a mouse, described by Carter (1952), that had presumably started life as a $W^v/+$ heterozygote (W^v, "viable dominant spotting," reduces pigmentation) and showed an apparent deficiency of the W^v allele in the coat (full-colored patches) but a deficient transmission of the $+$ allele in breeding tests.

A case rather similar to Carter's is being studied in our laboratory (Russell, unpublished). A female of originally $+ +/c^{ch}p$ genotype was found to have some light patches (possibly of $c^{ch}p/0$ phenotype?), but, in mating with $c^{ch}p/c^{ch}p$, transmitted a highly significant excess of the $+ +$ chromosome ($36 + +/c^{ch}p$, 9 $c^{ch}p/c^{ch}p$, $2 + p/c^{ch}p$). It may be possible to obtain positive proof of nondisjunction by cytological tests now in progress. If not, somatic crossing-over proximal to both c^{ch} and p must be considered as a possibility. (Somatic reduction would require that haploid oogonia can go through maturation to produce viable eggs, which seems, *a priori*, unlikely.)

Two other mosaic mice observed by us in the past could have been the result of somatic crossing-over. These were a/a; c^{ch}/c heterozygotes, each of which showed spots of white (c/c?) and of near-black (c^{ch}/c^{ch}?) on the grayish-tan ground color. They transmitted c^{ch} and c in ratios very close to 1:1. No cytological tests were possible at the time. If the event responsible had been nondisjunction, rather than crossing-over, the dark spots should have been of genotype $c^{ch}/c^{ch}/c$ and therefore presumably lighter than near-black. Since, however, no detailed analysis of pigment was made, no firm decision is possible.

Klein (1963), in his extensive review on genetics of somatic cells, suggests another possible instance of somatic crossing-over in the mouse. This is the appearance, in tumors heterozygous for *H-2* factors, of stable variants selectively compatible with one of the parental strains. Unfortunately, it is not yet possible to distinguish between truly homozygous tumor cells and phenocopies.

II. Functional Mosaicism

Varied phenotypes within an area of uniform differentiation on a given animal need not always be caused by genetic events occurring in somatic cells. The genetic content may be uniform, and yet certain genes or whole chromosome portions may function in some cells and not function in others of the same tissue, the distinction being random—with the tissue not showing any other signs of differentiation within it. This phenomenon will be referred to as functional mosaicism.

A. *White Spotting, Probably not a Case of Functional Mosaicism*

Several mutations in the mouse (e.g., piebald = *s*, belted = *bt*, and a number of dominants) cause white spots in an otherwise pigmented coat. Could this situation represent funtional mosaicism?

White areas in pied mice probably lack pigment cells (Silvers, 1961). This absence has been explained in two ways: either (1) retarded migration of melanoblasts, or reduction, by some mechanism, of available numbers of melanoblasts, so that the pigment-cell population finally formed lacks enough members to cover the available terrain (Schaible, 1964); or (2) an altered quality of the tissue environment in the white regions which, in some way, inhibits the establishment of melanocytes in the hair follicles (Mayer and Maltby, 1964). Results of embryonic transplantation experiments do not yet allow a decision between these two hypotheses. Silvers (1961) has pointed out that the mechanisms may be different for different white-spotting genes.

In favor of retarded pigment-cell migration (or multiplication) is the finding, both in the guinea pig (Chase, 1939) and in the mouse (Russell, unpublished), that the presence of white-spotting factors makes for a clearer separation of colored areas when more than one pigment type is present [as, e.g., in e^p guinea pigs or in T(X; A) female mice variegated for wild type and recessive; see below]. Thus, the very diffuse and irregular outlines of somatic mutation spots that one finds in the absence of piebald factors (Section I, C) can, perhaps, be thought of as resulting from rapid bursts of migration from various centers with an intermingling on the peripheries.

The effect of embryonic irradiation on white spotting also seems to support the hypothesis of restricted melanocyte population. Thus, it was found (Russell and Major, 1957) that the incidence of small white ventral spots could be increased from 6.4 to 26.8% by 100 r given to offspring of C57BL ♀ × C57BL ♂ matings on day 10 postconception. On the other hand, offspring of C57BL ♀ × NB ♂ matings had no white spots, regardless of whether or not they were irradiated as embryos. The interpretation proposed for this was that, although pigment precursor cells are killed by the irradiation in both types of embryos, their places in C57BL × NB animals can be filled by a surplus of surviving cells, whereas the C57BL × C57BL background normally provides only barely enough pigment cells to fill up the surface, with the deficiency noted at the end of the lateroventrad migration, i.e., midventrally. The radiation finding of Russell and Major has recently been confirmed by Schaible (1964) using the same stage but a different genetic background. It is more in keeping with known facts to interpret the effect of radiation as killing of pigment cells than as altering the quality of midventral follicles to render them nonreceptive to melanoblasts.

Regardless, however, of which explanation of white spotting will finally be proved correct, the phenomenon seems to be one of histological differentiation, rather than of functional mosaicism as defined at the beginning of this section.

B. *Functional Mosaicism of Autosomal Factors*

Although little or nothing is known yet concerning the mechanisms involved, four instances should be mentioned in which variegating "alleles" at well-known coat-color loci have been observed. Two of these occurred at the *p* locus and two at the *a* locus. [The phenotypes produced by Varitint-waddler, *Va,* and some alleles at the dominant spotting, *W,* locus are often referred to as "variegated" since they produce white spots, dilute regions, and occasional full-color patches. Since these last may represent somatic mutations to wild type (see Section I, C, 3) and since the white spots are considered by Schaible to be of the piebald type discussed above (Section II, A), these genotypes will not be considered further here.]

Two p-locus mutants (provisionally named p^{m1} and p^{m2}) that arose in different radiation experiments at our laboratory produce, in the p^m/p condition, a coat in which wild-type areas and areas of typical p/p-phenotype are freely intermingled. (In $c^{ch}p^m/c^{ch}p$ the areas are of $c^{ch} +/c^{ch}$ and $c^{ch}p/c^{ch}p$ color, i.e., the linked c locus does not appear to be affected.) On the average, about half the coat is of the p/p color, but individual animals may vary considerably in this respect. That the condition is not caused by a somatically highly mutable "wild-type" allele is shown by breeding results: $p^m/p \times p/p$ crosses yielded at least 50% mottled animals in well over 1000 young observed, the rest being p/p. If the mottling were the result of a somatically mutable wild type, then mottled (plus, perhaps, fully wild-type) progeny should not exceed 25%. It is thus concluded that p^m is present in all cells but that—at random—it produces full-colored pigment in some and typical p/p pigment in others.

Could p^m be the result of a position effect? Major rearrangements appear unlikely in view of the facts that (1) litter size of heterozygotes is average and that (2) recombination in the c-p interval is definitely not reduced, at least in the case of p^{m1} (p^{m2} not yet tested). The karyotypes are normal. The results cannot yet rule out small rearrangements or other types of linked variable suppressors of p^+. If such are present, however, they must be firmly linked with the p locus since no recombinants were found in 1354 young.

A situation apparently analogous to p^m exists at the a locus in the "allele" a^m derived in radiation experiments at this laboratory. Animals of genotype a^m/a have agouti and nonagouti patches of fur freely intermingled at their edges. As with p^m, mottled a^m/a animals produce about 50% mottled progeny in crosses to a/a, and they are fully fertile. Evidence concerning possible linked genes or small rearrangements that might act as variable suppressors is only beginning to be accumulated, but is negative so far.

Another a-locus "allele" with somatically variable effect is A^{vy}, viable yellow (Dickie, 1962). Animals carrying this gene are often mottled with agouti patches ranging from small size to a completely agouti coat. Again, these are not the result of somatic mutation.

Can these four instances of variable effect be ascribed to alleles producing an intermediate level of gene product, with chance local factors of the environment determining whether an end product is or is not made? This seems unlikely, especially in the case of the p locus, where alleles producing uniformly intermediate end product are known; i.e., the *p*-locus end product can be present at various levels rather than being an all-or-none affair. At the *a* locus, alleles are known that produce agouti and nonagouti hairs on the same animal, but the distribution of these hairs follows a definite morphological pattern. The random mottling that is observed in p^{m1}, p^{m2}, a^m, and A^{vy}, and the apparent all-or-none expression, resembles the situation in which there is heterozygosis of certain X-linked genes or certain autosomal genes involved in X-autosome translocations. These will be discussed in the next section.

C. *The Mammalian X Chromosome*

Functional mosaicism in the mouse has been best documented in the case of the X chromosome. The "inactive" X or, as I have preferred to call it, single-active-X chromosome hypothesis is by now so well known that it need not be discussed in detail (see Russell, 1964b, for a recent review). The hypothesis includes two main points: (1) that only one X chromosome is active in somatic cells of mammals regardless of the number actually present, and (2) that the choice of which X is the active one is random, but that, once differentiation has occurred, it remains fixed in subsequent cell generations.

Evidence that one X was active (Russell, 1961) came from the study of "variegated-type position effects" in the mouse, from cytological and cytochemical evidence that the two X chromosomes in a normal female do not act alike, and from the study of sex chromatin. That X differentiation must be random and fixed (Lyon, 1961, 1962) was evident from mosaic phenotypes in females heterozygous for X-linked or X-translocated genes and was borne out later by cytological findings. Most of the expected consequences of the hypothesis—dosage compensation, the coexistence of two cell populations in heterozygous females, and variability of such females—are indeed found.

There have, however, been more and more indications recently that the hypothesis should not be taken in its simplest form (Russell, 1964b). Evidence from X-autosome translocations in the mouse indicates that inactivation proceeds from a certain point or region of the X (Russell *et al.*, 1962; Russell, 1963). By studying variegation characteristics of several translocations involving the same two chromosomes (linkage group 1 and the X), it was found that the degree of inactivation is dependent on the position of the rearrangement points. A given gene may be inactivated in a high proportion of cells in the case of one T(X; 1), a low proportion in another, and not at all in a third. This finding, combined with the typical spreading effect that is observed when two loci are studied together in the same translocation, suggests that inactivating influences spread in gradients from a certain part of the X, probably not its centromere region. That this postulated "flow" of the inactivating influence affects X-chromosomal loci themselves and not just translocated autosomal loci was shown by a translocation recently described by Searle (1962) in which the gene Ta^+ had apparently become separated from the inactivating region of the X and was now invariably active.*

The conclusion that inactivation may spread for a certain distance from a certain point suggests that there may be portions of the X chromosome that do not normally come under this influence and are always active. Supporting evidence for this comes from the finding of a few X-linked genes that do not conform to the simple inactivation hypothesis, from the lack of complete phenotypic normality in abnormal sex-chromosome constitutions, and from cytological data (Russell, 1964b, review).

D. *Mechanisms in Functional Mosaicism*

The problem of how genes are turned on and off in a particular sequence during development is, of course, the basic problem of differentiation. What is unique about the mammalian X chromosome—and, perhaps, certain autosomal genes also (Section II, B)—is the fact that the differentiation is between homologs rather than between different parts of the genome. Furthermore, this differentiation occurs in a normal genome, rather than, as in *Drosophila,* in one containing rearrangements (Lewis, 1950, review) or extra chromatin (Cooper, 1956).

Although a number of authors have suggested possible mechanisms for X-chromosome differentiation (Russell, 1964b, review), we are undoubtedly still a long way from the facts. Only one point seems relatively clear. Although the altered state observable after a certain stage in development is that of the "inactive" X, differentiation must, instead, somehow single out the X that remains active, for there is always only one of that type, whereas any number of additional X's can become heteropyknotic. It is perhaps not unreasonable to think of X differentiation as being under the control of some part of the autosomal complement, such that certain autosomal gene products in double dose are necessary to retain activity of *one* X. The findings in polyploid cells support this idea.

Elucidation of the mechanisms involved in the induction of one X

---

* It has recently been found (Searle, private communication) that there is, in the case of that particular translocation, nonrandom inactivation of the X's, the translocated X being almost invariably the active one.

chromosome as a continuing active one thus constitutes the first problem. Another set of problems centers around the ways in which an entire chromosome or, perhaps, its major portion becomes *in*activated. One may have to look for mechanisms that can selectively affect replication rhythms, for it is easier to think of late replication (Taylor, 1960; and others) as a cause of inactivity (nonavailability of gene products at the proper time), than vice versa. To postulate a controlling center for replication time of the chromosome as a whole seems, however, an oversimplification, in view of the increasing evidence (Section II, C) that inactivity may not extend to the very ends of an autosomal piece translocated with the X and, in fact, possibly not even the entire length of the X. If this is so, and if inactivity is the result of late replication, then it may be that the influence that delays replication "flows" along the chromosome, but only for a certain distance.

Does this influence extend for a fixed distance and then end abruptly or does it peter out near its limits? The findings with X-autosome translocations support the latter alternative. Thus, when the sequence along the translocated autosomal piece is rearrangement point–c locus–p locus, animals are heavily mottled with c areas and only slightly, or not at all, with cp areas, but not with p areas alone. The reverse situation exists if the sequence is rearrangement point–p locus–c locus. It then becomes important to determine whether a gene near the limits of the inactivating influence is affected as often but only partially so, or whether, on the other hand, it has a smaller probability of being affected by *complete* inactivation. In an attempt to answer this, the genotype $(c^+p^+)R/cp^+$ has been constructed (R = rearrangement point). If c^+, which is at a considerable distance from R, were only partially affected, mottling should be with some intermediate color, e.g., resembling c^{ch}/c. As nearly as can be determined, however, mottling is with white only, i.e., c^+ is apparently completely inactivated, only less often so.

It thus appears that inactivation is all-or-none, but may be variable at the extremes of the range of the inactivating influence. If this should be true also of the nontranslocated complement, i.e., of the normal X chromosome, it would pose new problems of dosage compensation for certain X-linked genes. Genes located in portions of the X chromosome that are invariably inactivated would always be present in single dose and thus require no dosage compensation. Those located beyond the range of the inactivating influence would always be present in double dose and possibly come under some system of dosage compensation similar to that proposed for *Drosophila* (Stern, 1960, review). But the few that are at the extremes of the range could be present in single dose in some cells of the body of a female and in double dose in others. Perhaps this would not lead to such violent disorder as might at first be anticipated. Obviously, many autosomal genes must be able to function successfully in either single or double dose, for large segments of autosome, when involved in translocations with the X, become functionally monosomic.

E. *Functional Mosaicism as a Tool in Studying Gene Action*

While the mechanisms that bring about functional mosaicism may themselves shed light on the nature of gene action (when they are elucidated), the very existence of functional mosaicism provides a tool for studying certain properties of genes and of chromosomal portions.

Since the X-chromosome influence appears to cause total inactivation within a certain range, the homologous genes are expressed in an effectively hemizygous state. It thus becomes possible to use females heterozygous for X-autosome translocations as a test system to determine whether specific alleles introduced on the intact autosome are amorphs or hypomorphs. Both types have been found (Russell *et al.*, 1964). In addition, the system can be used to find out if certain autosomal mutations (possibly deficiencies) known to be homozygous lethal also act as cell lethals. Twelve independent brown lethals (general symbol b^l) and a pink-eyed lethal, p^l, have already yielded variegated $R(+)/p^l$ and $R(+)/b^l$ females, indicating that these mutations are not cell-lethal. It was, of course, already apparent that some X-linked mutations (*Mo* series, *Str*, etc.) known to be hemizygous lethal are not cell-lethal, for these mutations are, in fact, detected in functionally mosaic heterozygous females. Moreover, many of them have arisen by somatic mutation in males where they are present in genetically (not functionally) hemizygous condition in part of the body (Section I, C, 1).

In the course of the experiments designed to determine whether the b^l and p^l lethals were cell-lethal, it was found that female translocation heterozygotes were less viable if their intact autosome carried the lethal than if it carried the viable recessive. For instance, whereas in the cross $R(+)/b \times b/b$, 40.9% of 672 classified females were brown-variegated (Russell and Bangham, 1961), the cross of $R(+)/b \times +/b^l$ gave only 12.4% brown-variegated females in 218 classified, the expectation for equal viability being 20.5% ($P = 0.004$). The $R(+)/p^l$ type similarly appears in reduced numbers.

Certain conclusions can be drawn from this concerning the time of X-chromosome inactivation. For the particular p^l mutation used, we determined in independent experiments that p^l/p^l embryos call forth an implantation reaction, but die by day 6½ or possibly before, but not earlier than day $2\frac{1}{2}$ (no observations to date between days $2\frac{1}{2}$ and 6). If the time of p^l-lethal action were to precede the time of onset of X inactivation, $R(+)/p^l$ should be of normal viability, for p^l in each cell would then, at the critical time, still be "covered" by an active p^+. The reduced viability of $R(+)/p^l$ thus indicates that X-chromosome inactivation begins before day $6\frac{1}{2}$.

The fact that surviving $R(+)/p^l$ are variegated, i.e., p^l is expressed in a hemizygous state, could indicate one of two things. (1) X differentiation is already complete at the time of p^l-lethal action, i.e., all cells are already effectively $+/0$ or $0/p^l$, with those embryos succumbing in which the latter cell type by chance exceeds a certain threshold proportion. If this is so, one must suppose that death is caused by some organismic effect, for if it were the result of removal of $0/p^l$ cells, the surviving embryos would consist of $+/0$ cells only and not be variegated. (2) Alternatively, X inactivation may have occurred in only some cells by the end of the critical stage, i.e., the embryo may consist of effectively $+/0$, $0/p^l$, and $+/p^l$ cells. Again, the proportion of $0/p^l$ cells would determine whether or not the embryo succumbs, but *regardless* of the mechanism of death ($0/p^l$ cell removal or organismic), survivors would still become variegated because the cells that had been $+/p^l$ by the end of the critical period would differentiate later into $+/0$ and $0/p^l$.

It should be noted that in the case of alternative (1) the period of X differentiation is confined to an interval beginning *and ending* before day $6\frac{1}{2}$; this interval could be very short. In the case of alternative (2), X differentiation begins before day $6\frac{1}{2}$, but extends for some time past that stage.

The X-autosome translocations may, perhaps, serve as tools in the solution of an entirely different problem, the requirements for male fertility. In all of the six different translocations studied by us and one studied by Searle (1962), the males, although copulating freely, are completely sterile as a result of disturbances in spermatogenesis. One proposed explanation of this sterility (Russell, 1964a) is that there may be an upset in the rhythms of chromosome condensation and movement during meiosis. Thus, one translocated chromosome may have "divided loyalty" in its affinity for the Y on the one hand and for an autosome on the other (the X-Y bivalent and autosomes being governed normally by different rhythms). Juan Valencia (1964) has suggested a different mechanism. The "sex vesicle" which appears in prophase of the first meiotic division is normally formed by the X and Y chromosomes. In translocation males, however, it would consist of Y and presumably only part of an X, namely that part contained in the translocated chromosome that pairs with the Y. If it can be supposed that the sex vesicle has some positive function for the completion of normal meiosis, sterility could be explained by a deficient sex vesicle. It should be noted that a translocation studied by Cattanach (1961), which probably consists of insertion of a piece of linkage group 1 into the X (Ohno and Cattanach, 1962), is not completely male-sterile. In keeping with Valencia's idea, mice with this translocation would not form a deficient sex vesicle. The finding, however, that translocation males with two normal autosomes (i.e., with the insertion acting as a duplication) are, if they survive at all, more fertile than are balanced translocation males (i.e., with one normal and one deficient autosome) cannot be explained on the basis of Valencia's suggestion. It may fit better with the idea of divided affinity.

Summary

The considerable body of information that has become available in recent years on both genetic and functional mosaicism in the mouse provides some answers to problems of mutability, cell lineage, and gene action.

A. *Genetic Mosaicism*

1. Among spontaneous genetic mosaics, there has been one chimera that can be explained on the basis of either retention of a fertilized polar body or fusion of two independent zygotes.

2. Spontaneous mutability appears to be relatively very high at one or more of those stages in which genetic change would lead to half-and-half mosaics, namely, the postmeiotic gamete (mutation in one strand only), the first cleavage, or the 2-cell stage. Spontaneous rate becomes low in subsequent cleavages. In at least some genetic situations, it then rises again somewhat around day 10 postconception. Nothing is known concerning later stages because the mutant spots would become too small for analysis. The relatively high frequency of half-and-half mosaics is found both for forward mutations (or deficiencies) observed in animals heterozygous for standard coat-color markers and for reverse mutations of certain unstable genes. Somatic loss of autosomes is rare or may be selected against.

3. In over forty gonosomic mosaics whose breeding results were analyzed, there was no evidence for selection against mutant cells in the gonad or in the progeny. The distribution of these mosaics with respect

to proportion of germinal tissue consisting of mutant cells centered about a mean of 48.3% and was rather broad. The results fit one of two alternatives. (a) The gonad primordium is set aside as a random assortment of a small number of cells, averaging about 5, from a cell population that is 50% mutant. The primordial cells may contribute unequally to the mature germinal tissue. Or (b) some segregation into cell lineages has occurred before the time when the gonad primordium is set aside.

4. A number of animals have been observed that can be interpreted on the basis of somatic events producing *two* new genotypes, i.e., somatic crossover, nondisjunction, or reduction, with the first one the most likely. No definite proof for any of these events has, however, been obtained to date.

5. Instances of induced somatic forward "mutations" and of certain spontaneous reverse mutations, by providing labels to cell lineages, have been used to make interpretations concerning migration and multiplication of pigment-cell precursors. Observations on white spotting may also be useful for this.

B. *Functional Mosaicism*

A functional differentiation of genes or of whole-chromosome portions that is random and not related to histological or morphological differentiation leads to a state referred to as functional mosaicism.

1. Four mottling alleles at autosomal loci have been found. They are not somatically mutable alleles but, rather, genes that have all-or-none expression at random. No major rearrangements seem to be involved.

2. Functional mosaicism in the mouse is best documented in the case of the X chromosome. The single-active-X hypothesis states that only one X is active, that the choice of this X is random, and that, once differentiation has occurred, it remains fixed in subsequent cell generations. Recent evidence suggests a modification of this hypothesis to the effect that inactivation may not involve the whole chromosome, but may spread for a certain distance from a certain point.

3. Mechanisms that need elucidation are (a) how one X is singled out as the active one, and (b) how major portions of a chromosome can become *in*activated. Inactivity may be the result of late replication. An influence that delays replication may "flow" a certain distance from a controlling center in the chromosome. Results indicate that genes near the limits of this influence are still completely inactivated, but less often so.

4. Functional mosaicism has been used as a tool in determining

whether certain alleles at autosomal loci are amorphs or hypomorphs. It has also been used to show that a considerable number of mutations known to be lethal do not act as *cell*-lethals.

5. The study of an X-autosome translocation, in conjunction with an autosomal allele whose time of lethal action is known, indicates that X-chromosome inactivation begins before day $6\frac{1}{2}$ postconception.

ACKNOWLEDGMENTS

The author wishes to express gratitude to W. L. Russell for making available results of experiments that are as yet unpublished and to the many members of the Mammalian Genetics Section who have helped faithfully in the accumulation of the various sets of data that are discussed in this paper.

This research was sponsored by the United States Atomic Energy Commission under contract with the Union Carbide Corporation.

REFERENCES

ALTENBURG, E., AND BROWNING, L. S. (1961). The relative absence of fractional mutations in X-ray treated sperm of *Drosophila*. *Genetics* 46, 203-211.

BHAT, N. R. (1949). A dominant mutant mosaic house mouse. *Heredity* 3, 243-248.

BÖÖK, J. A., AND SANTESSON, B. (1961). Nuclear sex in triploid XXY human cells. *Lancet* II, 318.

BRADEN, A. W. H. (1957). Variation between strains in the incidence of various abnormalities of egg maturation and fertilization in the mouse. *J. Genet.* 55, 476-486.

CARLSON, E. A., AND SOUTHIN, J. L. (1963). Chemically induced somatic and gonadal mosaicism in *Drosophila*. I. Sex-linked lethals. *Genetics* 48, 663-675.

CARTER, T. C. (1952). A mosaic mouse with anomalous segregation ratio. *J. Genet.* 51, 1-6.

CATTANACH, B. M. (1961). A chemically-induced variegated-type position effect in the mouse. *Z. Vererbungslehre* 92, 165-182.

CATTANACH, B. M. (1964). Autosomal trisomy in the mouse. *Cytogenetics* 3, 159-166.

CHASE, H. B. (1939). Studies on the tricolor pattern of the guinea pig. II. The distribution of black and yellow as affected by white spotting and by imperfect dominance in the tortoise shell series of alleles. *Genetics* 24, 622-643.

CHU, E. H. Y., THULINE, H. C., AND NORBY, D. E. (1964). Triploid-diploid chimerism in a male tortoiseshell cat. *Cytogenetics* 3, 1-18.

COOPER, K. W. (1956). Phenotypic effects of Y chromosome hyperploidy in *Drosophila melanogaster*, and their relation to variegation. *Genetics* 41, 242-264.

DICKIE, M. (1962). A new viable yellow mutation in the house mouse. *J. Heredity* 53, 84-86.

DUNN, L. C. (1934). Analysis of a case of mosaicism in the house-mouse. *J. Genet.* 29, 317-326.

FISHER, R. A. (1930). Note on a tri-colour (mosaic) mouse. *J. Genet.* 23, 77-81.

GARTLER, S. M., WAXMAN, S. H., AND GIBLETT, E. (1962). An XX/XY human hermaphrodite resulting from double fertilization. *Proc. Nat. Acad. Sc. U. S.* 48, 332-335.

HOLLANDER, W. F., GOWEN, J. W., AND STADLER, J. (1956). A study of 25 gynandromorphic mice of the Bagg Albino strain. *Anat. Record* 124, 223-239.

KLEIN, G. (1963). Genetics of somatic cells. *In* "Methodology in Mammalian Genetics" (W. J. Burdette, ed.), pp. 407-468. Holden-Day, San Francisco, California.

LEWIS, E. B. (1950). The phenomenon of position effect. *Advan. Genet.* 3, 73-115.

LYON, M. F. (1961). Gene action in the X-chromosome of the mouse (*Mus musculus* L.). *Nature* 190, 372-373.

LYON, M. F. (1962). Sex chromatin and gene action in the mammalian X-chromosome. *Am. J. Human Genet.* 14, 135-148.

MAYER, T. C., AND MALTBY, E. L. (1964). An experimental investigation of pattern development in lethal spotting and belted mouse embryos. *Develop. Biol.* 9, 269-286.

MULLER, H. J., CARLSON, E., AND SCHALET, A. (1961). Mutation by alteration of the already existing gene. *Genetics* 46, 213-226.

OHNO, S., AND CATTANACH, B. M. (1962). Cytological study of an X-autosome translocation in *Mus musculus*. *Cytogenetics* 1, 129-140.

RAWLES, M. E. (1947). Origin of pigment cells from the neural crest in the mouse embryo. *Physiol. Zool.* 20, 248-266.

RUSSELL, L. B. (1961). The genetics of mammalian sex chromosomes. *Science* 133, 1795-1803.

RUSSELL, L. B. (1962). Chromosome aberrations in experimental mammals. *In* "Progress in Medical Genetics" (A. G. Steinberg and A. G. Bearn, eds.), Vol. 2, pp. 230-294. Grune & Stratton, New York.

RUSSELL, L. B. (1963). Mammalian X-chromosome action: inactivation limited in spread and in region of origin. *Science* 140, 976-978.

RUSSELL, L. B. (1964a). Experimental studies on mammalian chromosome aberrations. *In* "Mammalian Cytogenetics and Related Problems in Radiobiology" (C. Pavan and C. Chagas, eds.), pp. 61-86. Pergamon Press, New York.

RUSSELL, L. B. (1964b). Another look at the single-active-X hypothesis. *Trans. N.Y. Acad. Sci.* Ser. II, 26, 726-736.

RUSSELL, L. B., AND BANGHAM, J. W. (1961). Variegated-type position effects in the mouse. *Genetics* 46, 509-525.

RUSSELL, L. B., AND MAJOR, M. H. (1956). A high rate of somatic reversion in the mouse. *Genetics* 41, 658 (abstr.).

RUSSELL, L. B., AND MAJOR, M. H. (1957). Radiation-induced presumed somatic mutations in the house mouse. *Genetics* 42, 161-175.

RUSSELL, L. B., AND SAYLORS, C. L. (1960). Factors causing a high frequency of mice having the XO sex-chromosome constitution. *Science* 131, 1321-1322 (abstr.).

RUSSELL, L. B., AND SAYLORS, C. L. (1963). The relative sensitivity of various germ-cell stages of the mouse to radiation-induced nondisjunction, chromosome losses, and deficiencies. *In* "Repair from Genetic Radiation Damage" (F. Sobels, ed.), pp. 313-342. Pergamon Press, New York.

RUSSELL, L. B., AND WOODIEL, F. N. (1963). A mosaic mouse probably formed from two meiotic products of oogenesis. U. S. AEC Report ORNL-3489, pp. 75-76. Oak Ridge National Lab., Oak Ridge, Tennessee.

RUSSELL, L. B., BANGHAM, J. W., AND SAYLORS, C. L. (1962). Delimination of chromosomal regions involved in V-type position effects from X-autosome translocations in the mouse. *Genetics* 47, 981-982 (abstr.).

RUSSELL, L. B., BANGHAM, J. W., AND MONTGOMERY, C. S. (1964). The use of X-autosome translocations in the mouse for the study of properties of autosomal genes. *Genetics* **50**, 281-282 (abstr.).

RUSSELL, W. L. (1951). X-ray-induced mutations in mice. *Cold Spring Harbor Symp. Quant. Biol.* **16**, 327-336.

RUSSELL, W. L. (1964). Evidence from mice concerning the nature of the mutation process. *In* "Genetics Today," *Proc. Intern. Congr. Genet. 11th, The Hague, Netherlands, 1963* (S. J. Geerts, ed.), Vol. 2. Pergamon Press, New York (in press).

SCHAIBLE, R. H. (1964). Developmental genetics of spotting patterns in the mouse. *Dissertation Abstr.* **24**, (10). Iowa State Univ.

SCHAIBLE, R. H., AND GOWEN, J. W. (1960). Delimitation of coat pigment areas in mosaic and piebald mice. *Genetics* **45**, 1010 (abstr.).

SEARLE, A. G. (1962). Is sex-linked *Tabby* really recessive in the mouse? *Heredity* **17**, 297 (abstr.).

SILVERS, W. K. (1961). Genes and the pigment cells of mammals. *Science* **134**, 368-373.

STERN, C. (1960). Dosage compensation—development of a concept and new facts. *Can. J. Genet. Cytol.* **2**, 105-118.

TAYLOR, J. H. (1960). Asynchronous duplication of chromosomes in cultured cells of Chinese hamster. *J. Biophys. Biochem. Cytol.* **7**, 455-464.

VALENCIA, J. (1964). Private communication.

WOLFE, H. G. (1963). Two unusual mutations affecting pigmentation in the mouse. *In* "Genetics Today." *Proc. Intern. Congr. Genet. 11th, The Hague, Netherlands, 1963* (S. J. Geerts, ed.), Vol. 1, p. 251. Pergamon Press, New York.

WOODIEL, F. N., AND RUSSELL, L. B. (1963). A mosaic formed from fertilization of two meiotic products of oogenesis. *Genetics* **48**, 917 (abstr.).

Genetic Repression
of *R* Action in Maize

R. ALEXANDER BRINK

Department of Genetics, University of Wisconsin, Madison, Wisconsin

Chromosomes function in the reproduction, recombination, and transport of genes, and in the regulation of gene activity. Mediation of these processes presumably involves chromosome components different from the genes themselves. The nature of these secondary chromosome constituents and the manner in which the latter are integrated with the genes, as the primary components, are largely unanswered questions.

One approach to the problems in this area is the study of genetic phenomena that manifest the action of chromosomal materials that may be gametically transmissible, but are not resolvable into conventional genes. Classic cases are variegated position effects in *Drosophila melanogaster* (Lewis, 1950) and unstable loci in maize (McClintock, 1956). Variegated position effects involve transpositions of euchromatic chromosome segments to heterochromatic regions. It is presumed that heterochromatin is present at unstable loci in maize also, although cytological confirmation in these cases is lacking. A counterpart of these phenomena which, however, is limited to somatic tissues, is the mosaic phenotype of female mice heterozygous for sex-linked genes conditioning coat color. Features common to these several classes of cases are (1) variegated phenotypes that are superposed in a relatively discordant fashion on the highly ordered pattern of normal development and (2) somatic or gametic transmission of the anomalies via the chromosomes. Substantive gene changes are not involved; it is the expression, not the essential constitution of the genes that is altered. The phenotypes that usually result suggest partial or complete inactivation of the genes concerned, in an irregular manner. The writer recently has portrayed variegated position effects in *Drosophila,* unstable alleles in flowering plants, and mosaicism for sex-linked characters in the female mouse in terms of a common basic chromosomal process, namely, repression of gene action by pycnosis (Brink, 1964).

Paramutation at the R locus in maize will be considered here as another example of this kind of genetic repression. The evidence concerning it, however, is distinctive in certain respects. It is found, for example, that one widely occurring class of R alleles is never, or only rarely, recoverable in standard form from heterozygotes of certain kinds. The pigment-producing potential of all the gametes in this class is reduced, and the allele is gametically transmitted thereafter in changed form. Such heritable alterations in R are directed both in the sense of arising as responses to presence in the genome of a particular other R allele and as regularly involving a unidirectional change in pigmenting action in a given kind of heterozygote. Furthermore, newly arisen paramutant forms of R commonly revert partially toward the standard form, and so are metastable. These properties are not characteristic of mutation. The latter term has long been used in a collective sense as encompassing heritable variations of qualitatively diverse kinds. Mutations as a class, however, are characteristically sporadic in occurrence and are undirected; and the mutant ordinarily is stable. The R changes in question differ from mutation in these fundamental respects.

The evidence from paramutation points to presence at or near the R locus of chromosome components which, unlike conventional genes, are extraordinarily labile under certain conditions and can be heritably altered in particular ways at will. The evidence concerning the phenomenon will be reviewed in the present report.

Experimental Materials and Methods

The R locus in maize, situated in the distal half of the long arm of chromosome 10, is represented by numerous alleles conditioning the formation and distribution of anthocyanin in seed and plant. The several categories of R factors used in the paramutation studies are listed in Table I. Within each category, except possibly that of the ultimate recessive, r^g, individual alleles occur that differ from each other in minor ways. Several of the R^r alleles introduced into our cultures from one or another geographic source, for example, differ in grade of aleurone mottling in single dose, and in intensity and distribution of anthocyanin in vegetative tissues. All R^g alleles condition green anthers, and many give green seedlings also. Others, however, promote abundant anthocyanin formation in the primary roots. Furthermore, self-colored mutants from the stippled allele, which fall in the R^g class, although alike in aleurone and plant phenotype, vary widely in level of paramutagenic action. The symbols listed in Table I, therefore, are collective terms of convenience. Differences between alleles within a given category often are important in the design of an experiment, thus making it necessary to specify the particular allele used.

A further fact, unique in studies of this kind, is that the pigment-producing action of a paramutable R allele varies with the genetic "history" of the allele. An R^r allele of a given origin, extracted from otherwise isogenic R^rR^r, R^rr^r, and R^rR^{st} plants, for example, is demonstrably different in the three cases. Paramutable R factors do not conform to the basic Mendelian rule that contrasting alleles are regularly recoverable from heterozygotes without change.

All the R alleles used in the present studies have been introduced into a common highly inbred, dent corn strain, known as W22, as a means of reducing extraneous genetic variation to a minimum. A second, unrelated inbred line, designated W23, and carrying the r^g allele for colorless aleurone and green plant has been widely used as the pistillate parent in testcrosses.

Standard procedure in evaluating the pigment-producing action of an R allele is to apply pollen from a W22 plant carrying the factor in question to a W23 r^gr^g individual and then to score the resulting Rr^gr^g kernels. The R allele under test is thus transmitted through the pollen and is present in the resulting seed in single dose.

The kernels from a testcross ear customarily are scored for aleurone color by matching them singly under low magnification against a standard set of six seeds defining seven grades of pigmentation ranging from 1 (colorless) to 7 (self-colored).

R alleles condition both seed and seedling color, and these functions vary individually by mutation. Appropriately chosen R alleles that overlap in their aleurone color effects on segregating ears may be classified definitively, therefore, by noting seedling color after sprouting the seeds.

Paramutation of R^r in R^rR^{st} and R^rr^r Heterozygotes

The aleurone pigment-producing potential of a paramutable R allele may be either lowered or raised according to the class of heterozygotes through which the factor is passed, and the changes thus arising are gametically transmissible.

A striking reduction in the pigmenting action of standard R^r (a particular allele in our initial collection of unknown origin but indistinguishable from several other R^r factors since obtained from various North

TABLE I

Phenotypic Effects of the Main Categories of R Alleles

Allele	Phenotype			Paramu-table	Paramu-tagenic	Notes
	Seed	Seedling	Anther			
R^r	Self-colored in 2 or 3 doses, darkly mottled in 1 dose	Red	Red	+	−	Varies in grade of seed mottling in 1 dose, and in intensity and distribution of plant pigmentation
R^g	Self-colored in 2 or 3 doses, darkly mottled in 1 dose	Green, but some give red roots	Green	+	−	Occurs as mutants from R^r
R^g	Self-colored in 1, 2, or 3 doses	Green	Green	−	+ or −	Andean forms
R^{st}	Stippled	Green	Green	−	+	Finely spotted aleurone
R^{mb}	Marbled	Green	Green	−	+	Coarsely spotted aleurone
R^{nj}	Pigmented crown	Pinkish	Pink, but variable	−	−	Navajo
R^{sc}	Self-colored in 1, 2, or 3 doses	Green	Green	−	+ to −	Self-colored mutants from stippled or marbled

TABLE I (*Continued*)

Allele	Phenotype			Paramutable	Paramutagenic	Notes
	Seed	Seedling	Anther			
R_1^{ch}	Self-colored in 2 or 3 doses, mottled in 1 dose	Red	Red	+	—	Gives cherry pericarp with *Pl*
rr	Colorless	Red	Red	—	—	Occur as mutants from *Rr*
rg	Colorless	Green	Green	—	—	Occur as direct mutants from *Rg*, rarely from *Rr*
Paramutant forms						
Rr'	Self-colored in 2 or 3 doses, lightly mottled in 1 dose	Red	Red	+	+ (Weakly)	Paramutant form of *Rr*
Rg'	Self-colored in 2 or 3 doses, lightly mottled in 1 dose	Green	Green	+	+ (Weakly)	Paramutant form of *Rg*

American sources) occurs when the allele is passed through a hetero-zygote with stippled. The results of testcrosses made by McWhirter and Brink (1962) of W22 R^rR^r and R^rR^{st} plants on W23 r^gr^g ♀ ♀, sum-marized in Table II, serve to illustrate this change.

TABLE II

FREQUENCY DISTRIBUTIONS AND MEAN ALEURONE COLOR SCORES FOR THE $R^rr^gr^g$
KERNELS FROM TESTCROSSES ON W23 r^gr^g ♀ ♀ OF R^rR^r AND F_1 R^rR^{st} PLANTS

Staminate plant number	Parent genotype	Aleurone color							Mean score
		1	2	3	4	5	6	7	
783-1	R^rR^{st}	—	90	10	—	—	—	—	2.10
783-2	R^rR^{st}	—	15	63	20	2	—	—	3.09
783-3	R^rR^{st}	—	76	24	—	—	—	—	2.24
783-4	R^rR^{st}	—	68	32	—	—	—	—	2.32
783-5	R^rR^{st}	—	83	17	—	—	—	—	2.17
803-2	R^rR^r	—	—	—	—	14	86	—	5.86
803-3	R^rR^r	—	—	—	—	9	91	—	5.91
803-5	R^rR^r	—	—	—	—	8	92	—	5.92
803-7	R^rR^r	—	—	—	—	9	91	—	5.91
803-10	R^rR^r	—	—	—	—	28	72	—	5.72

The controls were five R^rR^r plants from a W22 stock culture main-tained by continuous self-pollination. The pooled mean aleurone color score for the $R^rr^gr^g$ kernels resulting from the five r^gr^g ♀ $\times$ R^rR^r ♂ test-crosses was 5.86, based on 100 kernels from each ear. The R^rR^{st} plants tested were F_1 hybrids between an R^rR^r and an $R^{st}R^{st}$ plant from stock cultures. The mean aleurone color score for the $R^{r'}r^gr^g$ kernels from the r^gr^g ♀ $\times$ R^rR^{st} ♂ was 2.38. It will be noted from Table II that the effect of passing R^r through an R^rR^{st} plant is to shift the entire distribution of $R^{r'}r^gr^g$ testcross kernels about three classes to the left on the 1–7 color scale. Such invariability in the change of R^r to $R^{r'}$ is characteristic of the paramutagenic action of the stippled allele. The change in aleurone phenotype following passage of the R^r allele through an R^rR^{st} plant is illustrated in Fig. 1.

Heritability of the change induced in R^r action in R^rR^{st} plants is readily demonstrable by applying to r^gr^g ♀ ♀ pollen collected from the R^rr^r (control) and $R^{r'}r^r$ (paramutant) offspring from r^rr^r ♀ $\times$ R^rR^r ♂ and r^rr^r ♀ $\times$ R^rR^{st} ♂ crosses, respectively. The $R^rr^gr^g$ kernels resulting from control testcrosses are darkly mottled; those from the $R^{r'}r^r$ matings are lightly mottled.

Kermicle (1963) has shown that the several $R^{r'}r^r$ offspring from a cross between W22 $r^r r^r$ and a single W22 $R^r R^{st}$ plant are heterogeneous in terms of aleurone pigment-producing action of the paramutant $R^{r'}$ allele. Eighteen $R^{r'} r^r$ sibs of this origin were tested in duplicate matings on W22 $r^g r^g$ ♀ ♀. A very high correlation, 0.98, was observed between the $R^{r'} r^g r^g$

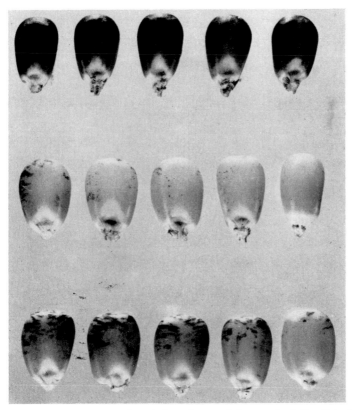

FIG. 1.   Effects on aleurone color of three forms of the standard Rr allele in single dose. *Top,* $R^r r^g r^g$ kernels from an $r^g r^g$ ♀ × $R^r R^r$ ♂ mating. *Middle,* paramutant $R^{r'} r^g r^g$ kernels from an $r^g r^g$ ♀ × F_1 $R^r R^{st}$ mating. *Bottom,* partially reverted $R^{r'} r^g r^g$ kernels from an $r^g r^g$ ♀ × $R^{r'} r^r$ ♂ mating in which the $R^{r'} r^r$ parent was derived from an $r^r r^r$ ♀ × F_1 $R^r R^{st}$ ♂ cross.

scores for kernels on duplicate ears. Mean scores for the 18 pairs of ears, however, ranged from 2.16 to 4.93, with a general mean of 3.19.

A progeny test confirmed the conclusion that the heterogeneity was genetic. Three of the above mentioned $R^{r'} r^r$ plants that gave low, intermediate, and relatively high color scores, respectively, were again mated to $r^r r^r$ individuals. Eighteen plants within each set of offspring were then testcrossed on $r^g r^g$ ♀ ♀ . The mean color scores for the three second generation groups of testcross kernels were in accord with the rank of the parent plants.

A significant additional observation from this experiment was that the individuals within each of the three groups of second generation $R^{r'} r^r$ plants were again heterogeneous with respect to $R^{r'}$ pigment-producing action. Each group of plants in this instance represents a single R^r gamete derived from the $R^r R^{st}$ ancestor. The variability in each group, therefore, reflects an inherent instability of the paramutant $R^{r'}$ alleles.

Two conclusions may be drawn from Kermicle's study. Pigment-producing action of R^r invariably is reduced markedly in $R^r R^{st}$ plants, but to varying levels. Second, the altered $R^{r'}$ allele is metastable.

Occasional $R^r r^g r^g$ kernels from $r^g r^g$ ♀ $\times R^r R^{st}$ ♂ testcrosses are as darkly pigmented as those from $r^g r^g$ ♀ $\times R^r R^r$ ♂ matings. In an experiment in which contaminants could be identified, Brown (1963a) showed that failure of these seeds to display the paramutant phenotype initially was not due to loss of paramutability by R^r. Plants grown from 76 such dark seeds selected from a population of about 142,000 testcross kernels were mated again with $R^{st} R^{st}$ individuals. The retest was completed on 64 of the entries. The R^r allele in question was found to be sensitive to paramutation in every case.

There is no evidence that the R^{st} allele is changed on passage through an $R^r R^{st}$ plant either in aleurone spotting action or in capacity to induce paramutation on being introduced subsequently into another $R^r R^{st}$ individual.

In contrast to the above results, the aleurone pigment-producing potential of R^r gametes from $R^r r^r$ plants is somewhat higher on the average than those from $R^r R^r$ individuals. Brink and Blackwood (1961) compared three families of W22 $R^r R^r$ plants with three closely related families of W22 $R^r r^r$ individuals in matings on W23 $r^g r^g$ ♀ ♀ . Five plants in each family were used in the testcrosses. The mean aleurone color scores for the $R^r r^g r^g$ kernels from the three sets of $r^g r^g$ ♀ $\times R^r R^r$ ♂ matings were 5.20, 5.34, and 5.30, on the 1–7 scale. The corresponding values for the $R^r r^g r^g$ seeds from the parallel $r^g r^g$ ♀ $\times R^r r^r$ ♂ testcrosses were 5.82, 5.90, and 5.74. The difference in mean score between the $R^r R^r$ and $R^r r^r$ groups is 0.44 class intervals, a value that is statistically significant at the 1% level.

A more closely controlled test of R^r action when the allele is derived from $R^r R^r$ and $R^r r^r$ plants has been carried out recently in our laboratory by Styles, the unpublished results of which he has permitted us to cite. The foundation material that Styles used was a uniform $R^g r^g$ family obtained by crossing an $R^r R^r$ with an $r^g r^g$ plant from stock cultures. $R^r r^g$ and $R^r R^r$ lineages were established from this family that were then maintained through three generations by continuous self-pollination. $R^r r^g$ and $R^r R^r$ plants of the two lineages were testcrossed on W22 $r^g r^g$ ♀ ♀ in each generation, and the resulting $R^r r^g r^g$ kernels were scored for aleurone pigmentation on the 1–7 scale.

Ten plants in the $R^r r^g$ foundation family yielded $R^r r^g r^g$ testcross kernels with a mean aleurone color score of 6.36. It will be noted that this value approaches the self-colored level, which is 7 on the scale used. As the generations progressed, the R^r testcross scores for the $R^r r^g$ plants in the $R^r r^g$ lineage were 6.71, 6.87, and 6.90, respectively. The corresponding values by generations for the $R^r R^r$ lineage were 5.95, 6.02, and 6.03. Thus, the mean R^r scores for the $R^r R^r$ lineage were lower throughout than those for the $R^r r^g$ lineage.

Styles also observed that the $R^r R^r$ segregates in each of the last two generations in the $R^r r^g$ lineage consistently gave lower testcross scores than their respective $R^r r^g$ sibs.

Partial Reversion of Paramutant R

A paramutant R allele derived directly from an R R^{st} plant is metastable; under certain conditions it regularly reverts partially toward the standard R level of aleurone pigment-producing action, as illustrated in Fig. 1. This phenomenon has been studied in our laboratory by Kermicle (1963) whose principal results we shall now summarize.

Reversion of $R^{r'}$ toward R^r is partial only; no instance has been observed yet in which a paramutant R has regained the level of action characteristic of the parent form. The amount of reversion of a given R' allele that occurs is the same in heterozygotes with various nonparamutagenic r^g, r^r, R^g, and R^r alleles. Partial reversion also can occur autonomously, i.e., in the absence of another R allele. Kermicle found that in plants carrying one chromosome 10 deficient for a segment including the R region, the amount of reversion of a paramutant R' allele carried by the normal homolog is equal to that occurring in $R'r$ and $R'R$ individuals.

The time course of partial reversion was measured by testcrossing on $r^g r^g$ ♀ ♀ a progressive series of $R^{r'} R^{r'}$ individuals obtained by selfing F_1 $R^r R^{st}$ individuals and their $R^{r'} R^{r'}$ descendants through five generations.

The results are shown in Fig. 2. It is apparent from the diagram that $R^{r'}$ male gametes from first generation $R^{r'}R^{r'}$ progeny possessed a much higher pigment-producing potential than those formed by their F_1 R^r R^{st} parents. An additional small increase in level of $R^{r'}$ action occurred in generation 2, but no further change was observed thereafter. Thus, under this mating system, $R^{r'}$ stabilized in two generations. As Fig. 2 also shows, constancy was attained at a pigmenting level about 1.5 class intervals, on

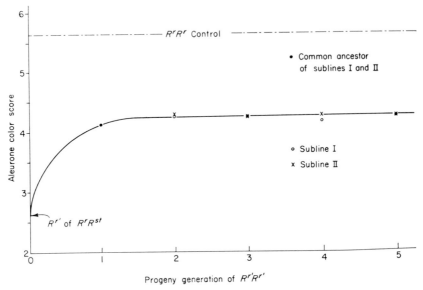

FIG. 2. Partial reversion of paramutant $R^{r'}$ in homozygous $R^{r'}R^{r'}$ plants over five successive generations (Kermicle, 1963).

the 1–7 scale, below that of the standard R^r allele from an R^rR^r stock culture.

Less reversion of $R^{r'}$ occurs on the average in $R^{r'}R^{r'}$ offspring obtained by selfing R^rR^{st} plants than in the $R^{r'}r^r$ progeny from $rr \times R^rR^{st}$ matings. As will be discussed later, $R^{r'}$ is weakly paramutagenic, whereas r^r is nonparamutagenic. Conceivably, therefore, this difference rests on a slight paramutagenic effect of each $R^{r'}$ allele on the other in $R^{r'}R^{r'}$ homozygotes.

Kermicle observed that an $R_6^{g'}$ allele which had been reduced to a very low level of action by passing it through R^{st} heterozygotes for two successive generations did not revert detectably when extracted in an

$R_6^{g'} R_6^{g'}$ homozygote. Either $R_6^{g'}$ was stabilized in this case or reversion was subliminal.

Self-colored (R^{sc}) mutants from the stippled allele varying in level of paramutagenicity affected reversion differentially. Nonparamutagenic R^{sc} mutants were indistinguishable in their influence on the process from R_5^g, a nonparamutagenic mutant from standard R^r, whereas weakly paramutagenic R^{sc} factors reduced the amount of reversion. No reversion occurred if an $R^{r'}$ allele was passed through a heterozygote carrying a strongly paramutagenic R^{sc} mutant.

The pigment-producing action of a partially reverted R allele was again reduced if the factor was made heterozygous with a strongly paramutagenic allele such as R^{st}. The change in level of R action involved in reversion, therefore, is reversible.

Changes in Action of R^r and R^g Alleles from Stock Cultures in Heterozygotes with Each Other

Evidence recently has been adduced by Styles (1964) in our laboratory that the aleurone pigment-producing potential of R^r and R^g alleles that are paramutable in heterozygotes with R^{st} may be altered when these alleles are bred as heterozygotes with each other for a few generations. These studies are incomplete, but the direction in which the results point is of such interest for the R paramutation problem in general that mention of them will be made here.

Styles has observed that when any two paramutable alleles which will be called R_1 and R_2, distinguishable from each other by plant color markers and differing slightly but consistently in aleurone-pigmenting action when tested in $R\ R$ or $R\ r$ stock cultures, are bred as R_1R_2 heterozygotes by continuous self-pollination the level of action of one of the alleles is altered. The pigmenting action of the stronger allele, as measured in testcrosses on $r^g r^g\ \female\ \female$, tends to decline in the heterozygote to the level of its weaker partner. As pigmenting action of the R allele declines, the level of action of the factor following passage through an $R\ R^{st}$ heterozygote also falls.

These relations are not easy to establish because the differences in grade of aleurone color involved are near the limits that may be distinguished by the kernel scoring methods available. If the findings are confirmed, however, an interesting conclusion follows. The results mean that paramutable R alleles are inherently metastable. Initial differences between them, as observed in stock cultures, are not fixed, and presumably could be eliminated by breeding each of them continually as a heterozygote with the R allele lowest in the series in terms of aleurone-pigmenting action.

It may be assumed that the R-locus components undergoing change in these cases are the same as those altered when the R allele is passed through an $R\,R^{st}$ plant. R alleles reacting in this way in R_1R_2 hetero-zygotes are to be considered not only paramutable but also as weakly paramutagenic. The latter property is disclosed by R_1 if R_2 enters the heterozygote at the higher aleurone-pigmenting level.

Acquisition of Paramutagenicity by R^r in Stippled Heterozygotes

Passage of a paramutable R allele through a heterozygote with stippled results in two recognizable changes in R action: pigment-producing po-tential is reduced, and paramutagenic potential is increased. The latter fact was demonstrated by Brown and Brink (1960) using a series of eight green seedling mutants (R^g) derived from standard R^r (red seedling) and not differing from the latter in aleurone-pigmenting action. The phenom-enon was termed secondary paramutation.

The pooled mean aleurone color score for the $R^gr^gr^g$ seeds resulting when R^rR^g control plants, carrying alleles derived in both cases from stock cultures, were testcrossed on r^gr^g ♀ ♀ was found to be 5.48 on the 1–7 scale. The corresponding mean value observed when the male parents in the testcrosses where heterozygous for one or another R^g allele and $R^{r'}$ (the latter derived from R^rR^{st} plants) was 4.68. The difference in score was in the same direction and also statistically significant, for each of the eight R^g mutants tested. Evidently standard R^r becomes paramuta-genic in an R^rR^{st} heterozygote.

The level of paramutagenicity thus acquired, however, is much lower than that of the R^{st} allele. As noted above, the mean score for the $R^gr^gr^g$ kernels resulting from the series of r^gr^g ♀ $\times$ $R^{r'}R^g$ ♂ matings was 4.68. The $R^{g'}r^gr^g$ testcross kernels from r^gr^g ♀ $\times$ R^gR^{st} ♂ matings in which the same eight mutant R^g alleles were represented was 2.44.

The probable relation of secondary paramutation to Styles' findings mentioned in the preceding section is noteworthy. Styles' results show that a paramutable R allele is potentially paramutagenic also. The de-tectable, but still low, paramutagenicity of an R factor that has been passed through an RR^{st} plant may now be regarded as enhancement to an overt level of a property of the allele normally present in a nearly subliminal form.

Association of the R Locus with Paramutation

The previously mentioned series of R^g mutants from standard R^r were used to prove R-locus dependence of the paramutant R phenotype (Brink *et al.*, 1960). These mutants are equivalent to R^r in aleurone-pigmenting action and in paramutability in heterozygotes with stippled. They are distinguishable from R^r, however, in conditioning green rather than red seedlings. $R^r R^g$ and $R^r R^{g\prime}$ plants derived from $R^r R^{st} \times R^g r^g$ and $R^g R^{st} \times R^r R^r$ matings, respectively, were testcrossed on $r^g r^g$ ♀ ♀. The testcross kernels were scored for grade of aleurone color and then identified with respect to R^r and R^g composition on the basis of seedling color. The mean color scores for the $R^r r^g r^g$ and $R^g r^g r^g$ kernels regularly were significantly different from each other. The paramutant phenotype in each case was associated with the particular allele, R^r or R^g, that had been derived from an R^{st} heterozygote, and the more darkly pigmented phenotype followed the allele of stock culture origin. Thus, reversing the origin of R^r and R^g as between a stock culture plant and an R^{st} heterozygote correspondingly reversed the order of R^r and R^g in level of aleurone-pigmenting action. A paramutant R and an oppositely marked normal R persisted in their respective states in a common cytoplasm. These results prove that paramutation is chromosomal and that the changes involved occur close to or at the R locus.

Brown (1963) recently has adduced additional evidence for an intimate association between paramutation and the R locus. As noted previously, each of ten R^g mutants (colored aleurone, green seedling) from standard R^r becomes weakly paramutagenic when passed through an $R^g R^{st}$ plant. That is to say, capacity to become paramutagenic is retained when R^r mutates to R^g. Brown found that this relation did not hold for mutations of R^r to r^r (colorless aleurone, red seedling). Twenty such r^r mutants were tested in $R^g r^r$ heterozygotes, following extraction of r^r from $R^{st} r^r$ plants. None of them was detectably paramutagenic. Evidently the capacity to become paramutagenic is lost when R^r mutates to r^r.

Two lines of evidence point to a correspondingly close relationship between the R locus and the paramutagenic action of the R^{st} allele. In the first place, R^{st} from our cultures has proved invariably to be paramutagenic when appropriately tested. Second, as McWhirter and Brink (1962) found and as will be discussed later in this report, para-

mutagenic action may be unchanged, abolished, or altered in degree
when R^{st} mutates to self-colored aleurone. Both the sensitivity of certain
R alleles to undergo paramutation and the capacity of other R alleles
to promote such change overtly, therefore, are closely associated with
the R locus.

Continuous Variation in Paramutation

The pigment-producing potential of standard R^r may be reduced by
paramutation to any one of a wide range of levels. This fact was established by McWhirter and Brink (1962) in a study of 83 independently
occurring mutants of stippled to self-colored (R^{sc}) aleurone. The R^{sc}
mutants in heterozygotes with standard R^r were found to vary greatly in
paramutagenic action in contrast to the parent R^{st} allele, which is
strongly paramutagenic.

The results of testcrosses on $r^g r^g$ ♀ ♀ of heterozygotes between standard
R^r and the 83 R^{sc} mutants from R^{st} are summarized in Fig. 3. The
arrows in the diagram point to the control entries based on parallel
matings with $R^r R^{st}$, standard $R^r R^r$, and $R^r r^g$ staminate plants.

Sixteen of the 83 R^{sc} mutants proved to be nonparamutagenic, namely,
those entered on the right-hand side of Fig. 3, from R^{sc}_{58} through R^{sc}_{113}. The
testcross scores for these $R^r R^{sc}$ heterozygotes did not differ significantly
from those given by standard $R^r R^r$ plants. The mutation of R^{st} to R^{sc} in
these cases has been accompanied by loss of the paramutagenic property.

The remaining 67 R^{sc} mutants were paramutagenic, but in varying
degrees. They may be divided, rather arbitrarily, into three groups.
Thirty-six mutants were paramutagenic at, or near, the high level
characteristic of the parent stippled allele. Mutation of R^{st} to R^{sc} in
these cases has not resulted in detectable changes in paramutagenicity.
Sixteen of the remaining R^{sc} mutants, which gave $R^{r'}$ aleurone color
scores in the 4.22 to 5.01 range and did not differ significantly from each
other in this respect, may be characterized as weakly paramutagenic.
The 15 mutants comprising the residual group, with mean scores for $R^{r'}$
action varying from 3.42 to 4.22, may be described as very weakly paramutagenic.

These tests show that accompanying the mutation of R^{st} to R^{sc} paramutagenicity may be unchanged, lost, or it may be quantitatively altered.
The data at hand are not statistically adequate to establish the fact

that each R^{sc} mutant is unique, but when arranged as in Fig. 3, they suggest that the variation in paramutagenicity is continuous.

The obverse aspect of the evidence summarized above, namely, that the pigment-producing action of standard R^r may be altered to one or another level in a series that is seemingly continuous is equally meaningful for an understanding of the paramutation process. The evidence

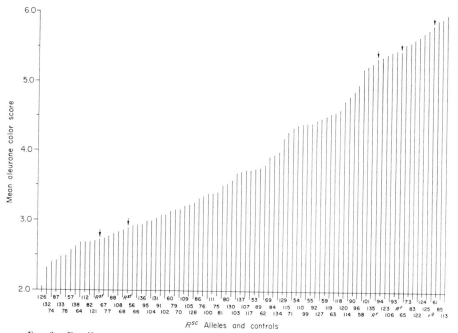

R^{SC} Alleles and controls

Fig. 3. Family mean aleurone color scores for the $R^r r^g r^g$ kernels from $r^g r^g$ ♀ × $R^r R^{sc}$ matings, arranged in order of increasing magnitude to show the continuous variation in level of paramutation of the standard R^r allele. Eighty-three R^{sc} mutants from R^{st} were represented in the $R^r R^{sc}$ ♂ parents (McWhirter and Brink, 1962).

suggests that the R^r component that changes when paramutation occurs is a compound structure that can be varied quantitatively over a wide range.

Compound Nature of the Stippled Allele

Stippled appears to be a compound allele comprising a gene for self-colored aleurone and green seedling (R^g) whose action in this relation, in the nonmutated condition, is repressed by an adjacent inhibiting factor. The spotting pattern characteristic of stippled kernels could be accounted for on the assumption that the inhibitor is removed frequently, but sporadically, by transposition to other chromosome sites during endosperm development, thus allowing the R^g gene to express itself in small colored areas irregularly distributed in the aleurone. Such a mutation occurring at the macrospore stage, or earlier, could result in a self-colored kernel on an otherwise stippled ear. If the transposition process in this case is analogous to that involved in variegated pericarp in maize, it would be expected that most of the sites to which the inhibitor transposes would be in the vicinity of the R locus (Van Schaik and Brink, 1959) and that transposition from the new position back to the old would occasionally occur, thus reconstituting the R^{st} allele (Orton, 1960). McWhirter and Brink (1962) screened more than a million gametes from $R^{sc}R^{sc}$ plants, however, without finding a back mutation to R^{st}. Seventeen mutations were observed in this population, but none corresponded to the stippled phenotype. There is no direct evidence, therefore, that implicates transposition in this mutation.

Ashman (1960) found that there was no relation between R^{st} to R^{sc} mutation and crossing-over in the region proximal to the R locus marked by the golden-1 gene, about 14 units away. Similarly, McWhirter and Brink (1962) observed that the mutation occurred independently of crossing-over with K10, a distal heterochromatic knob that gives 1–2% recombination with the R locus.

The mutation of R^{st} to R^{sc} occurs frequently enough (approximately 2 per 1000 gametes) so that more than one mutant kernel is sometimes recoverable from a single W22 ear. Comparison of such R^{sc} mutants with each other showed that they often differed markedly in paramutagenic action in R^rR^{sc} heterozygotes. This fact suggests that the alterations in aleurone pigmentation and paramutagenicity are coincident events.

Other evidence shows, however, that the inhibitor of aleurone pigmentation postulated above as a component of the R^{st} allele and the element responsible for the paramutagenic action of stippled are different from each other. Ashman (1960) identified a transposable modifier (M^{st}) of R^{st} normally located about six crossover units distal to the R locus that effected a tenfold increase in the number of colored spots on stippled seeds without, however, altering paramutagenic action of the R^{st} factor. This result and the fact that R^{st} mutates to R^{sc} in some cases without change in paramutagenicity point to the conclusion that aleurone pigment repression and paramutagenicity are referable to different components of the R^{st} allele.

Progressive Paramutation in Successive Generations

Evidence from several experiments recently made in our laboratory shows that the pigment-producing potential of R^r decreases if the allele is kept heterozygous with a paramutagenic allele through successive generations. This conclusion is contrary to an earlier report by the writer (Brink, 1958) who observed in a preliminary trial that $R^r r^g r^g$ test-cross kernels from $r^g r^g$ ♀ × $R^r R^{st}$ ♂ matings in which the staminate parent was the product of two successive backcrosses of $R^r R^{st}$ heterozygotes to $R^{st} R^{st}$ plants were no lighter in color than $R^r r^g r^g$ seeds from $r^g r^g$ ♀ × F_1 $R^r R^{st}$ matings. It is now clear that such a result is not typical. The reason for the exception in this instance, however, is not certainly known. A possible explanation is that since the stippled parent used in producing the F_1 $R^r R^{st}$ plants belonged to a different W22 subline than that used in the backcrosses, the R^{st} alleles in the strains compared may have differed in level of paramutagenic action. An R^{st} variant has been discovered in certain of our W22 stocks since the testcrosses in question were made that is somewhat less paramutagenic than the standard allele. This variant may have been used inadvertently in the $R^r R^{st}$ × $R^{st} R^{st}$ backcrosses, but not in producing the F_1 $R^r R^{st}$ plants with which the backcrossed stock was compared. In any case, it is clear, on the basis of the data from several experiments since made, that the conclusion first drawn was incorrect and that paramutation is, in fact, progressive in successive generations.

Cooper (1964), for example, observed that the $R^{r'} r^g r^g$ kernels produced following testcrosses of F_2 $R^r R^{st}$ plants on $r^g r^g$ ♀ ♀ were significantly less pigmented than those from comparable F_1 $R^r R^{st}$ matings. The F_1 plants used were obtained by applying pollen from an $R^r R^r$ stock to two $R^r R^{st}$ individuals in a single family. $R^r R^{st}$ offspring from the two kinds of male parents, when testcrossed on $r^g r^g$ ♀ ♀, gave mean aleurone color scores for the $R^{r'} r^g r^g$ seeds of 6.45 and 6.39 based on 14 and 18 ♂ ♂, respectively. (The aleurone color scores used in Cooper's experiments were based on a graded scale applying to 22, rather than 6, reference kernels, and so are not directly comparable to most of the other scores reported in this article.) The F_2 $R^r R^{st}$ plants tested were derived from six self-pollinated sibs in the same family. The aleurone color scores in this series, in which the number of F_2 individuals tested in each ear progeny varied from 8 to 14, were 3.72, 3.36, 3.30, 3.17, 3.08, and 2.97, respectively. The mean values for the F_1 R^rR^{st} and F_2 R^rR^{st} groups, 6.42 and 3.27, are significantly different statistically.

Another test by Cooper (1964) in which the pigment-producing action of the R^r allele was measured in testcrosses on r^gr^g ♀ ♀ after one and two generations of heterozygosity with R^{st} gave mean aleurone color scores of 6.99 and 4.24 for F_1 and F_2, respectively, based on 10 plants in each testcross group. The difference found in this experiment also was highly significant statistically.

Progressive reduction in R^r-pigmenting action during successive generations of heterozygosity with the stippled factor is in evidence also when the R^r allele is extracted in homozygous form from F_1 R^rR^{st} and F_2 R^rR^{st} plants, by self-pollination, and is then tested by crossing the $R^rR^{r'}$ plants on r^gr^g ♀ ♀. Cooper (1964) compared otherwise similar $R^rR^{r'}$ individuals of these two origins in three experiments, each involving eight plants of each class. The mean aleurone color scores for the $R^{r'}$ r^gr^g testcross kernels were 10.40 and 5.65 from the first experiment, 11.82 and 4.92 in the second, and 12.40 and 5.77 in the third, for $R^rR^{r'}$ plants representing one and two generations of prior heterozygosity for R^{st}, respectively. The difference in each case was statistically significant at the 1% level.

As noted earlier, self-colored (R^{sc}) mutants from the stippled allele vary widely in paramutagenicity. Some mutants are as active as R^{st} itself, others are inactive, and the remainder form a continuous series between these limits. McWhirter and Brink (1962) found that a particular mutant, R^{sc}_{83}, was not detectably paramutagenic in F_1 $R^rR^{sc}_{83}$ plants. The pigment-producing action of R^r was slightly and significantly reduced below the standard value, however, if the factor was passed through R^{sc}_{83} heterozygotes for three successive generations. R^{sc}_{83}, therefore, is very weakly paramutagenic; its effect on R^r is subliminal in F_1, but becomes overt among the descendants of selfed $R^rR^{sc}_{83}$ plants.

McWhirter and Brink (1962) also observed that an $R^{r'}$ factor whose aleurone-pigmenting ability had been lowered slightly by a single passage through a heterozygote with one or another of the weakly or very weakly paramutagenic alleles, R^{sc}_{89}, R^{sc}_{99}, R^{sc}_{110}, or R^{sc}_{128} could subsequently be further reduced in level of action by passage through plants carrying the strongly paramutagenic factor, R^{st}.

It is evident, therefore, that the change in R^r action resulting from a single passage through a heterozygote with a paramutagenic allele is not necessarily terminal. Further change may be effected by maintaining heterozygosity for additional generations either with the same or a different, but more strongly, paramutagenic allele.

Occurrence of Paramutation in Somatic Cells

The fact is now well established that in heterozygotes between standard R^r and a paramutagenic allele such as R^{st}, R^r changes to a paramutant form, $R^{r'}$, in somatic cells. There is direct evidence also that the change is not dependent upon conjugation of the R^r and R^{st} alleles at zygotene in meiosis.

Newton and Darlington (1929) observed that when more than two chromosomes of a given kind are present in a plant conjugation of these chromosomes in meiosis is two by two at any given level. If, therefore, zygotene pairing of the R^r and R^{st} alleles is a condition of paramutation, only a part of the R^r gametes formed by a trisomic plant also carrying a neutral representative of the locus, such as r^g, on the third chromosome 10, should be paramutant and the remainder should be normal in pigmenting action. Only the R^r gametes from R^r-R^{st} zygotene pairings, constituting about one-third of the total, should be paramutant on this hypothesis. Those from R^r-r^g pairings and also those carrying nonconjugated R^r should be equivalent in pigment-producing potential to R^r gametes derived from $R^r r^g$ plants. Testcrosses on $r^g r^g$ ♀ ♀ were made with sib $R^r r^g$, $R^r R^{st}$ and $R^r/R^{st}/r^g$ (trisomic) plants in a family obtained from a $R^{st}/R^{nj}/r^g$ ♀ $\times$ $R^r R^r$ ♂ mating (Brink, 1959). The $R^r r^g r^g$ kernels resulting from the $r^g r^g$ ♀ $\times$ $R^r r^g$ ♂ testcrosses were darkly pigmented, as expected for an R^r allele in standard form. With the exception of a few contaminants, all the $R^r r^g r^g$ kernels from the matings on $r^g r^g$ ♀ ♀ of both $R^r R^{st}$ ♂ ♂ and $R^r/R^{st}/r^g$ (trisomic) ♂ ♂ were of the weakly pigmented, paramutant class, and did not differ significantly from each other. Evidently, therefore, paramutation of R^r occurs in a plant whose nuclei also carry a R^{st} allele, even though conjugation of the two alleles at meiosis does not take place.

Standard R^r affects plant as well as seed pigmentation. Leaves and stems of the W22 inbred line are so weakly colored, however, that changes in R^r action during sporophytic development are not directly observable. One is limited to the determination of the net change in R^r action in an $R^r R^{st}$ individual after growth is completed by collecting pollen from the inflorescence at the apex of the plant, applying the pollen to $r^g r^g$ ♀ ♀ , and then scoring the resulting seed for aleurone pigmentation.

What does such pollen represent in terms of sampling R^r paramutations if the latter are assumed to have occurred progressively in the plant as development proceeded? On this supposition the pigment-producing potential of an R^r allele contained in a given pollen grain from an R^rR^{st} plant would reflect the sum of the changes the allele has undergone throughout the whole of a cell lineage, from the embryo onward, of which the corresponding pollen mother cell is a terminal representative. A mass collection of pollen from a tassel constitutes a cross section, as it were, of the end point conditions of R^r in all the cell lineages extending into the tassel.

If paramutation occurs progressively during plant development and the change in R^r in one cell lineage is independent of that in others, then it would be expected that sectoring for paramutation would occur in the tassel. The frequency of such sectoring would reflect the variation in paramutation in different somatic cell lineages. Tests can be made for sectoring, of course, by sampling pollen from different parts of a tassel or from different tassels in the same plant, if the latter produces more than one fertile male shoot.

The W22 inbred strain usually forms a single, tassel-bearing stem. Well-grown, widely spaced plants, however, sometimes also produce a basal branch (tiller) from which pollen may be collected a few days after anthesis in the main tassel. Cooper (1964), working in our laboratory, compared the aleurone color scores of the $R^{r'}r^gr^g$ kernels resulting from the applications to r^gr^g ♀ ♀ of pollen collected separately from the main and tiller tassels of six sib plants heterozygous for standard R^r and a paramutagenic R^{sc} allele. The aleurone pigment-producing potential of R^r in tiller pollen was found to be significantly higher in all six cases than that from the respective main tassels on the same plants. Evidently, in such heterozygotes, there is less change in R^r action, on the average, during development of a fertile branch from the base of the plant than during growth of the main shoot. Similar tests with stock R^rR^r plants that formed tillers gave no difference between pollen samples from the two sources.

Cooper also found sectoring within the main tassel on several R^rR^{sc} plants. One such individual from which pollen was taken in a pre-arranged order from four branches around the central axis and also from the main spike gave results in testcrosses on r^gr^g ♀ ♀ suggestive of a half-shoot chimera.

Ordinarily in a plant heterozygous for standard R^r and a strongly paramutagenic allele like R^{st} all the pollen grains formed carry paramutant $R^{r'}$ alleles whose aleurone pigment-producing potential is markedly reduced. The change in R^r action is not to be viewed, however, as a one-step process. The data from the tests for the amount of paramutation in evidence in successive sexual generations reviewed earlier, as well as those for the occurrence of chimerism, suggest that paramutation is a progressive process during plant development. Pollen collected from an R^rR^{st} tassel embodies an array of paramutant $R^{r'}$ alleles which represents terminal states of R^r in all the cell lineages extending into the sporogenous tissue and over which successive changes in R^r action have been distributed during the vegetative cycle. This interpretation of the course of R^r change during plant development is in harmony with the more direct evidence obtained by others for progressive occurrence of paramutation in sporophytic tissues in *Malva parviflora,* the *cruciata* form of *Oenothera,* and *Pisum sativum,* reviewed in a later section.

Although induced changes in R^r action are not visibly expressed during growth of W22 inbred maize plants, McWhirter and Brink (1963) obtained direct evidence for the occurrence of paramutation in vegetative cells of this strain in a study of the phenomenon in the endosperm. A given paramutable R allele was found to produce less aleurone pigment in seeds heterozygous for a strongly paramutagenic factor than in control kernels on the same ear carrying a nonparamutagenic factor.

The genotypes used as pistillate parent in these tests were r^rr^g and $r^r(I)_3/r^g$. The $r^r(I)_3$ allele is a mutant isolated from the progeny of R^rR^{st} plants that conditions near-colorless aleurone and is paramutagenic in standard R^r heterozygotes at about the same level as R^{st}. The r^r and r^g genes give colorless aleurone and are nonparamutagenic.

The genotypes of the staminate parents employed in the test matings were $R_5^gR_5^g$, R_5^g/R_{134}^{sc}, and $R_5^gR^{st}$. R_5^g is a highly paramutable mutant derived from standard R^r and distinguishable from the latter in conditioning green, rather than red, seedlings. R_{134}^{sc} is a mutant from R^{st} that gives self-colored aleurone in a single dose, colored scutellum, and green seedling. It is paramutagenic, but at a low level.

The R_{134}^{sc} factor was used to obtain an $R_5^{g'}$ allele for the testcross with a pigment-producing potential slightly lower than that of R_5^g in standard form. Such conditioning was effected by passing R_5^g through an R_5^g/R_{134}^{sc} plant before employing it in the test for occurrence of paramutation in the developing endosperm. Conditioned $R_5^{g'}$ probably is not more sensitive to paramutation than normal R_5^g, in an absolute sense, but its lowered initial action makes it especially suitable for detecting further reduction by the particular scoring procedure used in our experiments.

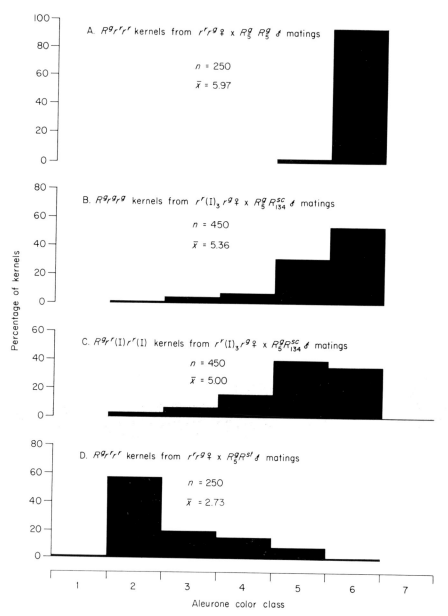

FIG. 4.   Percentage of R_5^g rr kernels in seven aleurone color classes in the matings demonstrating paramutation of R_5^g during endosperm development (B and C). The distribution for standard R_5^g from a stock $R_5^g R_5^g$ culture is shown in (A), and that for R_5^g from $R_5^g R^{st}$ plants in (D) (McWhirter and Brink, 1963).

Reference to diagram A in Fig. 4 shows that the $R_5^g r^r r^r$ kernels from the $r^r r^g ♀ \times R_5^g R_5^g ♂$ matings gave a mean aleurone color score of 5.97 on the 1–7 scale. The corresponding class of seeds from the $r^r r^g ♀ \times R_5^g R^{st} ♂$ crosses, as shown in diagram D, scored only 2.73. These results confirm the sensitivity of R_5^g to paramutation.

The results of the test for occurrence of paramutation in the developing endosperm are illustrated in diagrams B and C. The pistillate parent used in this mating was $r^r(I)_3/r^g$, i.e., it was heterozygous for a highly paramutagenic and a nonparamutagenic allele, distinguishable from each other by their effects on seedling color. The staminate parent was an R_5^g/R_{134}^{sc} plant, from which R_5^g was obtained in conditioned form. It will be noted from diagram B that the $R_5^{g'} r^g r^g$ kernels resulting from $r^r(I)_3/r^g ♀ \times R_5^g R_{134}^{sc} ♂$ testcross gave a mean aleurone color score of 5.36, whereas the $R_5^{g'}/r^r(I)_3/r^r(I)_3$ seeds, as shown in diagram C, gave a value of 5.00. Thus, the kernels carrying the paramutagenic $r^r(I)_3$ factor were less heavily pigmented than the controls, which received the nonparamutagenic allele, r^g, from the pistillate parent. The difference in score, 0.36, was found to be highly significant statistically. Repetition of this experiment using a different, near-colorless, paramutagenic allele, $r^g(I)_4$, in a heterozygote with the nonparamutagenic allele, r^r, as the pistillate parent, again showed that the pigment-producing action of conditioned $R_5^{g'}$ was significantly reduced in an endosperm carrying a strongly paramutagenic factor. It is apparent, therefore, that paramutation occurred in these vegetative cells and that a measureable amount of change in R-pigmenting action was effected during the short span of growth represented by an endosperm.

Manifestation of Paramutation in Sporophytic Tissues

The R^r allele in maize conditions both seed and plant color. Evidence has been adduced that the two effects of R^r rest upon different components of the locus that are separable by crossing-over (Emmerling, 1958). The standard test used in our laboratory for paramutation of R^r involves scoring seed color only. The question arises, therefore, whether plant color as well as seed color is affected by passing the R^r allele through a stippled heterozygote. The answer is not obvious from examination of either seedling or adult $R^r r^g$ plants. $R^r r^g$ seedlings resulting from $r^g r^g ♀ \times R^r R^{st} ♂$ matings overlap considerably with control $R^r r^g$ seedlings in pigmentation of shoot and root. Adult $R^r r^g$ plants sometimes show reduced anthocyanin formation in glumes and anthers, but the effect varies from plant to plant in a family and from one year to another. Special measures are necessary, therefore, to determine whether action of the plant color determinant of the R^r allele, like that for aleurone color, is reduced in R^rR^{st} individuals.

Brink and Mikula (1958) found that if seedlings were grown at 90°F less pigment was developed in the coleoptiles and leaf sheaths of $R^{r'}r^g$ than of R^rr^g control plants. Change in seedling root pigmentation, however, was not demonstrable by this procedure. This evidence and the fact that fully grown $R^{r'}r^g$ plants sometimes show markedly reduced glume and anther color, as compared with control R^rr^g individuals, makes it clear that expression of both seed and plant color components of the R^r allele are affected by the paramutation process.

Certain R^g alleles derived from strains originally collected from Indian reservations in the United States condition green anthers and red roots. Bray (1964) observed that following testcrosses on r^gr^g ♀ ♀ of R^gR^{st} plants carrying one of these factors, the R^gr^g offspring showed marked reduction of anthocyanin formation in both seeds and roots. These alleles, however, may not carry distinct seed and plant color determinants. Bray observed that when such R^g factors mutated to colorless aleurone the potentiality for root pigmentation was simultaneously lost.

The Origin and Geographic Distribution of Paramutable and Nonparamutable R Alleles

Tests of numerous North and South American forms and of a few forms from elsewhere show that R alleles giving self-colored aleurone when homozygous fall into two well-defined groups, paramutable and nonparamutable. The latter class appears to be limited in distribution to Ecuador, Peru, Bolivia, and Chile. All such alleles obtained from other parts of the world, including the United States, Canada, Guatemala, Argentina, Turkey, India, and Ethiopia, are paramutable on passage through heterozygotes with stippled.

The paramutable class of R alleles, which will be termed group A here, are characteristically somewhat weaker in aleurone pigment-producing action than those in the nonparamutable or B group. Many of them give mottled aleurone in single dose. This feature, however, is not strictly diagnostic, since the mottling occasionally ranges into self-color. Two characteristics in addition to sensitivity to paramutation in R R^{st} plants attest to the metastability of group A alleles: (1) pigmenting action is slightly enhanced on passage through R r heterozygotes, and (2) heritable change may occur when these alleles are made heterozygous with each other.

The nonparamutagenic alleles regularly give self-colored aleurone in single dose. They do not undergo change in level of R action in heterozygotes with stippled, marbled, or other alleles, whether overtly paramutagenic or nonparamutagenic. That is to say, group B alleles are both strong in aleurone-pigmenting action and stable. Many group B alleles are paramutagenic at one or another level in heterozygotes with representatives of group A.

It is important to note, however, that within group B is a subclass of self-colored alleles that is neither paramutable nor paramutagenic. One may reasonably assume that this subclass represents the primitive condition at the locus. It is postulated that the paramutagenicity of other group B alleles is an acquired property, as is the paramutability of group A factors also.

Likewise, it appears that the components of the stippled and marbled alleles that condition aleurone spotting also are adventive to the locus and are distinct from the elements involved in R paramutation.

R paramutation when looked at from this point of view involves a dichotomy in evolution of the R locus. From the conventional condition, exemplified in the present instance by nonparamutable, nonparamutagenic alleles now occurring in races indigenous to Ecuador, Peru, Bolivia, and Chile, two categories of R loci have arisen by acquisition of elements of two different kinds, possibly by transposition from positions elsewhere in the genome. One element conferred paramutagenicity on the locus, without affecting aleurone pigment-producing action locally. So far as our tests extend, R loci of this kind are restricted in distribution to certain maize races in the Andean region. A second element, also adventive to the locus, rendered other R alleles paramutable in heterozygotes with certain representatives of the Andean group. In addition to rendering the R locus sensitive to paramutation in heterozygotes with overtly paramutagenic factors this element conferred metastability on the R locus, one reflection of which is a tendency to give mottled aleurone in single dose. R alleles of this class appear to be of general occurrence outside the Andean region.

R Action in Structurally Altered Chromosome 10

The R locus lies in the distal half of the long arm of chromosome 10. Its position there is not known precisely, but the available data suggest the vicinity of .7. Brink and Blackwood (1961), Brink and Notani (1961), and Brink (1961) tested the effect on R action of three reciprocal translocations (T) involving breaks in this general region. The reciprocal translocations used and the respective breakpoints, according to Longley (1961), were: T2-10a(2L.16 and 10L.55), T4-10b(4L.15 and 10L.60), and T9-10a(9L.14 and 10L.92). The chromosome 10 breakpoints in T2-10a and T4-10b are proximal to R and show approximately 9% recombination with the locus. The T9-10a reciprocal translocation involves a break distal to R, and the amount of recombination in this case is about 5%. The recombination values are based on tests with reciprocal translocation heterozygotes in which crossing-over is markedly reduced in the vicinity of the breakpoints. It may be inferred, therefore, that the break-point in each case is well removed from the R locus.

Following introduction of the standard R^r allele from stock cultures into the respective structurally altered chromosomes 10, by crossing-over, the translocation lines were propagated for two generations or more as TR^r/r^r heterozygotes before the tests for effect on R^r action were begun.

The principal conclusions reached in this study are summarized as follows:

(1) The effects on R^r in terms of aleurone-pigmenting action and sensitivity to paramutation of the two reciprocal translocations, T2-10a and T4-10b, involving breaks in L10 proximal to R and T9-10a, in which the break is distal to R, were essentially alike.

(2) Two changes in R^r action in the structurally altered chromosomes were observed: (*a*) the aleurone pigment-producing potential of R^r was enhanced, and (*b*) the allele became relatively insensitive to paramutation in TR^r/R^{st} heterozygotes.

(3) Supplementary tests showed no effect on R^r action in the first generation following introduction of R^r into a reciprocally translocated chromosome and also that the enhanced pigmenting action and comparative insensitivity to paramutation of R^r in a translocated chromosome was retained for at least one generation following return of the allele, by crossing-over, into a normal chromosome 10. Thus, there was a lag in the occurrence of change in R^r action when R^r was transferred either in or out of the structurally altered chromosome.

(4) Passage of an enhanced TR^r through a heterozygote with a sensitive R^g on a normal chromosome derived directly from $R^g R^g$ stock cultures reduced the pigment-producing action of the enhanced R^r allele and also increased sensitivity to paramutation in TR^r/R^{st} plants.

It was observed in these experiments that the $R^r r^g r^g$ kernels resulting from testcrosses of control F_1 $R^r r^r$ plants were slightly but significantly darker then those from corresponding matings involving $R^r R^r$ stock culture plants (Brink and Blackwood, 1961). The possible importance of this difference was discounted at the time, in view of the additional observation that R^r derived from F_1 $R^r r^r$ *and* $R^r R^r$ plants appeared to be equally sensitive to paramutation in $R^r R^{st}$ individuals. It was later realized that continued heterozygosity for r^r through several generations, rather than only one, might render R^r relatively insensitive to paramutation. If this were the case then the F_1 $R^r r^r$ plants that were used as controls in testing for the effects of reciprocal translocations on R^r action in TR^r/r^r plants with a longer history of heterozygosity for r^r were inadequate for the purpose.

The uncertainty concerning validity of the original conclusion that translocations involving breaks in the long arm of chromosome 10 in themselves enhanced R^r action and rendered the allele less sensitive to paramutation led to repetition of the experiment with $R^r r^r$ control plants having similar histories of heterozygosity for r^r as the TR^r/r^r individuals. Three sets of stocks were used, carrying the T2-10a translocation and R^r alleles originally derived from Argentina, Turkey, and Oklahoma strains, respectively. Testcrosses on $r^g r^g$ ♀ ♀ of TR^r/R^{st} and $R^r R^{st}$ control ♂ ♂ were made through four generations. That is to say, the three parental sets of TR^r/r^r and control $R^r r^r$ lines were advanced by successive matings to $r^r r^r$ plants through four generations and also were crossed in each generation to $R^{st} R^{st}$ individuals for the paramutability tests. Two control $R^r R^{st}$ and two TR^r/R^{st} families (each family based on a single ear) for each of the R^r alleles were tested in generations 1 and 2. No fewer than four and up to ten families were sampled in each group in generations 3 and 4, except in the case of the Oklahoma R^r allele, which was not represented in generation 4.

The aleurone color scores for the $R^{r'} r^g r^g$ kernels representing the $r^g r^g$ ♀ × TR^r/R^{st} ♂ testcrosses exceeded those for the control $r^g r^g$ ♀ × $R^r R^{st}$ ♂ testcrosses in all four generations in the case of the Argentina R^r allele. The differences were small in generations 1 and 2, but exceeded one class interval, on the 1–7 scale, in generations 3 and 4. In none of the 18 control $R^r R^{st}$ families sampled was it found that R^r had become markedly insensitive to paramutation.

There was no evidence that the translocation reduced sensitivity of the Turkey R^r allele to paramutation in generations 1 and 2, but a pronounced influence was in evidence in generations 3 and 4. One generation 3 control family in this case gave a mean color score of 5.17, which was equal to the mean score (5.16) for the highest corresponding $TR^r/$ R^{st} family. On the other hand, no overlapping of the two sets of mean scores was observed in generation 4, in which four families of each kind were tested.

One of the two control families tested in generation 1 in the Oklahoma R^r series gave a mean color score of 5.30. This is a clear case of an R^r allele that has become relatively insensitive to paramutation when carried on a structurally normal chromosome 10. It is an exception, however, to the general rule. The $R^{r'}$ $r^g r^g$ testcross kernels in the generation 2 test of the Oklahoma R^r allele gave a mean score of 3.25 in the control matings and 5.22 in the case of the TR^r/R^{st} parents. The corresponding values for generation 3 were 3.14 and 5.14, respectively. This R^r allele, therefore, like the other two tested, was less sensitive to paramutation in R^{st} heterozygotes when carried in a T2-10a, rather than a structurally normal, chromosome 10.

These results confirm the conclusion deduced from the earlier experiments of this kind, namely, that sensitivity of R^r to paramutation is significantly influenced by a structural change in the long arm of chromosome 10 well removed from the R locus itself. Acquisition of such insensitivity appears to be irregular as the generations progress. Whether occurrence of the change in R^r action associated with a reciprocal translocation is conditional upon maintenance of the allele in a heterozygous condition with r^r is not known. There is evidence from other sources that standard R^r is less stable in $R^r r^r$ then in $R^r R^r$ plants.

Paramutability of R^r When Carried by Chromosome K10

Tests by Brink and Weyers (1960) disclosed that the standard R^r allele becomes relatively insensitive to paramutation in R^{st} heterozygotes when inserted in a chromosome 10 carrying a large, nearly terminal, heterochromatic knob on the long arm. The knob strongly depresses crossingover in this region and gives 1–2% recombination with the R locus. It causes characteristic meiotic irregularities in K10/10 heterozygotes (Rhoades, 1952), but it was found that effect of the knob on paramutation was independent of these disturbances.

Limited tests showed that the paramutagenic action of stippled was somewhat lower in R^r/R^{st}K10 than in $R^r R^{st}$ plants, but the difference was not statistically significant.

Brink and Weyers (1960) tested the paramutability of a single R^r allele recovered as a crossover in a normal chromosome from an R^rK10/r^r plant. Testcrosses on $r^g r^g$ ♀ ♀ of progeny from the R^r/r^r crossover plant and of a noncrossover R^rK10/r^r sib, following pollination by a common

$R^{mb}R^{mb}$ individual, gave mean color scores for the $R^r r^g r^g$ kernels of 3.46 and 5.10, respectively. This result suggested that the sensitivity of R^r to paramutation increased if the allele was returned from a knobbed to a normal chromosome 10.

Since this observation was made, Brink (1963) recovered eleven additional R^r crossovers from $R^r K10/r^r$ plants in an $R^r K10/r^r$ ♀ $\times$ $R^{st} R^{st}$ ♂ detasseling plot and then evaluated them for sensitivity to paramutation. Four sib, noncrossover $R^r K/R^{st}$ plants were used as controls for each of the $R^r R^{st}$ crossovers tested. The crossover R^r alleles were found to be more sensitive to paramutation in nine of the eleven paired comparisons, and the difference was in the opposite direction in two cases. The mean difference between the eleven pairs of scores was 0.66 class intervals on the 1–7 color scale. The probability of obtaining a difference of this size by chance alone lies between 1 and 2.5%. These data, therefore, also suggest that when R^r is returned from a K10 to a normal chromosome 10 the sensitivity of the allele to paramutation is increased.

Level of R Action in Relation to Mode of Sexual Transmission

It is an extraordinary fact that the level of R action is differentially affected by transmission of the allele through male and female gametophytes produced by the same plant.

Many R alleles, including that termed standard R^r in our collection, give markedly different phenotypes in reciprocal crosses with colorless aleurone plants. The Rrr kernels resulting from rr ♀ $\times$ RR ♂ matings are mottled; the RRr seeds from $R R$ ♀ $\times$ rr ♂ are solidly pigmented. It has been commonly thought that the difference was due to the dosage of R in the endosperm nuclei in the two cases. The primary endosperm nucleus in maize, as in most flowering plants, is a fusion product of two haploid polar nuclei of maternal origin with a haploid sperm. $RR \times rr$ reciprocal crosses, therefore, yield endosperms with two doses or one dose of R, according to the direction of the cross. An unpublished observation made by Roman several years ago and a recent analysis by Kermicle (1963) show, however, that the marked difference in pigmentation following reciprocal crosses between RR and rr is not due to R dosage. Kermicle's evidence proves that a given R allele transmitted through a male gametophyte to the endosperm regularly has a lower pigment-producing potential than when transmitted through the female gametophyte.

The way was opened for Kermicle's study by Roman's analysis (1947,

1948) of the genetic behavior of reciprocal translocations between heterochromatic B type and normal chromosomes in maize. Roman observed
that in plants carrying the TB-4a interchange the B⁴ chromosome, which
possesses the centromere and proximal third of the B type chromosome,
undergoes nondisjunction at the second pollen grain mitosis in a high

FIG. 5. Difference in aleurone pigmentation following reciprocal crosses between
(a) r^gr^g and (b) $10^{(r^g)}/10^B/B^{10(R^{r'})}$ plants. Upper ear is from a (b) ♀ × (a) ♂ mating.
The colored kernels are of $R^{r'}R^{r'}/r^g$ endosperm constitution and are mostly self-colored.
The lower ear is from an (a) ♀ × (b) ♂ mating. Approximately two-fifths of the
colored kernels have $r^gr^g/R^{r'}R^{r'}$ endosperms, and three-fifths are $r^gr^g/R^{r'}$. No difference
was found in pigmentation of these two kernel classes (Kermicle, 1963).

proportion of the cases, with the result that the two gametes formed
within the pollen grain differ from each other. One carries the B⁴
chromosome in duplicate, and the other is deficient in this chromosome.
Roman demonstrated that both sperm are functional and that the
hyperploid gamete preferentially fertilizes the egg. This mechanism
provides a means of introducing into the endosperm via the pollen two
representatives of a given gene instead of only one, as normally occurs.

One may then compare at the same dosage level the effects during endosperm development of male and female transmission of a gene. Kermicle (1963) used a reciprocal translocation between a heterochromatic B chromosome and chromosome 10, termed TB-10a, in which the breakpoint in chromosome 10 is at .35 in the long arm proximal to the R locus (Roman and Ullstrup, 1951). Male transmission of the B^{10} chromosome was found to correspond closely to that of the B^4 chromosome earlier studied by Roman.

In summarizing the results of Kermicle's study of the effect on endosperm pigmentation of male and female transmissions of R, as presented in a recent doctoral thesis, the convention will be adopted of writing endosperm genotypes with the R alleles of female origin before and those of male origin after a diagonal line.

Kermicle found that the effect of mode of transmission on level of R action in the endosperm was significantly greater if the R allele was in paramutant, rather than standard, form. TB-10a R^r/r^g plants carrying an R^r allele in standard form were crossed reciprocally with $r^g r^g$ individuals. The aleurone color scores for the $r^g r^g/R^r$ *and* $r^g r^g/R^r R^r$ kernels resulting from the $r^g r^g$ ♀ $\times$ TB-10a R^r/r^r ♂ matings were 6.15 and 6.45, respectively, on the 1–7 scale. The corresponding value for the $R^r R^r/r^g$ seeds resulting from the reciprocal cross, TB-10a R^r/r^r ♀ $\times$ $r^g R^g$ ♂, was 7.00 (self-colored). In contrast, the $r^g r^g/R^{r'}$ and $r^g r^g/R^{r'} R^{r'}$ kernels from $r^g r^g$ ♀ $\times$ TB-10a R^r/R^{st} testcrosses gave scores of 3.95 and 3.79, respectively. The reciprocal mating, TB-10a R/R^{st} ♀ $\times$ $r^g r^g$ ♂, yielded $R^{r'} R^{r'}/r^g$ seeds with an average score of 6.96. (See Fig. 5.)

It is evident from these latter results that two doses of paramutant $R^{r'}$ transmitted to the endosperm via the male gametophyte produce no more pigment than one dose of $R^{r'}$ received by the same route. Furthermore, in both these cases pigmentation is at a much lower level than in $R^{r'} R^{r'}/r^g$ seeds in which $R^{r'}$ has been conveyed to the endosperm through the female gametophyte.

Two lines of evidence support the conclusion that r^g is amorphic in this relation and so is unimportant in comparing color grade in $rr/R^r R^r$ and $R^r R^r/r$ kernels. Aleurone tissue that was hemizygous for $R^{r'}$, following R^g/R-deficient ♀ $\times$ $R^r R^{st}$ ♂ matings, was found to be weakly mottled, as in $R^{r'} r^g r^g$ seeds resulting from $r^g r^g$ ♀ $\times$ $R^r R^{st}$ ♂ crosses. Second, $R^{r'} R^{r'}/r^g r^g$ kernels resulting from $R^{r'} R^{r'}$ ♀ $\times$ TB-10a $r^g r^g$ ♂ matings were found to be self-colored, in contrast to $r^g r^g/R^{r'} R^{r'}$ seeds from $r^g r^g$ ♀ $\times$ TB-10a $R^{r'}/r^r$ ♂ matings, which were weakly colored. The endosperm genotypes are identical in these two cases, and so the low color grade in the latter instance can not be attributed to a depressing effect of two r^g alleles in a nucleus on $R^{r'}$ expression.

The question may be asked whether the large difference in color grade of the $r^g r^g / R^{r'} R^{r'}$ and $R^{r'} R^{r'} / r^g r^g$ kernels just mentioned is due to the fact that the former is borne on $r^g r^g$ and the latter on $R^{r'} R^{r'}$ plants. Kermicle tested this possibility by pollinating $r^g r^g$ and $R^g r^g$ plants with individual $R^{g'} R^{g'}$ ♂ ♂ and then comparing aleurone color of the two resulting sets of $R^{g'} r^g r^g$ seeds. The mean score for the $R^{g'} r^g r^g$ seeds borne on $R^r r^g$ ♀ ♀ was 4.87 and that of the kernels produced on $r^g r^g$ individuals was 5.01. The difference in score is not statistically significant and, moreover, is in the direction opposite to that expected if the self-colored condition of $R^r R^r / r^g r^g$ kernels resulting from $R^r R^r$ ♀ × TB-10a r^g / r^g ♂ matings were due to presence of R^r in the maternal parent.

Kermicle found also that the TB-10a translocation per se had no effect on $R^{r'}$ expression.

Persistence in subsequent generations of the difference in level of R action associated with mode of transmission by the parent is currently under study. A further question of basic interest for the paramutation problem on which adequate data are not yet available is whether the difference in R action in question applies to paramutable, but not to nonparamutable, R alleles.

Effects on R^r and R^{st} of High Energy Irradiation

Preliminary results reported by Linden (1963) from experiments carried out at the Puerto Rico Nuclear Center, Mayaguez, indicate that high energy irradiation of R^r and R^{st} pollen often changes the paragenetic properties of these alleles. Tassels from $R^r R^r$ and $R^{st} R^{st}$ plants in the pollen-shedding stage were given 2000 r from a gamma source. Irradiated R^r and R^{st} pollen collected the next day was placed on the silks of untreated $R^{st} R^{st}$ and $R^r R^r$ individuals, respectively. Irradiation of R^r pollen before crossing to a normal stippled stock led to considerable heterogeneity among the F_1 offspring, as was manifested after mating the latter to $r^g r^g$ ♀ ♀. No R^r kernels of paramutant phenotype appeared on about 10% of the testcross ears, and pronounced but less striking evidence of interference with the paramutation process was observed in an additional 15–20% of the cases. Complete inactivation of R^{st} as a paramutagenic allele was not observed following irradiation of R^{st} pollen, but seeming reductions in paramutagenicity occurred in several instances. A useful new tool for the study of paramutation will be available if

Linden's preliminary findings that the radiosensitivity of R^r and R^{st} to paragenetic change is much higher than to mutation are confirmed.

Is a Gene-Dependent Cytoplasmic Particle Associated with R Paramutation?

The mechanism whereby the R^r allele invariably is changed during plant development to a paramutant form, $R^{r'}$, in response to presence in the same cells of R^{st} or other paramutagenic alleles, remains unknown. One might suppose that particles are produced by the R^{st} gene that are released into the cytoplasm and are then incorporated at the R locus in the homologous chromosome where they reproduce in phase and partially repress R action. Tests recently made by Brink and associates (1964), for occurrence of such a gene-dependent particle in the cytoplasm, however, gave a negative result. It was argued that if paramutation is mediated in this way, transmission of the particle to the endosperm, independently of the gene that produces it, might occur via the female gametophyte. The endosperm provides favorable conditions for the early detection of paramutation after fertilization. It is the product of secondary fertilization and matures in the seed. Furthermore, it has been shown, as previously noted, that a paramutant aleurone phenotype results if a sensitive R gene is introduced via the pollen into an endosperm that has received a strongly paramutagenic allele from the pistillate parent. The question at issue is whether, in such a case, the paramutagenic allele functions directly in the developing tissue or the change in R-pigment-producing action is a response to a particular cytoplasmic element formed in the parent by the paramutagenic allele which is then passively transmitted in effective concentration through the female gametophyte to the endosperm? Several experiments were made to test the latter possibility the results of one of which will be presented here to illustrate the negative results observed.

A special stock, designated $4\text{-}R_6^{g'}R_6^{g'}$, served as the staminate parent in the testcrosses in question. The strain carries an $R^{g'}$ allele, originally derived by mutation from standard R^r, whose aleurone-pigmenting action had been moderately reduced by passage through an R^{st} heterozygote and then stabilized by four generations of self-fertilization. Earlier tests had shown that $R_6^{g'}$ in this conditioned form was especially suitable for detecting further change in aleurone-pigmenting action. The genotypes of the three pistillate parents used in the testcrosses were $R_1^g/r\text{-}x_1$, $R_{61}^{sc}/r\text{-}x_1$, and $R_{132}^{sc}/r\text{-}x_1$. Both R_1^g and R_{61}^{sc} are nonparamutagenic. R_{132}^{sc}, on the other hand, is strongly paramutagenic. The r-x_1 symbol represents an R deficiency that is regularly female transmissible. The three classes of hemizygotes were mated to $R_6^{g'} R_6^{g'}$ in sets of one individual each; each set received pollen from a single $R_6^{g'} R_6^{g'}$ plant.

The question posed in this experiment was whether the $R_6^{g'}/r$-x_1/r-x_1 kernels resulting from the R_{132}^{sc}/r-x_1 ♀ × $R_6^{g'} R_6^{g'}$ ♂ testcross, in which the pistillate parent carried the strongly paramutagenic R_{132}^{sc} allele, would be

TABLE III

MEAN ALEURONE COLOR SCORES OF THE $R_6^{g'}/r$-x_1/r-x_1 KERNELS RESULTING FROM MATING 4-$R_6^{g'} R_6^{g'}$ ♂ ♂ TO R_1^g/r-x_1, R_{61}^{sc}/r-x_1, AND R_{132}^{sc}/r-x_1 ♀ ♀, RESPECTIVELY (R_{132}^{sc} IS STRONGLY PARAMUTAGENIC; R_1^g AND R_{61}^{sc} ARE NONPARAMUTAGENIC)

4-$R_6^{g'} R_6^{g'}$ ♂ plant number	Genotype of ♀ parent		
	R_1^g/r-x_1	R_{61}^{sc}/r-x_1	R_{132}^{sc}/r-x_1
T1281-1	4.44	4.54	5.08
T1281-2	4.76	5.02	4.84
T1281-6	4.86	5.20	5.08
T1281-10	4.22	5.22	4.54
T1281-12	4.64	4.18	4.76
T1281-13	5.08	4.86	4.20
T1281-14	5.02	4.14	4.66
T1281-15	4.88	4.20	4.80
T1281-16	4.16	4.44	5.00
T1281-17	4.12	4.82	4.10
T1281-19	4.20	4.22	4.50
T1281-20	4.36	4.10	4.26
T1281-22	4.94	4.56	4.56
T1281-23	4.50	4.24	4.22
T1281-24	4.10	4.22	4.48
T1281-25	4.68	4.20	4.18
Mean	4.57	4.51	4.58

less pigmented than the same class of kernels from the other two matings in each of which the female parent genotypes carried a nonparamutagenic R allele. A positive result would support the assumption that the R_{132}^{sc} allele alone had formed paramutagenic particles that had been transmitted to the endosperm via the r-x_1 (R-deficient) female gametophyte. The results of the three sets of testcrosses are summarized in Table III.

The data in Table III show that the mean color scores for the $R_6^{g'}/r$-x_1/r-x_1 kernels from the three kinds of testcrosses are almost identical. The endosperms carrying cytoplasm derived from the female parent possessing a strongly paramutagenic allele are pigmented at the same level as those of the two controls. If, therefore, paramutation is mediated in the sporophyte by a gene-dependent particle that is released into the cytoplasm, the particle is not detectable by a change in level of action of a newly introduced, sensitive R gene in the endosperm progeny receiving such cytoplasm, but lacking the paramutagenic allele.

Paramutation in Other Organisms

The first case described of irregular genetic behavior recognizable now as due to paramutation is the rabbit ear rogue in garden peas. It is of interest that this anomaly was one of the exceptions to Mendelism underlying the skepticism which Bateson (1926) maintained to the end of his career regarding adequacy of the classic form of the chromosome theory of heredity.

The rabbit ear rogue, in which leaflets and stipules are conspicuously narrowed, occurs sporadically in many cultivated pea varieties. Bateson and Pellew (1916, 1920) showed that rogues bred true and that, when rogues were crossed with type plants and the hybrids were then allowed to self-pollinate, the offspring often were mostly, and sometimes exclusively, rogues. F_1 plants were observed whose phenotype in early developmental stages was intermediate between rogue and type, but which became patently rogue at the upper nodes. The progressive phenotypic change in such individuals was shown to be associated with a corresponding increase in the proportion of rogue offspring from seeds borne at successively higher nodes. Another remarkable observation made was that, as the stem of a heterozygous plant was ascended, the proportion of gametes carrying the rogue factor appeared to increase more rapidly on the male than on the female side (Bateson, 1926).

Brotherton (1923, 1924) confirmed the atypical breeding behavior of rogues and offered an explanation of the phenomenon in terms of "mass somatic mutation" in rogue $\times$ type heterozygotes. Primary rogues were assumed to arise in a pea variety by infrequent mutation of a single gene x to X. In the vegetative cells of Xx hybrids, x was extremely unstable and usually mutated to X before meiosis occurred.. An allele of the x gene, called x_1 was identified in Mummy, a nonrogue producing variety, that rarely mutated to X in Xx_1 plants.

Lilienfeld (1929) found among *Malva parviflora* plants grown from seed collected in the wild a form with deeply incised leaves, termed *laciniata*. Crosses between true wild type and *laciniata*, or mutants from *laciniata,* gave three wild type to one mutant in F_2. Homozygous mutants of a given kind usually bred true. F_1 hybrids between different mutants, on the other hand, were "heterostatic." For example, *laciniata* changed progressively in the direction of its partner in F_1 hybrids with normal - 2, a mutant from *laciniata* conditioning nonincised leaves and thus resembling wild type phenotypically. F_1 plants, which were intermediate in phenotype initially, became progressively more normal in appearance as development proceeded. Progeny tests, using seed from different branches, showed that hand in hand with the morphological transformation action of the *laciniata* allele changed in the direction of normal - 2.

The *cruciata* character in *Oenothera,* distinguished by flowers in the form of a slender cross, does not obey classic genetic rules, although it is inherited as a simple Mendelian recessive in the closely related genus *Epilobium.* Renner (1937, 1959), on the basis of studies extending over more than 20 years, postulated that in *Oenothera* a single locus was involved at which, however, an unusual phenomenon, termed "somatic conversion," occurred whereby the action of one allele in a heterozygote was heritably altered in the direction of the other during plant development. Only normal offspring appeared when a normal plant was selfed or was crossed with another normal. Similarly, *cruciata* $\times$ *cruciata,* or *cruciata* selfed, yielded only *cruciata* progeny, although expression of the character varied depending upon the source of the parents. Heterozygotes between normal and *cruciata,* of whatever lineage, collectively designated *Cr cr,* were always inconstant. Sectoring frequently occurred in these F_1 hybrids. Renner found (as he notes deVries had also reported much earlier) that in such cases the distribution of F_1 phenotypes varied in accordance with the form of the flowers that produced the seed, namely, *cruciata,* intermediate, or normal. Usually the change in a *Cr cr* plant was in the *cr* (cruciata) allele toward *Cr* (normal). Sometimes, however, *Cr* was altered in the direction of *cr.* Thus both *Cr* and *cr* were shown to be labile. Renner points out that somatic conversion in *Oenothera* probably has no relation to the meiotic phenomena in *Saccharomyces, Neurospora,* and *Aspergillus* to which the term conversion also has been applied.

Hagemann (1961 a, b) has reported the occurrence in *Lycopersicon esculentum* of a locus (*sulfuria*), conditioning chlorophyll formation, at which paramutation occurs. Groups of alleles were identified at the locus, the members of which were alike in phenotypic effect as homozygotes. In heterozygotes with normal, however, the alleles within each group gave rise to quite unlike percentages of leaf mottling as a result of "somatic conversion." In *sulfuria-pura*/normal heterozygotes, for example, different alleles varied in conversion activity from 0.5 to 100%. Hagemann demonstrated that the forms to which the normal allele is changed in heterozygotes with a given paramutagenic allele are not equivalent, but vary considerably.

Three alleles are known at the B locus on chromosome 2 in maize, B, B^{w}, and b, respectively, effecting intense, weak, and no (or little) anthocyanin formation in husks, sheaths, and culm. Coe (1959) found two weakly colored plants in a family of 140 otherwise BB individuals (intense sun red) which gave only weakly colored descendants on continuous selfing. Crosses between the newly arisen weak mutant, termed B', and intense plants (BB) yielded exclusively weak offspring in F_1 and F_2. The F_1 hybrid between $B'B'$ and bb plants was weak and on self-pollination gave weaks and greens in a 3:1 ratio. $B'b \times BB$ matings resulted in equal numbers of $B'B'$ (weak) and Bb (intense) offspring. Other chromosome 2 markers present in these families assorted regularly. Recurrence of B' mutants was observed occasionally in the foundation BB stock, but not in all sublines. Coe concludes that in BB' heterozygotes the B' allele "converts" B to B', which then persists in the new form.

Coe (1961a) found no evidence for clustering on the ear of new B' mutants in heterozygotes between a stable B factor and the B which was known to give rise to such mutants occasionally. He concluded from this result that the mutation of B to B' in stock BB plants probably originates at meiosis (Such primary mutation is to be distinguished, of course, from the change of B to B' in heterozygotes between BB and $B'B'$ individuals that occurs in somatic cells).

Twenty haploid offspring from matings in which $B'B'$ plants were used as pistillate parents in crosses with BB ♂ ♂ were found by Coe (1961b) to be weakly colored, like their diploid sibs. Four haploids obtained from BB ♀ $\times$ $B'B'$ ♂ matings, on the other hand, were intensely pigmented. Since the central nucleus of the female gametophyte is fertilized in ovules in which the embryo develops parthenogenetically from the egg to give a haploid plant, Coe concludes that the change of B to B' does not involve an infectious agent that could be transmitted in the developing seed from endosperm to embryo.

Observations by Anderson-Kottö and Gairdner (1936) on the inheritance of apospory in *Scolopendrium vulgare* (*Phyllitis scolopendrium*) suggests the occurrence of paramutation in this ornamental fern. These investigators reported the chromosome number of the species to be $n = 30$, $2n = 60$. Manton (1950) found in other stocks that the values were $n = 36$, $2n = 72$. Since chromosome number is the variable with which we are concerned here, some uncertainty attaches to the validity of the data upon which Anderson-Kottö and Gairdner's unusual claims rest. The writer has been told that the strains used by these investigators have been lost, so that reexamination of the original material is now impossible.

Anderson-Kottö and Gairdner isolated a mutant termed "peculiar," conditioned by a single recessive factor, among the offspring of a normal sporophyte of the variety *crispum muricatum*. Peculiar plants are much smaller than normal ones. Fully grown fronds are several cell-layers thick; but apart from the veins, the leaf blade consists of prothallial tissue only. A distinctive feature is the outgrowth of the leaf edge into a prothallial sheet upon which rhizoids, archegonia, and antheridia are formed. This structure upon coming in contact with soil establishes itself independently of the parent sporophyte. The gametophyte of aposporous origin is sexually functional and gives rise to sporophytes of the peculiar phenotype after fertilization.

Anderson-Kottö and Gairdner observed that, among the progeny of peculiar homozygotes, sporophytes regularly occurred with fewer than twice the number of chromosomes present in the parent gametophyte. It was considered probable that in gamete formation part of the nuclear divisions were regularly meiotic, others regularly mitotic, and that the rest were abnormally meiotic, thus giving rise to sex cells with chromosome numbers ranging between 30 and 60.

The surprising observation was made that homozygous normal segregates from reciprocal hybrids between peculiar and normal plants likewise invariably displayed the capacity to form sex cells with fewer than the expected chromosome number. F_1 sporophytes from reciprocal crosses were identical in this respect. The investigators assumed that the cytological irregularities in sex-cell formation shown by the extracted normals were due to an abnormal cytoplasmic condition induced by the peculiar gene in the heterozygote. This is a possible explanation of the phenomenon, but it is scarcely reconcilable with the further claim made, namely, that little or no cytoplasm is transmitted to the zygote by the sperm. An alternative explanation, not mentioned by the investigators, is that in heterozygotes between peculiar and normal plants the normal allele invariably acquires as a response to its partner in the same nucleus the capacity to disturb chromosome behavior in sex-cell formation.

Sandler, *et al.* (1959) encountered a phenomenon in *Drosophila melanogaster,* termed segregation-distortion, that is parallel in certain respects to paramutation in plants. Directed changes arose in certain genotypes affecting the distribution of chromosome II through sperm that were heritable in the absence of the genetic agent which effected the changes initially. A chromosome II originally derived from a stock of wild flies was found to be transmitted by heterozygous males in ratios as high as 20:1 in some instances, instead of 1:1. Subsequent studies (references in Sandler and Rosenfeld, 1962) disclosed that *SD* is genetically unstable in certain genotypes and stable in others. Furthermore, sensitivity of an *SD+* allele can be changed by passing the factor through heterozygotes with an insensitive allele for one generation or more. Also, when *SD* males are aged, the segregation ratios which they give are genetically altered. Likewise, *SD* was found to induce a specific heritable change in the X chromosome which acted to suppress segregation-distortion in certain genotypes.

Twenty years ago Noujdin (1944) reported that homozygosity and heterozygosity for the scute-8 inversion in *Drosophila melanogaster* led to differences in the expression of the yellow and achaete genes, located near one of the breakpoints, that persisted through a few generations. Noujdin (1946) also described heritable alterations of the wild-type allele of bobbed bristles toward recessiveness that were believed to have arisen in another genotype containing a structurally modified X chromosome and heterochromatin in excess of the normal complement.

Several one-generation parental effects on position-effect variegation in *Drosophila melanogaster* have been reported by Spofford (1959, 1961). Some of these can reasonably be attributed to the maternal cytoplasm, but in others the evidence suggests nuclear changes. The cellular basis of the changes is difficult to determine in these cases because of the transitory nature of the phenotypic effects.

Summary and Discussion

Particular attention will be directed to five groups of facts in an attempt to bring to focus the diverse evidence presented concerning paramutation at the *R* locus in maize.

(1) *R* alleles which, when homozygous, condition self-colored aleurone fall into two categories with reference to paramutation: A, paramutable; and B, nonparamutable. The B category may be divided into two subclasses, one of which is paramutagenic and the other nonparamutagenic. The B class of alleles appears to be limited in distribution to races indigenous to Ecuador, Peru, Bolivia, and Chile. Alleles of the other class are of general distribution outside the Andean region.

(2) Alleles in category A are characteristically metastable. Their level of action may be heritably altered in either direction and in different ways. The most striking change observed is the marked reduction in aleurone-pigmenting action that occurs when standard R^r, or a like representative of the A category, is passed through a heterozygote with stippled, marbled, or a highly paramutagenic, self-colored mutant from either of these spotting factors. A change in the opposite direction occurs, however, if an A-type allele is propagated in $R^r r^r$ plants. R action is enhanced in this case, as compared with that of R in stock RR cultures. It has not been determined whether enhancement also occurs in R/R-deficient individuals. Kermicle showed, however, that the paramutant form of R^r may change autonomously. He observed that $R^{r'}$ alleles derived directly from $R^r R^{st}$ plants revert partially toward the standard level of action in $R^{r'}/R$-deficient hemizygotes, as well as in $R^{r'} R^{r'}$, $R^{r'} R^r$, $R^{r'} r^r$, and $R^{r'} r^g$ individuals. Styles has observed recently that R^r and R^g alleles of category A derived from stock cultures may change slightly in level of action in heterozygotes with each other. Structural changes in the long arm of chromosome 10, in which the R locus lies, enhance R-pigmenting action and also render the allele less sensitive to paramutation in R^{st} heterozygotes. Insertion of a class A allele into a chromosome 10 carrying a large, nearly terminal, heterochromatic knob also leads to decreased sensitivity to paramutation. Finally, as Kermicle has demonstrated, there is a marked difference in level of R or R' action in the immediately resulting endosperm depending on transmission of the factor to the tissue through the male or the female gametophyte. Limitation of this characteristic to class A alleles and heritability of the difference through the sporophyte are still open questions.

(3) The levels of action of a given paramutable R allele are found to vary continuously following passage of the factor through a series of heterozygotes carrying appropriately chosen paramutagenic alleles. By the same token, it is evident that, within class B, alleles occur that vary continuously in paramutagenicity.

(4) Heritable changes in level of pigmenting action of paramutable R alleles arise in somatic cells. McWhirter showed that the change is progressive in successive generations under appropriate conditions. It is probably progressive during development of the individual also. The latter relation has not been directly demonstrated in maize, but it is known to hold for paramutation in *Pisum, Malva,* and *Oenothera.*

(5) A given paramutagenic, class B allele is stable for the level of paramutagenic action. Changes in paramutagenicity, however, occasionally

occur. Those which have been studied were associated with mutations of stippled to self-colored aleurone. Since these mutants occur in $R^{st}R^{st}$ plants as single self-colored kernels on otherwise stippled ears, the change may take place at meiosis. Such changes can occur, however, without recombination of outside markers in the R region.

The basis of paramutation is a matter of speculation. A working hypothesis may be formulated, however, that encompasses the available evidence and, at the same time, serves to relate paramutation to certain other genetic phenomena that appear to be of similar importance for chromosome organization.

The writer (Brink, 1964) has reviewed elsewhere the evidence from variegated position effects in *Drosophila,* unstable alleles in maize, and the mottled expression of sex-linked characters in the female of mammals in terms of a hypothesis that may be termed genetic repression by pycnosis. These phenomena are assumed to reflect the action of heterochromatin in interfering with chromosome uncoiling, an essential process in the sequence of events leading up to the specific activation of a gene during development of the individual. Schultz (1947) and Proko-fyeva-Belgovskaya (1948) have shown that in *D. melanogaster* the im-mediately adjacent euchromatin in an euchromatic-heterochromatic transposition tends to assume the condensed state of the heterochromatin. Accompanying the tight coiling is a partial or complete repression of gene action locally. There is now direct evidence of a causal relation between pycnosis and such gene inactivation. Beermann (1961) has pre-sented conclusive evidence that in *Chironomus* the puff formation of salivary gland chromosomes is an index of gene activity at the locus of the puff. Schultz (1963) has observed that if a chromosome band that normally puffs at a particular stage in *Drosophila* development is trans-posed to heterochromatin the puff in question does not form.

As a working hypothesis and without confirming cytological evidence, it may be supposed that repression of R action in maize in the case of class A alleles, referred to earlier, also is due to the presence of a particular segment of heterochromatin at or near the locus. It is postulated that this segment consists of a common element, called P_A for convenience in discussion, repeated varying numbers of times. The "P" in the symbol is intended to imply a relation to pycnosis, and the subscript "A" denotes a particular kind of such elements affecting chromosome condensation. The degree of repression of R action is assumed to vary in accordance with length of the P_A segment as determined by the number of P_A ele-ments present.

Stippled, marbled, and the paramutagenic self-colored alleles in category B may be represented as associated with a qualitatively different heterochromatic segment near the R locus consisting of repeating units termed P_B. The P_B segment does not interfere locally with R-pigment-producing action, and, unlike the P_A segment, it is ordinarily stable in somatic cells. The distinctive property of the P_B segment is to promote supernumerary replication of P_A units in somatic mitosis in P_A/P_B heterozygotes.

Various models might be suggested whereby the increase in numbers of P_A units is effected during somatic reduplication of the R region in a P_A/P_B plant, between which there is little choice at present. One such model will be briefly described for illustrative purposes. Assume that in an R^rR^{st} (P_A/P_B) plant the R chromosome enters a somatic mitosis already split into two chromatids which, of course, serve as templates for the formation of two daughter chromatids. Suppose that the postulated heterochromatic segment associated with R^r initially consists of two P_A units and that these units pair with each other so that a P_A-P_A loop is formed on each side of the principal chromosome axis. Each daughter chromatid is then assumed to copy both loops, instead of only one, thus changing constitution of the heterochromatic segment from P_A-P_A in the original strands to P_A-P_A-P_A-P_A in both progeny.

According to this hypothesis there is no transfer of material from the P_B to the P_A segment in paramutation. Rather the effect of P_B in the R^rR^{st} heterozygote is on the mode of replication of the P_A segment in the homologous chromosome. Details of the process are entirely obscure. One might suppose, however, that P_B prolongs somewhat the period during which the ordinarily compacted P_A segment is uncoiled in mitosis and so could serve as a template for the formation of new units. The directed nature of paramutation can be explained in this way if it is also assumed that, in respect to P_B action, supernumerary P_A units are formed in both daughter chromatids of the R^r chromosome rather than in one at the expense of the other.

Evidence for replication of certain chromosome constituents twice in the same mitotic cycle has been obtained in maize. Greenblatt and Brink (1962) showed, for example, that Modulator (Mp) which inhibits action of the P^{rr} gene for pericarp color when situated at the P locus must divide twice in a single nuclear division in the formation of twin mutations to light variegated and self-red from medium variegated pericarp. In the cases they analyzed, one replication occurred at the P locus and the second at another locus to which one daughter Mp had trans-posed and which was assumed to divide later in the mitotic cycle. Other mutations of medium to light variegated pericarp have been observed, however, in which the second Mp element (which in the presence of the variegated allele changes the pericarp phenotype from medium to light variegated) assorts regularly with the P locus. Transposition of Mp from the P locus to a very closely linked site has not been excluded in these instances. It is possible, on the other hand, that such medium to light variegated mutations include cases in which Mp has replicated twice in a single mitotic cycle without change of position. An event of this kind would be comparable to that postulated to account for the increase in number of P_A units associated with the R^r allele in response to the action of the P_B segment of R^{st} in an $R^r R^{st}$ plant.

Kermicle's evidence that partial reversion of a paramutant $R^{r'}$ allele toward the level of action of standard R^r following extraction from an $R^r R^{st}$ heterozygote occurs in hemizygous $R^{r'}/R$-deficient plants, leads to the conclusion that the number of repeating units in a P_A heterochromatic segment is subject to change not only in response to presence of a paramutagenic R factor in the homologous chromosome but also as a result of "self-regulation." Seemingly, the multiplication of P_A units to a level resulting in increased repression of R^r action adds to the instability of the locus. Under these circumstances the number of P_A units at the locus subsequently is regulated downward during mitosis possibly by the copying of some, but not all, of the P_A elements associated with the original paramutant $R^{r'}$ allele. The enhancement of R^r action that occurs when an allele from a stock $R^r R^r$ culture is passed through a $R^r r^r$ heterozygote is understandable in the same terms. Whether enhancement in this case is due to the presence of a single R^r allele in an $R^r r^r$ plant or to a positive effect of r^r on the process is a question that should be answerable by comparing the results of testcrosses on $r^g r^g$ ♀ ♀ of $R^r r^r$ and R^r/R-deficient hemizygotes.

Secondary paramutation, i.e., the small reduction in pigmenting potential of an R allele initially in standard form that occurs when the factor is passed through a heterozygote with a paramutant R' allele (R R') appears to be the same phenomenon that Styles has observed when certain R alleles from stock cultures are made heterozygous with each other. Styles found that if R_1 and R_2, as they occur in stock cultures, are "high" and "low," respectively, in aleurone-pigmenting potential then in the $R_1 R_2$ heterozygote the level of action of R_1 tends to fall to that of R_2.

Evidently, a wide spectrum of metastable states characterizes R alleles in class A. The variation is expressed not only in terms of sensitivity to paramutation in R^{st} heterozygotes but also as interallelic interactions between class A factors themselves. The different states may be assumed to reflect the multiplicity with which P_A units occur at the R locus. The P_A heterochromatic segment exerts a dual effect. It conditions the pigment-forming action of the R gene with which it is immediately associated, and it also influences the process whereby P_A units are replicated during somatic mitosis. The latter effect can be local (autonomous), as in the partial reversion of $R^{r'}$ in $R^{r'}/R$-deficient plants, or it can be exerted by one R allele on another in a homologous chromosome, as in secondary paramutation and in the R_1 R_2 heterozygotes mentioned above.

The effects of inserting R^r into a reciprocal translocation involving the long arm of chromosome 10, but remote from the R locus, disclose another dimension of the paramutation problem. The pigment-producing action of R^r becomes enhanced under these conditions, and the allele also shows reduced sensitivity to paramutation in R^{st} heterozygotes. Since sensitivity of R^r to paramutation is not immediately reduced on insertion of the allele into a translocated chromosome and since the changed state, once acquired, persists for at least one generation after the factor is returned by crossing-over to a structurally normal chromosome, the phenomenon is not position effect in the usual sense of the term. The evidence shows that the structural alterations, in some unknown way, favor directed changes at the R locus of the kinds mentioned which are then self-propagating. The enhancement of R action suggests that the change consists in a reduction in numbers of P_A units in the heterochromatic segment adjacent to the R gene. If this is so, then one must postulate that replication of the P_A units is subject to the influence of factors elsewhere in the same chromosome arm. Considered from the point of view of the general hypothesis advanced concerning the chromosomal basis of paramutation the evidence from structural alterations supplements that from the other sources in showing that replication of the heterochromatic P_A segment in somatic mitosis is not a process that is strictly determined locally, but is under the influence of a mechanism subject to disturbances by changes both in the corresponding region in the homologous chromosome and elsewhere in the same arm.

The marked difference in level of R^r aleurone pigment-determining action following transmission of the allele to this tissue through male and female gametophytes, respectively, shows that the chromosome constituents concerned with paramutability are highly sensitive to certain variations in developmental conditions. The latter cannot now be localized as between the later stages of sporophyte development and the gameto-phytes themselves, nor can they be characterized except in terms of repression of R action. It will be of interest to determine whether the transmission effect is exhibited only by R alleles of class A, i.e., R alleles which are paramutable. A suggestion that this may be the case is afforded by the fact that stippled, the self-colored mutants from which are non-paramutable throughout, conditions a frequency of aleurone spotting in direct relation to dosage of the allele. This evidence means, of course, that a male-transmitted R^{st} allele has the same determinative effect in the endosperm as each of the two alleles received via the female game-tophyte. Stippled, however, although nonparamutable, embodies a re-pressor of aleurone pigmentation not directly concerned with paramuta-tion and so may not be representative of class B alleles in general. Defini-tive evidence on the point in question may be obtainable from tests with nonparamutable R alleles that condition self-colored aleurone.

The occurrence in maize of some R alleles that are neither paramuta-ble nor paramutagenic, designated here for convenience only as a sub-class of category B (nonparamutable), and that condition anthocyanin formation in seed and plant in regular ways, shows that R expression is definitively regulated by a mechanism upon which paragenetic proper-ties may be superposed. It is suggested that the paramutation phenome-na described rest on chromosome components inserted at or near the R locus that are not normal to this position and whose effect in develop-ment is to override the regulatory mechanism proper to the R gene. As argued elsewhere (Brink, 1964), these adventive materials lack the specificity necessary for controlling the expression of genes individually. Their action suggests that they are concerned with regulating gene action in some more general way. Perhaps they govern changes at the chromosome, rather than the locus, level that are antecedent to the specific activation of individual genes.

ACKNOWLEDGMENTS

Paper No. 970 from the Department of Genetics, College of Agriculture, University of Wisconsin. These studies have been aided by grants from the Research Committee of the Graduate School from funds supplied by the Wisconsin Alumni Research Foun-dation and by grants from the National Science Foundation and the U.S. Atomic Energy Commission, Contract No. AT(11-1)-1300.

REFERENCES

ANDERSON-KOTTÖ, I., AND GAIRDNER, A. E. (1936). The inheritance of apospory in *Scolopendrium vulgare*. *J. Genet.* 32, 189-228.

ASHMAN, R. B. (1960). Stippled aleurone in maize. *Genetics* 45, 19-34.

BATESON, W. (1926). Segregation. *J. Genet.* **16**, 201-235.

BATESON, W., AND PELLEW, C. (1916). Note on the orderly dissimilarity in inheritance from different parts of a plant. *Proc. Roy. Soc.* **B89**, 174-175.

BATESON, W., AND PELLEW, C. (1920). The genetics of "rogues" among culinary peas (*Pisum sativum*). *Proc. Roy. Soc.* **B91**, 186-195.

BEERMANN, W. (1961). Ein Balbiani-ring als Locus einer Speicheldrüsen-mutation. *Chromosoma* **12**, 1-25.

BRAY, R. A. (1964). Mutation and paramutation at the R locus in maize. Ph.D. Thesis, University of Wisconsin Library, Madison, Wisconsin.

BRINK, R. A. (1958). Paramutation at the R locus in maize. *Cold Spring Harbor Symp. Quant. Biol.* **23**, 379-391.

BRINK, R. A. (1959). Paramutation at the R locus in maize plants trisomic for chromosome 10. *Proc. Natl. Acad. Sci. U. S.* **45**, 819-827.

BRINK, R. A. (1961). Relative insensitivity of enhanced R^r to paramutation in maize plants heterozygous for the stippled allele. *Genetics* **46**, 1207-1221.

BRINK, R. A. (1963). Unpublished material.

BRINK, R. A. (1964). Genetic repression in multicellular organisms. *Am. Naturalist* **98**, 193-211.

BRINK, R. A., AND BLACKWOOD, M. (1961). Persistent enhancement of R^r action in maize by structural alterations of chromosome 10. *Genetics* **46**, 1185-1205.

BRINK, R. A., AND MIKULA, B. (1958). Plant color effects of certain anomalous forms of the R^r allele in maize. *Z. Vererbungslehre* **89**, 94-102.

BRINK, R. A., AND NOTANI, N. K. (1961). Effect on R^r action in maize of a structural alteration distal to the R locus in chromosome 10. *Genetics* **46**, 1223-1230.

BRINK, R. A., AND WEYERS, W. H. (1960). Effect of an abnormal knob-carrying chromosome 10 on paramutation of R^r in maize. *Genetics* **45**, 1445-1455.

BRINK, R. A., BROWN, D. F., KERMICLE, J., AND WEYERS, W. H. (1960). Locus dependence of the paramutant R phenotype in maize. *Genetics* **45**, 1297-1312.

BRINK, R. A., KERMICLE, J. L., AND BROWN, D. F. (1964). Tests for a gene-dependent cytoplasmic particle associated with R paramutation in maize. *Proc. Natl. Acad. Sci. U. S.* **51**, 1067-1074.

BROTHERTON, W., JR. (1923). Further studies on the inheritance of "rogue" type in garden peas (*Pisum sativum* L.) *J. Agr. Res.* **24**, 815-852.

BROTHERTON, W., JR. (1924). Gamete production in certain crosses with "rogues" in peas. *J. Agr. Res.* **28**, 1247-1252.

BROWN, D. F. (1963). Paramutability of R^g and r^r mutants from the standard R^r allele in maize. Ph.D. Thesis, University of Wisconsin Library, Madison, Wisconsin.

BROWN, D. F. (1963a). Unpublished material.

BROWN, D. F., AND BRINK, R. A. (1960). Paramutagenic action of paramutant R^r and R^g alleles in maize. *Genetics* **45**, 1313-1316.

COE, E. H., JR. (1959). A regular and continuing conversion-type phenomenon at the B locus in maize. *Proc. Natl. Acad. Sci. U. S.* **45**, 828-832.

COE, E. H., JR. (1961a). A test for somatic mutations in the origination of conversion-type inheritance at the B locus in maize. *Genetics* **46**, 707-710.

COE, E. H., JR. (1961b). Some observations bearing on plasmid versus gene hypothesis for a conversion-type phenomenon. *Genetics* **46**, 719-725.

COOPER, H. B., JR. (1964). Paramutation and reversion of the R^r allele in maize. Ph.D. Thesis, University of Wisconsin Library, Madison, Wisconsin.

EMMERLING, M. (1958). An analysis of intragenic and extragenic mutations of the plant color component of the *Rr* gene complex in *Zea mays*. *Cold Spring Harbor Symp. Quant. Biol.* **23**, 393-407.

GREENBLATT, I. M., AND BRINK, R. A. (1962). Twin mutations in medium variegated pericarp maize. *Genetics* **47**, 489-501.

HAGEMANN, R. (1961a). Mitteilungen über somatische Konversion 1-Ausschluss des Vorliegens von somatischem Austausch. *Biol. Zentr.* **80**, 477-478.

HAGEMANN, R. (1961b). Mitteilungen über somatische Konversion 2. In welchem Ausmass ist die somatische Konversion gerichtet? *Biol. Zentr.* **80**, 549-550.

KERMICLE, J. (1963). Metastability of paramutant forms of the *R* gene in maize. Ph.D. Thesis, University of Wisconsin Library, Madison, Wisconsin.

LEWIS, E. B. (1950). The phenomenon of position effect. *Advan. Genet.* **3**, 73-115.

LILIENFELD, F. A. (1929). Vererbungsversuche mit schlitz-blättrigen Sippen von *Malva parviflora*. I. Die laciniata Sippe. *Bibliotheca Genet.* **13**, 1-214.

LINDEN, D. B. (1963). Radiation induced modification of paramutation expression. *Maize Genet. Cooperation News Letter* **37**, 133-134.

LONGLEY, A. E. (1961). Breakage points for four corn translocation series and other corn chromosome observations. *U. S. Dept. Agr.* (In cooperation with Calif. Inst. Technol.) **ARS 34-16**.

MCCLINTOCK, B. (1956). Controlling elements and the gene. *Cold Spring Harbor Symp. Quant. Biol.* **21**, 197-216.

MCWHIRTER, K. S., AND BRINK, R. A. (1962). Continuous variation in level of paramutation at the *R* locus in maize. *Genetics* **47**, 1053-1074.

MCWHIRTER, K. S., AND BRINK, R. A. (1963). Paramutation in maize during endosperm development. *Genetics* **48**, 189-203.

MANTON, I. (1950). "Problems of Cytology and Evolution in the Pteridophytes." Cambridge Univ. Press, London and New York.

NEWTON, W. C. F., AND DARLINGTON, C. D. (1929). Meiosis in polyploids. I. Triploid and pentaploid tulips. *J. Genet.* **21**, 1-15.

NOUJDIN, N. I. (1944). The regularities of the heterochromatin influences of mosaicism. *Zh. Obshch. Biol.* **5**, 357-389 (in Russian).

NOUJDIN, N. I. (1946). The role of hybridization in variability. I. Influence of heterozygous structure upon variegation of mosaic characters. II. Influence of extra heterochromatin upon variation of the wild type allelomorph for bobbed in *D. melanogaster*. *Zh. Obshch. Biol.* **7**, 175-208 (in Russian: English summary).

ORTON, E. R., JR. (1960). Reconstitution of the variegated pericarp allele in maize by return of Modulator to the *P* locus. Ph.D. Thesis, University of Wisconsin Library, Madison, Wisconsin.

PROKOFYEVA-BELGOVSKAYA, A. A. (1948). Heterochromatization as a change of the chromosome cycle. *J. Genetics* **48**, 80-98.

RENNER, O. (1937). Über *Oenothera atrovirens* Sh. et Bartl. und über somatische Konversion im Erbgang des *cruciata*—Merkmals der Oenotheren. *Z. induktive Abstammungs–Vererbungslehre* **74**, 91-124.

RENNER, O. (1959). Somatic conversion in the heredity of the *cruciata* character in *Oenothera*. *Heredity* **13**, 283-288.

RHOADES, M. M. (1952). Preferential segregation in maize. *In* "Heterosis" (J. W. Gowen, ed.), pp. 66-80. Iowa State College Press, Ames, Iowa.

ROMAN, H. (1947). Mitotic nondisjunction in the case of interchanges involving the B-type chromosome in maize. *Genetics* **32**, 391-409.

ROMAN, H. (1948). Directed fertilization in maize. *Proc. Natl. Acad. Sci. U. S.* **34**, 36-42.

ROMAN, H., AND ULLSTRUP, A. J. (1951). The use of A-B translocations to locate genes in maize. *Agron. J.* **43**, 450-454.

SANDLER, L., AND ROSENFELD, A. (1962). A genetically induced, heritable modification of segregation-distortion in *Drosophila melanogaster*. *Can. J. Genet. Cytol.* **4**, 453-457.

SANDLER, L., HIRAIZUMI, Y., AND SANDLER, I. (1959). Meiotic drive in natural populations of *D. melanogaster*. I. The cytogenetic basis of segregation distortion. *Genetics* **44**, 233-250.

SCHULTZ, J. (1947). The nature of heterochromatin. *Cold Spr. Harb. Symp. Quant. Biol.* **12**, 179-191.

SCHULTZ, J. (1963). Personal communication.

SPOFFORD, J. B. (1959). Parental control of position-effect variegation: I. Parental heterochromatin and expression of the white locus in compound-X *Drosophila melanogaster*. *Proc. Natl. Acad. Sci. U. S.* **45**, 1003-1007.

SPOFFORD, J. B. (1961). Parental control of position-effect variegation. II. Effect of sex of parent contributing white-mottled rearrangement in *Drosophila melanogaster*. *Genetics* **46**, 1151-1167.

STYLES, D. (1964). Unpublished material.

VAN SCHAIK, N., AND BRINK, R. A. (1959). Transpositions of Modulator, a component of the variegated pericarp allele in maize. *Genetics* **44**, 725-738.

Genetic Control and Regulation of Developmental Pathways

E. B. LEWIS

Division of Biology, California Institute of Technology, Pasadena, California

Introduction

There are many experimental approaches to the problem of growth and development. We would like to discuss what might be called the genetic approach. The underlying concept is that the genetic mechanisms which are believed to control and regulate biosynthetic pathways may be applicable with relatively little modification to the control and regulation of developmental pathways. In the case of a biosynthetic pathway it frequently has proved possible, especially in the microorganisms, to assemble a series of mutant genes that affect many if not all of the individual steps of that pathway. The difficulty of assembling such genes in the case of developmental pathways is well known. For example, many mutant genes are known in *Drosophila* which affect the size and shape of the eye; yet, the order in which such genes exert their effects during development and the biochemical basis of such effects are essentially unknown.

There is a phenomenon, however, which promises to provide the kind of materials needed to make a genetic attack upon the problem of growth and development, namely, pseudoallelism or the occurrence in the chromosome of clusters of closely linked genes with similar effects. These clusters have been variously called pseudoallelic series, complex loci, regions, operons, and polycistronic units. A discussion of this terminology and the general problem of defining the gene has been given elsewhere (Lewis, 1963) and need not be of concern here. Pseudoallelism should not be confused with subdivision of the gene itself into an array of sites, presumably corresponding to the individual base pairs of the deoxyribonucleic acid (DNA) molecule. Instead it refers to a higher level of organization in the chromosome, a level involving clusters of genes so closely related in function that they have come to lie in proximity or, as may often be the case, they arose in proximity by a process of tandem gene duplication and that proximity conferred an advantage which has tended to prevent their becoming separated by subsequent chromosomal rearrangement.

Many of the most well-analyzed genetic loci in *Drosophila,* and indeed in many other organisms, have turned out to be compound in this sense of being clusters of functionally, closely related units (review by Carlson, 1959). This paper is concerned with one such case, the "bithorax" series, which seems to control the course of development of certain body segments of the fly. Before discussing this case, however, it may be instructive to outline the methods available for the genetic analysis of developmental problems.

Genetic Methods for the Analysis of Development

The earliest method consisted of studying the effect of substituting a mutant allele for the normal or wild-type allele of a gene. By comparing the effects of substituting different mutant alleles or "multiple alleles" it was possible to determine the degree to which a specific developmental effect could be varied by changes in what was presumed to be one functional unit.

It soon became possible to study the effects of different doses of a gene through the use of deficiencies and duplications for parts of the chromosomes. The results indicated that, with some important exceptions, the mutant alleles of a gene tend to act like partial or complete inactivations of the wild-type allele from which they originated. This finding made possible the important deduction that a developmental abnormality associated with a mutant gene presumably arises because of a loss of some substance that is elaborated by the wild-type allele during the course of normal development.

An important advance came with the use of somatic mosaics to study the developmental effects of genes (Sturtevant, 1932). In this way it was found that the morphological effects of mutant genes in *Drosophila* are almost always expressed autonomously, i.e., there is little or no evidence in such cases for diffusion of substances between mutant and wild-type cells of the somatic mosaic (for example, Stern, 1956; Tokunaga, 1961; Roberts, 1964). A number of genetic processes can be used to produce somatic mosaics. These include somatic crossing-over, somatic mutation, somatic elimination of chromosomes, variegated-type position effects, and the normal inactivation or "fixed differentiation" of one of the two X chromosomes in somatic cells of female mammals (chapter by L. Russell in this volume).

The position effect phenomenon provides another method of investigating the control of developmental pathways. Position effects include a variety of gene interaction effects that take place at the nuclear, as opposed to the cytoplasmic, level. On the one hand, there is the somatic instability of gene action manifested when genes are brought next to heterochromatin. The possible significance of this phenomenon of variegation, or V-type position effect, for the problem of development has been discussed by Schultz (1956). On the other hand, there is a stable or S-type position effect which seems to depend upon the presence here and there in the chromosomes of clusters of functionally interrelated genes or pseudoalleles. One way of detecting the S-type of position effect is to compare the *cis* and *trans* heterozygotes for two such closely linked genes, say *a* and *b*. In the *cis* form, *a b* / + +, the mutant genes are together in the same chromosome and their wild-type alleles are in the opposite chromosome. In the *trans* heterozygote, *a* + / + *b*, the mutant genes are in opposite chromosomes, as are also the wild-type alleles. A *cis-trans* position effect is said to occur if the two heterozygotes differ phenotypically. In general, the *cis* form is wild type, or nearly so; whereas the *trans* form is mutant in phenotype. Two or more mutant genes which exhibit a *cis-trans* position effect are sometimes said to belong to the same functional unit or cistron (Benzer, 1955).

Suppressor genes promise to be especially useful tools in analyzing the genetic control and regulation of developmental, as well as biochemical, pathways.

Several mechanisms have been discovered which can account for suppressor genes that suppress in an allele-specific manner biochemical mutants at several different loci (review by Yanofsky, 1963). In *Drosophila* such a suppressor gene for mutants affecting a variety of morphological traits, including several of the bithorax mutant genes, has been known for some time (see discussion of the suppressor of Hairy-wing by Wagner and Mitchell, 1964). An understanding of the chemical basis for the action of such a suppressor might be an opening wedge in elucidating in turn the basis of gene action of the suppressible mutants.

The Bithorax Pseudoallelic Series

In the case of the bithorax pseudoallelic series it has been possible to bring together many of these genetic methods for analyzing development. We would like to summarize some of the results. Additional details have been given elsewhere (Lewis, 1951, 1955, 1963). Many spontaneous and X-ray-induced mutants of this series are now available, some eleven of

which are cytologically normal. When the "point" mutations were subjected to genetic recombination analysis, it was discovered that they
could be grouped into five major loci, with adjacent genes in the series
recombining with frequencies of the order of one recombinant per 10,000
gametes. A correlation of the genetic and cytological maps of the third
chromosome region containing these genes is shown in Fig. 1.

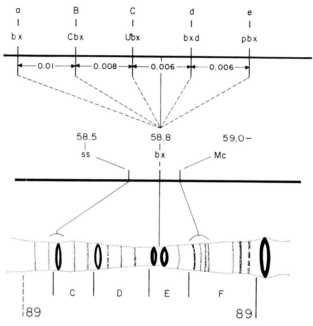

FIG. 1. A correlation of the genetic and cytological maps in the right arm of the
third chromosome in the region of the bithorax genes.

Developmental Effects of the Bithorax Mutants

The bithorax mutants are examples of homeotic mutants, i.e., their
effects can be described in terms of degree of transformation of one
structure (or organ) into a different, but embryologically homologous,
one. In the bithorax mutants the transformations involve portions of
the mesothoracic (MS), metathoracic (MT), and first-abdominal (AB$_1$)
segments. The patterns of segmentation in the normal fly and the various
mutant types are shown schematically in Figs. 2 and 3, respectively.

Mutants at the first locus in the series, which is designated here simply as the *a* locus, cause the anterior portion of the metathorax (AMT) to develop a structure closely resembling the anterior portion of the meso-thorax (AMS). This transformation is designated as T1. Photographs of a normal fly and one with an extreme *a* mutant phenotype are shown in Figs. 4 and 5, respectively. Mutants at the fifth or *e* locus of the series cause the posterior portion of the metathorax (PMT) to resemble the posterior portion of the mesothorax (PMS) (Fig. 7).

By combining the *a* and *e* mutants a virtually complete mesothoracic modification of the metathoracic segment can be achieved resulting in a four-winged fly (Fig. 6). In this way and also by utilizing genotypes which combine weak T1 and strong T2, or strong T1 and weak T2, effects it can be inferred that these two transformations vary more or less independently of one another, suggesting that two separate functions are involved. The relationship between the *a* and *e* mutant effects is shown schematically in Fig. 8.

Mutants at the fourth or *d* locus produce two effects, the T2 transformation and a conversion of the first-abdominal segment toward a thoracic one, the latter transformation being designated as T3. The most striking feature of T3 is the development of rudimentary to fully formed abdominal legs on the first abdominal segment of the adult fly (Figs. 9 and 10), and occasionally small partially winglike halteres on the dorsal part of this segment (Lewis, 1963). T3 appears to vary more or less independently of the T1 and T2 transformations. For example, the T2 effect which normally accompanies the T3 effect is nearly absent in certain genotypes involving alleles of the *d* gene.

Mutants at the third or *C* locus cause all three transformations to occur; one allele (Ubx^{61d} of Gloor) is viable when homozygous and expresses weak degrees of transformations of each type. The original mutant of this series (*Ubx* of W. F. Hollander) is lethal when homozygous, but in its interactions with other mutants in the bithorax cluster and in its larval phenotype, this mutant also seems to produce all three types of transformations. When homozygous this latter mutant is viable as a larva. The larva develops, in addition to a normal set of anterior spiracles, which are believed to be mesothoracic in origin, additional sets on the metathoracic and first-abdominal segments; this same transformation of the larval spiracle system is produced to a weaker extent in the homozygote for the double mutant *a d, or the a d e* triple mutant, or in the genotype *a d / C*. (In symbolizing genotypes in this paper, whenever symbols for a gene in the pseudoallelic series are omitted it is always to be understood that the wild-type alleles of those genes are present.) Therefore, the *C* mutant can be said to express all three transformations, T1, T2, and T3.

Finally the second or *B* mutant has effects which are more or less the inverse of those of the *a* and *e* mutants, i.e., the *B* mutant which is dominant causes the posterior portion of PMS to approach rather closely a

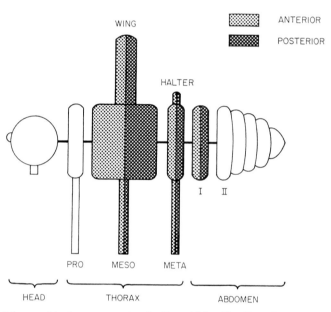

Fig. 2. Scheme of body segmentation in *Drosophila*. The line of separation between the anterior and posterior portions is deduced from the mutant effects and is anatomically well defined only in the case of the mesothorax.

level of development seen in PMT (Fig. 11). Occasionally, in this mutant AMS also achieves an AMT-type of development so that a halterlike structure (accompanied often by greatly reduced development of the mesothorax) arises on one or both sides of the second as well as on the third thoracic segment (Fig. 12). This transformation of the mesothorax toward the metathorax is designated as T4. The *B* mutant effects are seen to approximately the same extent whether the mutant is heterozygous (*B* / +) or homozygous (*B* / *B*), but the transformation of AMS is more frequent in the latter case. The T4 transformation is only partially independent of the other transformations. For example, the *a* and *B* double mutant combination shows a mutual partial suppression of the T1 and T4 transformations; the *B* and *e* double mutant combination has

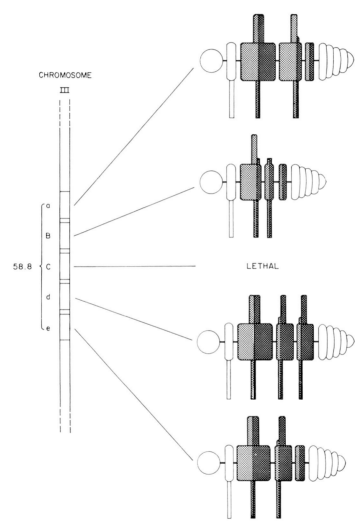

FIG. 3. A schematic illustration of the body segment pattern associated with each of the five bithorax loci. a, bithorax; b, contrabithorax; c, ultrabithorax, d, bithoraxoid; and e, postbithorax.

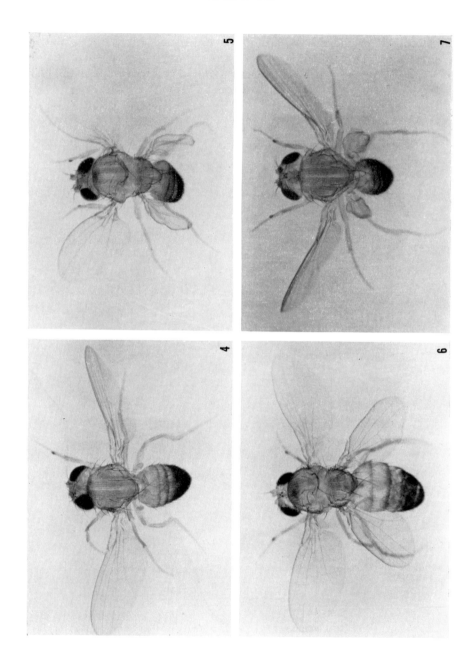

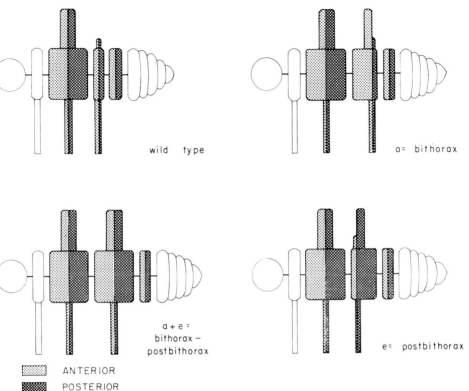

ANTERIOR

POSTERIOR

FIG. 8. Scheme for the body segmentation plan of the *a* and *e* mutants compared with that found in wild type and in the double mutant combination. Compare with Figs. 4–7.

FIG. 4. Photograph of a wild-type male. The mesothoracic wings have been extended to show the dorsal metathoracic and first-abdominal regions.

FIG. 5. Photograph of a male with an extreme T1 transformation (genotype: bx^3/Ubx^{105}).

FIG. 6. Photograph of a male showing a combination of extreme T1 and T2 transformations (genotype: $bx^3\ pbx/Ubx^{105}$).

FIG. 7. Photograph of a male with an extreme T2 transformation (genotype: pbx/Ubx^{105}).

a typical T4 change but complete suppression of the T2 transformation;
the *B* and *d* mutant combination has a possibly slight enhancement of
the T4 transformation with a slight weakening of the T3 (and complete
suppression of the T2) transformation.

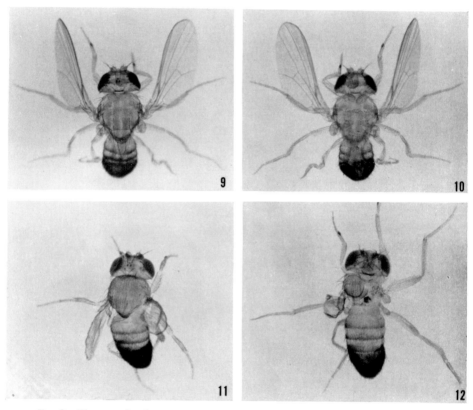

FIG. 9.   Photograph of an extreme example of the *d* phenotype (T2 + T3 transformations) (genotype: *bxd/Ubx*[109]). Dorsal view of a male showing a fourth pair of legs
which arise from the first-abdominal segment and which have the same symmetry and
the same number of segments as in the case of the thoracic legs.

FIG. 10.   Photograph of a ventral view of the same specimen shown in Fig. 9.

FIG. 11.   Photograph of a male homozygous for the *B* mutant illustrating the T4
transformation.

FIG. 12.   Photograph of a male homozygous for the *B* mutant showing asymmetric
express of the T4 transformation. On the right-hand side of the body the wing has
been reduced to a halterlike appendage and the dorsal mesothorax is all but obliterated, the tissue arising near the halter being that of the humerus or dorsal prothorax.

Gene Dosage Studies

By means of duplications, it has been possible to construct genotypes containing two dosages of a given bithorax mutant allele and one dosage of the corresponding wild-type allele; such duplication genotypes are phenotypically wildtype for any one of the recessive mutant genes a, d, or e or for any combination thereof. Even two doses of the dominant mutant C, which is normally lethal when homozygous, are suppressed by the presence of one set of wild-type alleles, i.e., C / C / $+$ resembles C / $+$ which is nearly wild-type except for a slight enlargement of the halter. It is presumed therefore that the mutant genes fail to make substances normally elaborated by the wild-type alleles. Paradoxically, this failure on the part of the mutant genes leads to tremendous overgrowths of tissue in the metathoracic or abdominal regions, as the case may be. Stated in another way, the wild-type alleles appear to produce substances which suppress the potential development of the metathorax toward a mesothoracic segment or of the abdominal segment toward a thoracic-like one. Since the T1, T2, and T3 effects are capable of being more or less independently expressed, it may be presumed further that the transformations result from the loss of three specific substances S1, S2, and S3, respectively, produced in turn by the a^+, e^+, and d^+ genes.

Somatic Mosaics

Two methods have been used to make somatic mosaics for the bithorax genes. The first method makes use of a ring X chromosome containing the normal alleles of all of the bithorax genes (derived from an insertional translocation between the X and third chromosomes of Oliver). This method depends upon occasional instability, especially in aged maternal cytoplasm (Brown and Hannah, 1952), of a ring X chromosome which results in its loss during early cell divisions of the developing embryo.

As shown in Fig. 13, with suitably marked first and third chromosomes, the loss of the ring X chromosome in a female embryo results in male tissue genotypically mutant for some one or more of the bithorax mutants (expressed by the symbol bx^k), and at the same time mutant for a body and bristle marker gene, yellow (y), carried in the normal X chromosome. Gynandromorphs mosaic for the homozygous C mutant genotype are shown in Figs. 14 and 15. Additional gynandromorphs have been obtained that are mosaic for the a e double mutant combination (Lewis, 1963). The results indicate that there is either complete or virtually

ZYGOTE

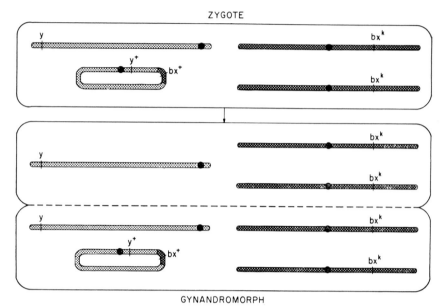

GYNANDROMORPH

Fɪɢ. 13. Scheme for the production of gynandromorphs mosaic for the bithorax mutants and for the body color mutant, yellow.

Fɪɢ. 14. Photograph of a gynandromorph mosaic for wild-type and homozygous *C* mutant tissue. On the right-hand side the anterior portion of the metathorax is greatly enlarged and expresses the yellow phenotype; on the same side the dorsal portion of the first-abdominal segment is greatly reduced as in the T3 transformation. The left-hand side of the body is wild type.

Fɪɢ. 15. Photograph of another gynandromorph mosaic for wild-type and homozygous *C* mutant tissue. On the right-hand side the entire dorsal mesothorax is yellow; in addition, a large portion of the anterior metathorax is mesothoracic-like and yellow, except for a nonyellow scutellar-like bristle (lower arrow); the latter bristle may be indicative of a slightly nonautonomous action of the yellow gene or of the bithorax gene. On the posterior region of the mesothorax (upper arrow) there is a patch of yellow hairs and bristles whose origin and homology are not known. The left-hand side is wild type except for the slightly enlarged halter typical of the duplication genotype, $C/C/+$.

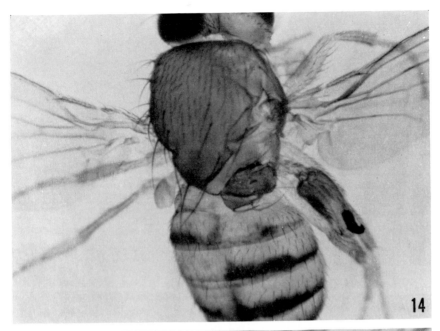

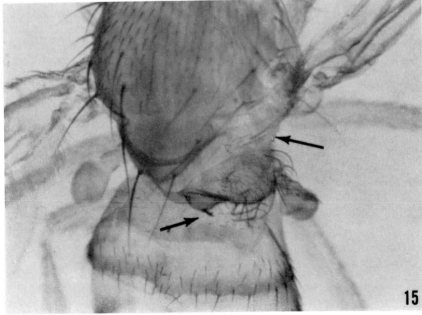

complete autonomy of expression of the bithorax mutant transformations associated with the a, C, and e genes, the only ones thus far studied
in mosaics. This suggests that there is little or no diffusion from one
cell to another of the hypothetical bithorax substances.

The second method utilizes somatic crossing-over to produce mutant
bithorax tissue in an otherwise wild-type background. This method
involves constructing females identical in genotype with those shown in
Fig. 13 except that the duplication-bearing X chromosome is a rod rather
than a ring, and the normal X chromosome carries in addition to the
yellow mutant another recessive mutant producing singed (sn^3) hairs and
bristles. The phenotype of such females is wild type. When X-rays (at
doses of 900 r and 1200 r) are applied to such females in the embryonic
or larval stage, the frequency of somatic crossing-over in the proximal
part of the X chromosomes is greatly increased and results in yellow
singed patches of bristles and hairs that are expected to lack the wild-
type alleles of the bithorax genes. Such tissue when it arises in the
dorsal metathoracic region has been found to express the a and e mutant
effects autonomously. When the irradiation is applied between day 4 and
5 of development, near the end of the third larval instar, a few of the
adults show a single yellow singed hair or bristle on the dorsal metathorax; single bristles and hairs of this type arise with approximately
the same frequency in the normal mesothoracic region as expected. These
results suggest that the wild-type alleles of at least the a gene are still
functioning late in larval development, preventing so to speak, a mesothoracic-like transformation of even a few cells of the dorsal metathoracic
imaginal disc.

Cis-Trans Effects

Many mutants of the bithorax pseudoallelic series exhibit pronounced
cis-trans effects. For example, the trans heterozygote, $a + / + C$ between
one of the less extreme a mutants (bx^{34e}) and the C mutant (Fig. 19),
invariably has a small winglike halter which represents a transformation
of the T1 type; on the other hand, the cis heterozygote, $a C / + +$
(Fig. 18), invariably is nearly wild type except for a slight enlargement of
the halter normally observed in $C / +$. For a comparison the wild-type
halter can be seen in Fig. 16. Since the a and C genes each seem to be
involved in effecting the T1 transformation in ways which cannot be
clearly differentiated, it has not been possible to decide whether the T1
transformation observed in this trans heterozygote depends upon a re-

duced activity of the normal allele of the *a* and/or of the *C* gene. In many of the other *cis-trans* position effects that exist in this series, however, a conspicuous polarity to the mutant interactions is observed (Lewis, 1955). For example, the *trans* heterozygote, *d* + / + *e*, invariably shows a T2 transformation similar to but not quite so extreme as that observed in the homozygous *e* mutant, but fails to show any trace of the T3 transformation typical of the *d* mutant; the *cis* heterozygote, *d e* / + +, on the other hand, is phenotypically wild type. The *trans* heterozygote, *a* + / + *e*, is normally wild type; however, when *a* is the most extreme allele available (*bx³*) and the temperature during development is elevated to 28°C this heterozygote shows a weak T2 transformation but no trace of the T1 transformation typical of the *a* mutant. Under the same elevated temperature conditions, the *cis* heterozygote, *a e* / + +, remains phenotypically wild type. The *trans* heterozygote, *C* + / + *d*, shows a polarized effect on the *d* locus in that it has an extreme T3 transformation combined with a weak to moderate T2 transformation (the latter being directly dependent upon the strength of the particular *d* mutant used). The *trans* heterozygote, *C* + / + *e*, has a polarized effect on the *e* locus in that it shows an extreme T2 transformation with no T3 transformation. The corresponding *cis* heterozygotes, *C d* / + + and *C e* / + +, are virtually wild type except for the enlarged halter typical of *C* / +.

In *trans* heterozygotes involving the the *B* mutant and either an *a, d,* or an *e* mutant, the phenotype is similar to the T4 transformation of *B* / + with little or no effect of the other mutants in evidence. *B* / + *C*, however, has a slightly suppressed T4 transformation and weak T1 and T2 effects; moreover, a striking position effect is present in that the *cis* heterozygote, *B C* / + +, is virtually wild type. (A somewhat similar but less marked position effect is observed for the *a* and *B* mutants.) In the presence of a partial suppressor of the *B* mutant, *trans* heterozygotes between *B* and other mutants act as if the *B* mutant partially inactivates the wild-type alleles of the *C, d,* and *e* loci. Thus there is a polarity to the bithorax pseudoallelic series such that mutants at one locus tend to inactivate the genes to the right (or distal in the chromosome arm) but not to the left of it. The same type of polarity is seen, also in rearrangements that appear to have separated the *a, B,* and *C* loci from the *d* and *e* loci. In three such rearrangements which have arisen in wild-type chromosomes, the activity of the wild-type alleles of *a, B,* and *C* appear to be unimpaired, whereas the wild-type alleles of the *d* and *e* genes appear to be almost completely inactivated.

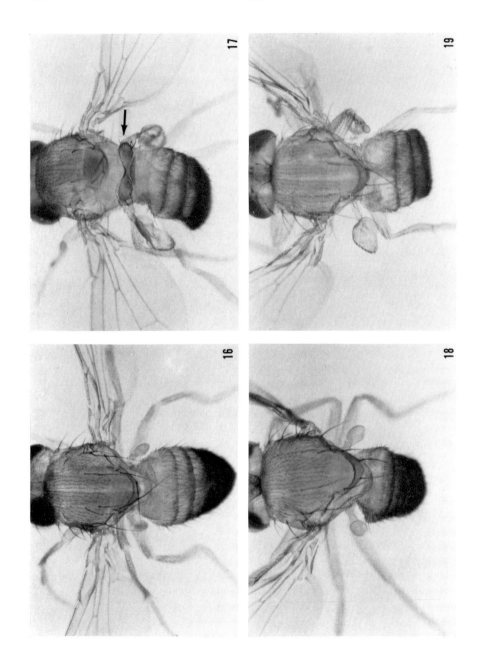

The *Trans*-Vection Effect

The *cis-trans* effect can be further intensified in some cases by introducing a chromosomal rearrangement in heterozygous condition into the *cis* and *trans* types (Lewis, 1954). In certain genotypes the effect is particularly striking. For example, the heterozygote between C and one of the a mutants (bx^{34e}) results in a weak T1 transformation (Fig. 19) as already noted; heterozygosity for certain chromosomal rearrangements involving the right arm of the third chromosome causes this *trans* heterozygote to develop a broad band of mesothoracic-like tissue in the dorsal anterior metathoracic region (Fig. 17). This intensification of the T1 transformation is confined to the *trans* heterozygote, i.e., such rearrangements do not modify the phenotype of the *cis* heterozygote (Fig. 18), which remains nearly wild type. This is a unique type of position effect in that the rearrangements are without effect on any other genotype except that of the *trans* heterozygote. This "*trans*-vection effect" (Lewis, 1954) has not yet been detected in any other case of pseudoallelism. The available evidence suggests that the position effect comes about by interference with the pairing of the homologous chromosomes in the region of the bithorax genes; moreover, the degree of the *trans*-vection effect seems to depend more or less directly on the degree to which that pairing is interrupted.

Discussion

A picture begins to emerge for the way in which the wild-type alleles of the bithorax pseudoallelic series control and regulate the development of certain portions of the body segments of *Drosophila*. The discussion

FIG. 16.   Photograph of a wild-type male.

FIG. 17.   Photograph of the *trans* heterozygote for an a and C mutant (genotype: $bx^{34e} +/+ Ubx$), which is at the same time heterozygous for a translocation between the second and third chromosomes. The band of hairy mesothoracic-like tissue in the region of the dorsal metathorax (see arrow) is absent in the corresponding *trans* heterozygote that fails to carry a chromosomal rearrangement (Fig. 19).

FIG. 18.   Photograph of the *cis* heterozygote between an a and C mutant (genotype: $bx^{34e} Ubx/++$).

FIG. 19.   Photograph of a *trans* heterozygote identical in genotype with that shown in Fig. 17 except that the third chromosomes are structurally normal. The dorsal metathorax shows only a few hairs in contrast to the pronounced mesothoracic-like band of tissue seen in Fig. 17; this difference between the two *trans* heterozygotes is an expression of the *trans*-vection.

which follows is admittedly highly speculative, but it is put forth because it may suggest new kinds of experiments and may help to synthesize the experimental findings already at hand.

The wild-type alleles of at least three of the five bithorax genes are assumed to elaborate substances which control the level of development achieved in the wild-type fly by the mesothoracic, metathoracic, and first-abdominal segments. The wild-type allele of d is assumed to manufacture a substance, S3, which suppresses the potential thoracic-like development of the first-abdominal segment. This gene may have been one of the genes responsible for the evolution of the insects from multilegged ancestors and therefore may have been the first gene of the series to arise during evolution. A very similar gene is evidently present in the Lepidoptera, since mutants are known in *Bombyx* which cause extra leglike appendages to arise on all of the larval abdominal segments and which cause extra first-abdominal legs and wings to arise in the adult moth (Itikawa, 1955; Tsujita, 1955).

The production of the hypothetical substance, S1, by the wild-type alleles of the C (or a) gene, and of S2 by the corresponding allele of the e gene, is assumed to be responsible for the suppression of the potential mesothoracic-like development of the metathorax. Possibly, the wild-type alleles of the a, C, and e genes are ancestrally related to the d^+ gene, i.e., they may have evolved from it by a process of tandem gene duplication, the resultant duplicate genes then undergoing functional divergence by mutation (Lewis, 1951).

The central problem is how the production of the hypothetical bithorax substances is regulated during development. At this point, it is useful to introduce the concept of the "operon" which Jacob and Monod (1961) invented to explain the regulation of gene activity in certain microbial systems of closely linked and functionally interrelated genes. This concept will be summarized briefly and then applied to the bithorax case.

The operon comprises structural genes, whose DNA message is "transcribed" into polypeptides, and an "operator" which is a region of the DNA strand where the initial stage of transcription, the synthesis of messenger RNA, commences. The operon model can be used to explain either "inducible" or "repressible" systems of gene activity. Only the inducible system will be considered here since a model based on it rather than the repressible system seems better able to explain the bithorax findings. In the inducible type of operon, the transcription process is assumed to be blocked (during the uninduced state) as the result of binding of a repressor substance to the operator region. "Induction" takes place when an exogenous inducer is added. The inducer is assumed to react with the repressor thereby preventing it from reaching the operator; as a result transcription can proceed.

In the lactose operon of *Escherichia coli,* Jacob and Monod (1961) found that certain mutants located in the operator region allowed transcription to proceed even in the absence of the inducer. Such "operator-constitutive" or o^C mutants are remarkable in being dominant and in being associated with a gain, rather than loss, of function. Moreover, they are dominant only when in the *trans* relationship to a mutant (x) at the adjoining structural gene, i.e., $o^C + / + x$ showed the dominant gain in function, whereas $o^C x / + +$ did not. This *cis-trans* effect is explained by assuming that the o^C mutant reduces the affinity of the operator region for the repressor; therefore, in the chromosome bearing this mutant transcription can proceed even in the absence of the inducer. In the absence of inducer, however, a normal polypeptide obviously can be made only when o^C is next to the wild-type allele of the structural gene, namely, in the *trans* heterozygote; in the *cis* form the mutant allele of the structural gene would result in transcription of a defective polypeptide.

Some elements of the operon concept appear particularly helpful in understanding how the bithorax genes control and regulate developmental processes. The bithorax genes *C, d,* and *e* may be thought of as the structural genes. They would elaborate the hypothetical substances S1, S3, and S2, respectively. (The *a* gene is presumably also a structural gene, but is assumed to make a substance whose effects have not been differentiable from those of S1). These substances might be messenger RNA molecules, polypeptides, or products of the enzyme activity of such polypeptides. A mutant allele of any one of the structural genes is assumed to reduce the rate of transcription of that gene and of any gene to the right of it in the series. In this way, the *cis-trans* effects and the polarity of the mutant effects can be readily accounted for. A specific mechanism, involving modulated codons in the DNA sequences, has been proposed recently by Ames and Hartman (1963) to explain how the rate of transcription might itself be regulated in an operon.

The *B* mutant corresponds to the o^C type of mutant. It first of all represents a dominant gain of function in the sense that it acts as if it produces an excessive amount of the bithorax substances in the metathorax. (The simplest interpretation, consistent with all of the findings involving combinations of B with other mutants of the series, is that an excessive amount of S1 only is all that is needed to bring about the T4 transformation or metathoracic-like modification of the mesothorax). This gain in function is observed in the *trans* heterozygote between B and a mutant of the C gene, but not in the corresponding *cis* heterozygote, i.e., $B + / + C$ has a strong T4 transformation which is all but obliterated in $B C / + +$.

It remains to consider how the bithorax series is regulated during the course of normal development. Formally, this can be understood by assuming that there is an inducer substance, X, for the bithorax operon and that a gradient in the concentration of X is present during embryogenesis. The origin of the gradient is pictured as follows. In very early embryogenesis the concentration of X would presumably be uniform throughout the egg; if X is a substance which cannot diffuse readily from one cell to another and if during embryonic development there is an anteroposterior gradient in the mitotic division rate, then the desired gradient will be set up, i.e., on these assumptions the relative concentration of X will be higher in cells of the posterior region of the embryo than it will be in cells of the anterior region. In the cells of the mesothoracic region of the developing embryo and larva it is assumed that the cellular concentration of X is too low to provide effective induction of the bithorax operon; therefore, the transcription of substances S1, S2, and S3 is effectively prevented in this region. In the metathoracic region, the cellular concentration of X is assumed to be sufficient to induce transcription of these substances; it is necessary to suppose that the resultant concentrations of S1 and S2 are sufficient to suppress the potential mesothoracic-like modification of the metathoracic region but that the concentration of S3 is still insufficient to bring about an abdominal type of development in the metathoracic region. Finally, in the cells of the first-abdominal region, higher concentrations of X would allow the cellular concentration of S3 to build up to a point where it would suppress the potential thoracic-like development of this segment.

The above account of the regulation of gene action in the bithorax case is only one of a number of models which might be constructed. Another model involving sequentially controlled gene reactions has also been developed (Lewis, 1955, 1963). Neither this model nor the operon one readily explains all of the observations. Moreover, it is obvious that some knowledge of the underlying biochemistry of gene action will be needed before any such models can be put to critical test.

Summary

The bithorax genes in *Drosophila* control the level of development achieved by certain body segments. Evidence is presented that they do so in a polarized and coordinated manner reminiscent of the genes in the operons of microorganisms. Possibly the bithorax genes are regulated by an inducible type of operonic system. The inducer in the bithorax case is assumed to be a substance which diffuses with difficulty between cells and which at first may be uniformly distributed in the embryo. As embryogenesis proceeds, it is postulated that a gradient in the inducer arises perhaps as a result of an anteroposterior gradient in mitotic division rates. The bithorax genes evidently exploit and amplify this gradient by producing a whole set of new substances that repress certain systems of cellular differentiation and thereby allow other systems to come into play. Possibly in this way the bithorax genes control the pathway of development of certain major body segments of the fly.

ACKNOWLEDGMENTS

This work was supported in part by a grant from the U. S. Atomic Energy Commission (AT-(04-3)-41). The author wishes to acknowledge the excellent technical assistance of Gladys del Campo. Figures 1–19 first appeared in the *American Zoologist* and are reprinted by permission.

REFERENCES

AMES, B. N., AND HARTMAN, P. E. (1963). The histidine operon. *Cold Spring Harbor Symp. Quant. Biol.* **28**, 349-356.

BENZER, S. (1955). Fine structure of a genetic region in bacteriophage. *Proc. Natl. Acad. Sci. U. S.* **41**, 344-354.

BROWN, S. W., AND HANNAH, A. (1952). An induced maternal effect on the stability of the ring-X chromosome of *Drosophila melanogaster. Proc. Natl. Acad. Sci. U. S.* **38**, 687-693.

CARLSON, E. A. (1959). Comparative genetics of complex loci. *Quart. Rev. Biol.* **34**, 33-67.

ITIKAWA, N. (1955). An example of the silkworm moth which has the 3rd wing incompletely developed. *Acta Sericol. (Tokyo)* **12**, 13-15 (in Japanese).

JACOB, F., AND MONOD, J. (1961). On the regulation of gene activity. *Cold Spring Harbor Symp. Quant. Biol.* **26**, 193-211.

LEWIS, E. B. (1951). Pseudoallelism and gene evolution. *Cold Spring Harbor Symp. Quant. Biol.* **16**, 159-174.

LEWIS, E. B. (1954). The theory and application of a new method of detecting chromosomal rearrangements in *Drosophila melanogaster. Am. Naturalist* **88**, 225-239.

LEWIS, E. B. (1955). Some aspects of position pseudoallelism. *Am. Naturalist* **89**, 73-89.

LEWIS, E. B. (1963). Genes and developmental pathways. *Am. Zoologist* **3**, 33-56.

ROBERTS, P. (1964). Mosaics involving aristapedia, a homeotic mutant of *Drosophila melanogaster*. *Genetics* **49**, 593-598.

SCHULTZ, J. (1956). The relation of the heterochromatic chromosome regions to the nucleic acids of the cell. *Cold Spring Harbor Symp. Quant. Biol.* **21**, 307-328.

STERN, C. (1956). Genetic mechanisms in the localized initiation of differentiation. *Cold Spring Harbor Symp. Quant. Biol.* **21**, 375-382.

STURTEVANT, A. H. (1932). The use of mosaics in the study of the developmental effects of genes. *Proc. 6th Intern. Congr. Genet., Ithaca 1932* Vol. 1, pp. 304-307. Brooklyn Botanic Garden, New York.

TOKUNAGA, C. (1961). The differentiation of a secondary sex comb under the influence of the gene engrailed in *Drosophila melanogaster*. *Genetics* **46**, 157-176.

TSUJITA, M. (1955). On the crossing-over between E^H and E^K of the E allelic series in the silkworm. *Japan. J. Genet.* **30**, 227-235.

YANOFSKY, C. (1963). Genetic control of protein structure. *In* "Cytodifferentiation and Macromolecular Synthesis," 21st Symposium Soc. Study of Development and Growth (M. Locke, ed.), pp. 15-29. Academic Press, New York.

WAGNER, R. P., AND MITCHELL, H. K. (1964). "Genetics and Metabolism," 2nd ed. Wiley, New York.

Macronuclear Differentiation and Subnuclear Assortment in Ciliates

D. L. NANNEY

Department of Zoology, University of Illinois, Urbana, Illinois

Ciliates are peculiar beasts. Their organization is intermediate between that of strictly unicellular organisms and that of unambiguously multicellular forms. They are compound in the sense that each individual contains dozens or even hundreds of sets of chromosomes, but they are not compartmentalized. The individual consists of a single cytoplasmic mass containing one (or a few) polygenomic nuclear structures. Since they are not precisely comparable to either microorganisms or macroorganisms, they might be best described as mezzoorganisms. The lack of compartmentalization must have its advantages, for the ciliates are ancient, numerous, and widely distributed; but it presents certain problems of organization and differentiation which may not be solved in precisely the same way as in other organisms.

The very singularity of ciliates constitutes a barrier to generalization, for one is constantly perplexed with an assessment of what is to be compared with what and which mechanisms may be considered as "general" and which as "special." This problem is not restricted to ciliates, of course, and all organisms are to some extent special. Experience, however, seems to justify the faith that biological mechanisms, when pursued to a sufficiently elemental level, are ubiquitous. It also suggests that the very peculiarities of organisms provide opportunities for analysis; different life forms have their activities organized in different patterns and exposed in diverse ways to experimental probes. Organismic unconventionality is not simply a deterrant, but also a challenge to the experimentalist.

Morphological Nuclear Differentiation

One of the peculiar problems of ciliates arises at the junction of the generations. Not being properly cellularized, ciliates cannot produce gametes which fuse and develop into new individuals. However, they maintain—isolated from the common nuclear mass—one or more diploid genomes which serve as a germinal reservoir. The micronucleus behaves in a reasonably conventional manner and undergoes meiosis at an appropriate time to produce haploid nuclei. These nuclear donations to the next generation do not possess a private cytoplasm in which to venture forth in search of a complement. The union of gametic nuclei from different sources is accomplished by the temporary union of the parental bodies (conjugation) when the haploid nuclei are exchanged and fuse into zygote nuclei. Even then the nuclei are not provided with personal domains, but persist in the communal cytoplasm; the nuclear anlagen of the next generation have been established, but they have

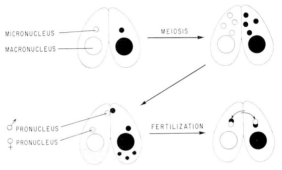

FIG. 1.   Prezygotic nuclear events at conjugation in *Tetrahymena*.

not been incorporated into a functional individual. This incorporation is accomplished in a unique way. The new nuclei simply requisition the bodies of the parents, destroy the quantitatively superior nuclear forces of the previous generation, and reconstruct an organism of their own specification.

To illustrate these processes, we may examine the events bridging the generations in one representative ciliate *Tetrahymena pyriformis* (Nanney, 1953; Elliott and Hayes, 1953; Ray, 1956; Nanney and Nagel, 1964). Individuals of complementary mating type attach in a region near the oral membranes and the micronuclei undergo meiosis (Fig. 1). Three of the meiotic products disintegrate and the fourth divides again to provide identical "male" and "female" pronuclei. The male nuclei then migrate through the region of contact and unite with the female nuclei of the mates. The mating individuals separate.

The zygote nuclei then prepare to commandeer the parental bodies (Fig. 2). They first undergo two nuclear divisions with spindles so oriented that two new nuclei come to rest at the extreme anterior end of the animal and two at the posterior end. The nuclei at the anterior end are then induced to begin the next phase of the reconstruction; under the influence of the anterior cytoplasm two of the nuclei begin their compounding activities. They increase in size and deoxyribonucleic acid (DNA) content and move back toward a central position in the animal. At this time three kinds of nuclei are present in the common cytoplasm; the macronuclear anlagen are entering a period of rapid DNA synthesis; the micronuclear anlagen remain as simple diploids; and the compound macronucleus from the previous generation not only fails to synthesize new DNA, but is scheduled for liquidation. As the new macronucleus

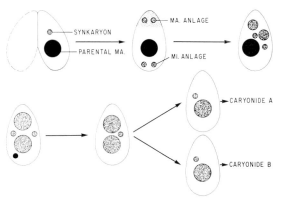

Fig. 2.   Postzygotic nuclear events at conjugation in *Tetrahymena*.

begins to develop, the old macronucleus rounds up, changes its staining properties, and is quickly resorbed. The invariable correlation between macronuclear development and macronuclear resorption indicates that the new macronucleus is instrumental in the destruction of the old one; whenever new macronuclei fail to grow—because of innate incapacity or artificial trauma—the old macronucleus persists (see also Sonneborn, 1947, 1954). An analogy might be drawn between a reorganizing ciliate and a bacterium infected with a virulent phage; in both cases a newly introduced genetic material commandeers the machinery employed by the old and regulates its behavior.

The reorganization process is completed after two more steps. After the resorption of the old macronucleus, the cytoplasm contains four nuclei— two macronuclei and two micronuclei with identical nucleic endowments. One of the micronuclei, however, through some mechanism of mutual exclusion, is discarded leaving only one micronucleus and two macronuclei. At this juncture the organism divides; the single micronucleus divides to provide germ lines for both daughters, but the macronuclei are separated into different individuals. These two daughters, possessing identical genetic constitutions, then produce through binary fission individual clones designated as "caryonides."

The events just described illustrate the profound modifications in nuclear structure and function which are associated with the sexual process. Nuclei with the same relevant nucleic information, but differing from each other in their historical experience and geographic location, may either remain static, enter a period of rapid DNA synthesis, or be completely dismantled; and these events occur in a regular temporal and spatial pattern. And lest we be tempted to consider the nuclear differences simply as transitory physiological variants, we should note that the differences developed in micronuclei and macronuclei during the conjugal maneuvers may persist in a common cytoplasm for hundreds of replications; macronuclei are not convertible into micronuclei, and micronuclei may generate new macronuclei only through precise and elaborate nuclear differentiation in conjugation. Unfortunately, the mechanisms involved in these nuclear differentiations have not been extensively explored; questions are raised, but answers must be deferred.

The gross nuclear differentiation associated with nuclear reorganization only provides a backdrop for a consideration of another striking characteristic of ciliates. Although the cytological descriptions lead to the expectation that the vegetative progeny of any conjugating pair should be genetically uniform, persistent phenotypic diversities, involving a wide range of characteristics, commonly arise within such populations. The major emphasis throughout the last three decades of ciliate genetics has been the rationalization of this intraclonal variation. We shall not attempt a comprehensive survey of these studies. Some of the variations reflect the gross appropriation of parental substance and parental structures, which condition in significant ways the characteristics of the progeny; but others are clearly due to differentiative events which occur in the somatic nuclei. We shall restrict this discussion to a small selection of these cases and in particular to certain cases in which "bean bag" analysis has been applied.

Caryonidal Distribution: Mating Type Differentiation in Syngen 1, *Paramecium aurelia*

The first demonstration that intraclonal variants might have a basis in nuclear differentiation came with Sonneborn's studies (1937, 1947, 1957) of mating types in syngen 1 of *Paramecium aurelia*. These strains undergo repeated autogamies, and any one autogamous event yields a homozygous individual. Nevertheless, at each nuclear reorganization (either autogamy or conjugation) a large fraction of the reorganized individuals yield clones heterogeneous for mating type. The patterns of assortment of mating types after a reorganization provide evidence for differences in the macronuclei developed from a single synkaryon. Specifically, most caryonides are found to be pure for a mating type, but sister caryonides are no more often alike than expected by chance (Fig. 3). Mating-type differences assort at precisely the same division at which newly developed macronuclei are segregated into daughter cells, even

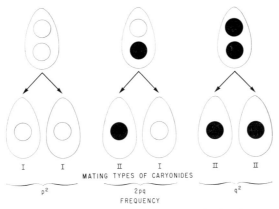

FIG. 3. Mating-type assortment after nuclear reorganization in *Paramecium aurelia* (syngen 1). The term p represents the frequency of type I caryonides and q the frequency of type II caryonides.

when segregation occurs under atypical circumstances. Genes control the mating-type potentialities, but which capacities are expressed depends upon differentiative events which occur independently in macronuclei developing in the same cytoplasm. Environmental influences (particularly temperature) may be shown to influence the probabilities of establishing the alternative nuclear states, but the significance of these observations is problematical.

This first example of nuclear differentiation is perhaps the simplest which has been encountered, but the mechanisms involved are obscure. Even the precise time of the differentiation has not been determined, although it occurs in the interval between the initiation of anlagen enlargement and the first macronuclear division. The fact that most caryonides are pure for mating type indicates an "all or none" process;

a particular macronucleus is usually totally committed to the manifestation of one of the two mating types. The occasional caryonides which are
not of pure mating type can be interpreted as due either to "unstable"
macronuclei or to mosaic macronuclei composed of stable and assorting
elements.

Subnuclear Assortment: Mating Type Differentiation in Syngen 1, *Tetrahymena pyriformis*

A second example of nuclear differentiation is also concerned with
mating types but in a related form—syngen 1 of *Tetrahymena pyriformis*.
Seven rather than two mating types occur in this organism, and the
progeny of a single mating pair commonly include several of these. As in
the previous case, the different caryonides have distinct properties and
no correlation can be demonstrated between sister caryonides (Nanney,
1956). The major difference between this system and that in syngen 1
of *P. aurelia* resides in the fact that a large fraction of the caryonides are
"impure," i.e., they contain individuals of two or more mating types, even
though one of the kinds is usually in great excess.

A detailed analysis of caryonides producing diverse mating types (Allen
and Nanney, 1958; Schensted, 1958) demonstrates that they may be treated
as mosaics, containing segregating units designated as "subnuclei." Unstable lines assort pure sublines in characteristic patterns and rates. In
particular, every unstable line—after a period of equilibration to adjust
for initial differences in the relative quantities of the different classes of
subnuclei—produces pure derivatives at a rate (R_f) of about 0.0113 per
fission. It is important to note that this assortment constant is identical
in all unstable lines, regardless of the mating types assorting, and that the
rates of stabilization to the two alternative types always approach
equality. These results would not be expected if the subnuclear types
replicated at differential rates; no subnuclear selection can be demonstrated in mature clones. The analysis of vegetative pedigrees thus provides some indication of the physical basis of mating-type variation
within caryonides; the macronucleus contains stable assorting units, and
the number of these units can be estimated to be approximately 90 just
prior to a macronuclear division.

Because the mating-type variants occur regularly even in homozygous
clones, they cannot be ascribed to the usual kinds of genetic assortments
which might be imagined and pose a problem in developmental differentiation. Cell lineage studies at early stages of the development of a

clone provide a means of assessing the mode of origin of the subnuclear differences. In evaluating such studies several factors have to be kept in mind, and before presenting the experimental results, these *a priori* considerations require discussion.

The Timing of Differentiation

Consider, for example, the problem of determining the time at which subnuclear differentiation occurs. For the sake of simplicity we may assume that the compounding is accomplished by synchronous replications of the chromosomes so that successive macronuclei contain 1, 2, 4, 8, 16, 32, and 64 diploid sets of chromosomes. We may also assume that the assorting "subnuclei," defined through vegetative pedigree studies, correspond to these diploid sets, but we should be aware that the physical nature of the subnuclei may be interpreted in other ways. If differentiation occurs when only one subnucleus is present, all the derived subnuclei will be alike, as will all the individuals within a caryonide. The fact that many caryonides are mixed demonstrates that most new macronuclei are heterogeneous and that, therefore, irreversible differentiation must occur at a time when more than one subnucleus is present. If determination occurs when two subnuclei are present (Fig. 4), the opportunity is provided for intranuclear differences. If both subnuclei differentiate alike, a pure macronucleus is produced, but if they differentiate diversely, many kinds of macronuclei become possible, depending upon which of the seven alternative states the two subnuclei assume. In all of them, however, the subnuclei of the two types are equally frequent at first.

If differentiation occurs at a later stage, a wider selection of subnuclear ratios is possible. Thus, if differentiation occurs when only two subnuclei are present, a particular kind of subnucleus should constitute 0, 50, or 100% of the total. If differentiation occurs when four subnuclei have been produced, a particular subnuclear type could comprise 0, 25, 50, 75, or 100% of the population; if it occurred at the 8-unit stage, the input could be 0, 12.5, 25, 37.5%, etc. The later the differentiation is, the greater the variety of inputs, and the higher the probability of producing macronuclei with small fractions of a rare type.

The Question of Coordination

While a quantitative analysis of subnuclear ratios provides information about the timing of differentiation, a qualitative analysis may suggest intranuclear interactions. In particular, differentiation at a particular time in the developmental sequence will have different consequences depending upon the coordination of the events within a single macro-nucleus. At one extreme the fixation of subnuclear types might be com-pletely independent for each of the subnuclei present at the critical time. Thus, if each of four subnuclei were determined independently to one of the five mating types (or six or seven, depending on the genotype) and if the probabilities of the various determinations were approximately the

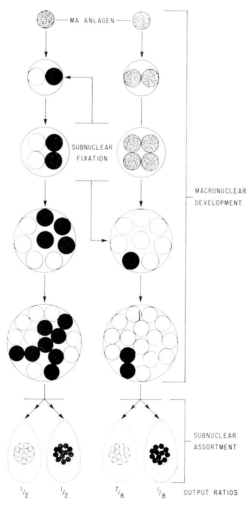

Fig. 4. Schematic diagram illustrating the relationship between the time of sub-nuclear differentiation and the maximum eccentricity of output ratios.

same, very few macronuclei would be monotypic [$5(1/5)^4$ or less than 1%]. A larger fraction should be ditypic [$140(1/5)^4$ or 22%], but the remaining 77% of the macronuclei should contain at least three types of subnuclei. If differentiation occurs when 8, 16, or 32 units are present, nearly all macronuclei should include subnuclei of three or more different kinds, and many should include the entire array potentiated by the genotype.

In contrast, if the differentiation of subnuclei is not independent and sister subnuclei tend to differentiate alike, eccentric input ratios would be possible, but the qualitative diversity anticipated under conditions of random determination would not be found.

The Problem of Differential Replication

The kind of macronucleus which is finally developed depends not only on its condition at the time of subnuclear fixation, but also on the events which occur subsequently. Consider, for example, the fate of a nucleus which has differentiated at the 2-unit stage and contains one subnucleus of each of two kinds. If, as suggested earlier, each subnucleus replicates in synchrony with the others, the fully developed macronucleus should contain equal numbers of the two kinds of units, and the caryonide, once assortment has been completed, should contain equal numbers of the two kinds of individuals. Alternatively, one might imagine that subnuclear replication is uncoordinated and that differential multiplication may permit the ratios of subnuclear types in the late nucleus to depart from the initial ratios; the "output ratio" might not correspond to the "input ratio."

Two different bases for differential replication must be considered: subnuclei of certain types might replicate more rapidly than those of other types to produce a special kind of intranuclear selection; or differential replication might be indifferent to subnuclear type and reflect entirely random factors. In this case the average output ratios would reflect the input ratios, but individual macronuclei might deviate in either direction from the mean; a kind of intranuclear "drift" similar to that occurring in later fissions could be occurring prior to the first macronuclear division.

The reason for discussing these factors relating initial and final macronuclear states is that the initial states cannot be directly ascertained and must be probed entirely through a consideration of the final states. "Output ratios" can be determined simply by allowing mosaic macronuclei to assort into pure lines and scoring the frequencies of the alternative types. Inferences concerning the input ratios must, however, be made with caution.

The major generalizations concerning output ratios for mating types (Nanney and Allen, 1959) are the following:

1. A majority of caryonides (80 of 127 in one series with limited sampling) are capable of producing sublines of two or more mating types.

2. Most of the mixed caryonides (51 of 64 resolved) yield only two types of pure sublines. Some (12 of 64) produce three, and a very small fraction (1 of 64) produce more.

3. Any combination of two mating types may be recovered from a single caryonide.

4. Most caryonides yield sublines of one predominant type; although minority outputs smaller than about 3% would not be detected in the limited surveys carried out, many outputs were in this range.

5. No marked associations of particular mating types can be demonstrated, but certain mating types tend to be "majority types" more frequently than others and more frequently than expected from their gross probabilities of appearance.

These facts lead to certain inferences concerning the differentiative events. The fact that most caryonides are mixed demonstrates that differentiation occurs at a time when more than one subnucleus is present; since some caryonides have three or four different kinds of subnuclei, the earliest possible time of differentiation for some macronuclei is the 4-unit stage. The fact that the minority outputs are often very small indicates one of two things. If subnuclei do not replicate differentially, the differentiation must occur late; a 3% minority output (the lowest commonly detectable in these experiments) would suggest fixation at least as late as the 32-unit stage. Alternatively, a small minority output ratio could be reconciled with an early differentiation if, after differentiation, the subnuclei did not replicate at equal rates. For example, differentiation at the 2-unit stage to yield unlike subnuclei, followed by replication of only one, could produce a macronucleus with a small minority type.

An experimental distinction between these alternatives has not been possible, but *a priori* considerations of considerable force may be developed. We may note that the differentiations occur regularly even in homozygotes and that—whatever a "subnucleus" may be—subnuclei probably do not differ from each other in their genetic composition. Moreover, the differentiations at these early stages in the development of a clone are cryptic; immediately after reorganization and for a period of dozens of fissions thereafter, the individuals are sexually immature and manifest no mating type. Overt functional differences among subnuclei at this time are difficult to imagine. And finally, the studies of subnuclear assortment at later stages provide no hint of differential replication. While selection or drift cannot be categorically denied, a reasonable physical basis for such phenomena is difficult to prescribe. The most plausible assumption is that they do not occur and that the small minority classes do reflect late differentiations; subnuclei are irreversibly determined only when a macronucleus approaches its full compound structure.

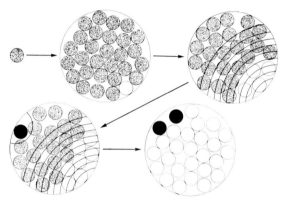

Fig. 5.   A model for mating type differentiation in syngen 1 of *Tetrahymena pyriformis,* illustrating the spread of a nuclear differentiation through a population of subnuclei, a possible basis for intranuclear coordination.

If this interpretation is correct, it leads to a second inference. We have discussed the expectations for *random* determination of subnuclei at different times during subnuclear proliferation. We noted in particular that differentiation after the 4-unit stage should lead to the recovery of most of the possible mating types from each macronucleus. Yet, only a small fraction of the macronuclei yield more than two kinds of subnucleus. If we reject differential replication, we are forced to the conclusion that subnuclei do not differentiate at random; the subnuclei within a single macronucleus at the time of determination are strongly disposed to differentiate in the same way.

Several different bases for this coordination might be imagined, but a useful model might be suggested (Fig. 5). We might suppose that as a macronucleus approaches the limit of its initial proliferation, the probability for a subnuclear fixation rises and eventually one of the subnuclei is differentiated at a type whose frequency is determined by some general probability function. If the first fixation conditions subsequent fixations, a differentiation might spread through the population at a more rapid rate than autonomous fixations would permit and result in the majority of the subnuclei being of the same kind. The near-random assortment of types within a macronucleus could reflect the autonomy of the primary events; the tendencies for types to vary in their average output ratios might be explained as owing to differences in the rates of spreading of secondary fixations. The subsequent events in the history of the caryonide are due to the maintenance of the subnuclear characteristics through replication and the assortment of subnuclei at macronuclear division.

Subnuclear Assortment: Allelic Repression or Heterozygote Resolution?

Mating-type differentiation represents only one of several instances of subnuclear assortment in *Tetrahymena* and differs from the others in what may be an important respect. Mating-type differentiation occurs in individuals of all known genetic constitutions; the specificities involved in the determination appear to be associated with a single genetic locus, the *mt* locus, and each of the known alleles potentiates an array of mating types (Nanney *et al.*, 1955; Nanney, 1959). The fixation of type may be imagined to be due to the selection for manifestation of one component from a polycistronic cluster. Each *mt* locus is, in a sense, pluripotent.

The other examples of subnuclear assortment occur only in heterozygous individuals. They include two different sets of esterase isozymes (Allen, 1960, 1961) and a set of acid phosphatase isozymes (Allen *et al.*, 1963) visualized through starch-gel electrophoresis. The H-serotype system (Nanney and Dubert, 1960) also manifests assortment. Significantly, this assembly of genetic variants, along with those related to mating types, constitutes the entire collection of simple gene differences which have been assembled for syngen 1, *T. pyriformis*. Whatever the basis for subnuclear assortment, it seems to be widespread in this form.

Detailed quantitative studies have been carried out thus far only for the H serotypes. These are the serological variants detected through immobilization tests on cells grown at temperatures above 20°C. A series of four alleles (H^A, H^C, H^D, and H^E) has been defined for the H locus, which is unlinked to the other known loci. Whenever heterozygotes are established, the clones initially manifest both component alleles, but eventually they yield sublines capable of expressing only one. Assortment studies equivalent to those for mating types yield identical results; the rate of stabilization (R_f) again approaches 0.0113 per fission. The subnuclei differentiated for serotypes behave in precisely the same way as those for mating types and must be assumed to have a similar physical basis.

Before tackling the question of mechanisms underlying the differentiations, a summary of pertinent studies on the serotype system (Nanney and Dubert, 1960; Nanney *et al.*, 1963, 1964) will be useful.

1. All six of the allelic combinations for serotypes have been examined and all show subnuclear assortment.

2. Each kind of heterozygote has a characteristic array of output ratios, and a "peck-order" of expression may be developed. H^E is manifested most frequently, followed by H^A, H^D, and H^C in this order.

3. Serotype output ratios, unlike those for mating types, are relatively insensitive to temperature variations.

4. An analysis of variance of output ratios in early fissions demonstrates that the characteristic macronuclear constitutions are established at different times in individuals with different genotypes. In particular, caryonides of H^A/H^D heterozygotes differ significantly from each other, and the primary subcaryonides (produced at the first macronuclear division) are highly correlated, indicating a fixation at a time prior to the first macronuclear division. In contrast, the H^A/H^E and H^C/H^D primary subcaryonides are uncorrelated, and the subnuclear constitution must be fixed between the first and second macronuclear divisions; no significant differentiation prior to the first division can be detected.

5. Dispersion studies of output ratios for caryonides (or primary caryonides, where appropriate) indicate that subnuclei are fixed late in macronuclear development and that little if any coordination of subnuclear differentiations occurs.

These observations are all consistent with the following model (Fig. 6). The compounding of the macronucleus occurs by the replication of diploid subnuclei. At some time near the completion of the compounding (but at different times in different genotypes) the subnuclei differentiate. This fixation involves the activation of one of the alleles in each subnucleus, coincident with a repression of the alternative allele. The differentiation of subnuclei is uncoordinated and occurs with probabilities characteristic for the allelic combination. According to this interpretation the chief problem is that of understanding the mechanism whereby genes interact in a system of mutual repression (Nanney, 1963). The phenomenon under study may be referred to as "allelic repression."

Alternative Interpretations

Unfortunately, this simple interpretation involves a basic assumption which cannot be directly tested yet, i.e., that the macronucleus is constituted of diploid genomes. We know from its increase in size and DNA content that the macronucleus becomes polygenomic. Electron microscopy, however, fails to reveal any membrane structures within the macronucleus; the macronucleus looks more like a bag of spaghetti than a bag of marbles. Many sets of chromosomes are, therefore, associated inside a single nuclear envelope without obvious compartmentalization, and their organization can only be deduced from indirect evidence.

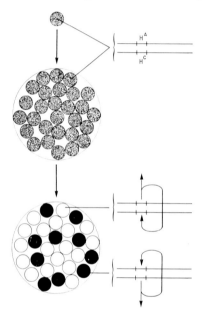

Fig. 6. A model for H-serotype differentiation in syngen 1 of *Tetrahymena pyriformis,* illustrating the late and autonomous subnuclear differentiation and the genic basis for "allelic repression."

Several different patterns of association have been considered, and these may be summarized into three categories:

1. The chromosomes are not organized at all, but replicate and assort independently.

2. The chromosomes of a haploid set are linked together into "suprachromosomal" arrays. These haploid sets replicate and assort independently.

3. The chromosomes of diploid sets retain their original associations; all subnuclei are genetically equivalent.

Each of these interpretations leads to somewhat different expectations. Macronuclear division occurs by an apparently simple constriction and yields daughter macronuclei of only approximately equal size. If the chromosomes are assorted individually and randomly, any particular chromosome might fail to be included in one of the daughters at division. The probability of such a loss would depend primarily on the total compoundness of the macronucleus; the larger the number of copies of the chromosome present, the lower the probability of its loss. Although the complete loss of both homologs of a pair would almost certainly be lethal, the loss of one of a pair should not impair vitality to any marked extent unless the remaining homolog possesses a recessive lethal. Selection in mass cultures would probably maintain approximate chromosome balance, in the sense that at least one homolog of each pair would be represented in reasonable frequency, but eventually individuals would be produced which contained only one homolog of a kind. The precise time at which a particular homolog was fixed in a lineage would be independent of that at which other homologs are fixed. This model would lead to vegetative assortment, but the assorting "subnuclei" would in fact be individual chromosomes.

The second alternative has somewhat different consequences. If haploid sets are maintained, unbalanced chromosome complements would not be generated, but again heterozygotes would be resolved into some sublines manifesting one allele and some manifesting the other. The fixation of one allele, however, should coincidentally result in the fixation of all alleles "linked" in the haploid array. One modification can convert this model into one with consequences very similar to those of the first. If the haploid "linkages" are sufficiently "loose" that exchanges can occur freely, either during a limited period of time early in the development of a clone or continuously throughout its history, a large number of kinds of subnuclei could be established, and simultaneous fixation of alleles would not be required. Haploid associations which are capable of reconstitution could scarcely be distinguished from no linkage at all.

The third alternative—the linkage of chromosomes into diploid associations—would not lead to the expectation of genetic assortment; all subnuclei would be genetically equivalent and any phenotypic diversification would have to be explained on an "epigenetic" rather than a "genetic" basis. Again, however, one has to qualify the evaluation, because somatic crossing-over, if sufficiently frequent, could lead to the production of subnuclei homozygous for particular markers and eventually to the production of individuals homozygous (in their macronuclei) for certain genes.

This discussion should make clear that any of the major models of macronuclear construction could lead to genetic assortment within a clone, provided that somatic recombination occurs at a sufficiently high rate; and any of these models could provide a physical basis for the "subnuclei" demonstrated in assortment studies. In one case they would be individual chromosomes, in another, haploid sets of chromosomes, and in the third they would be diploid units differentiated either genetically or epigenetically. The model proposed earlier is based on epigenetic diversification of genetically equivalent diploid units.

Simply to pose the problem in a concrete form, let us consider an alternative interpretation of the H-serotype phenomena. Let us assume that at some stage in the compounding process haploid units are established and that these are then autonomously replicated and passively assorted at macronuclear division. Some sublines would be established with one allele and some with the other. In a general way this model is capable of accounting for the observations on the H-serotype system and, indeed, for all the cases of "allelic repression."

One has to consider the model, however, with reference to the details of the systems before it can be fully evaluated. One thing which has to be considered, for example, is the meaning of the various output ratios. In some heterozygotes nearly all caryonides have output ratios of 80:20 or higher, and individual caryonides may have outputs at least as high as 95:5. Since the initial allelic input is always 1:1, these output ratios would require differential replication of the haploid units after they are established. The differential replication would have to be selective; units with the allele H^E would have to replicate more efficiently than those with H^A, and these in turn more rapidly than those with H^C, etc. The selective advantages required, however, to account for the output ratios would have to be lost once the macronucleus was fully developed, because selection during the assortment process could be detected, but has not yet been found. Hence, the haploidization model requires the subsidiary assumption of subnuclear selection during a limited period of the compounding process.

Even this assumption, however, does not clear all the difficulties. We noted that certain heterozygotes (H^A/H^E and H^C/H^D) do not differentiate during the early period of compounding—that the differences in output ratios arise in the interval between the first and second macronuclear divisions. Hence, if differential replication occurs, it must occur during the initial period of proliferation for some genotypes and during a later period for other genotypes. The selective system would require some very peculiar properties.

A more general problem arises in consideration of other cases of allelic repression. Thus far only one case of linkage has been detected in *Tetra-hymena* (Allen, 1964a) and this involves one of the esterase loci *(E-1)* and the *mt* locus. The linkage is not close and about 25% recombinations are recovered. This system, however, permits a test of the haploidization hypothesis in one of its forms. As noted previously, the *mt* alleles specify an array of potentialities, only one of which is manifested. The gene *mt^A*, for example, potentiates the array of *I*, II, III, V, and VI, whereas *mt^B* potentiates mating types II, III, *IV*, V, VI, and *VII*. If haploidization occurs, some subnuclei should be limited to one array and others to the other array. The critical test involves nuclei manifesting the differential types I, IV, and VII. We may first note that heterozygous nuclei are not infrequently found which appear to be pure for a differential type such as mating type IV; the haploidization interpretation would require in this case a complete selection against the haploid sets which did not contain the IV potentiality. One would expect under these conditions that selection would also act against markers linked to the *mt* locus. Yet, when the esterase characteristics of differentiated sublines were exam-ined, no relationship could be demonstrated between the mating types and the esterases (Allen, 1964b). To retain the haploidization hypothesis, therefore, one has to introduce an additional assumption to the effect that sufficient somatic recombination occurs during the development of the macronucleus to randomize the markers located on the same chromosome. Moreover, the randomization must occur continuously during the selective period to account for the independent output ratios for the different markers.

Thus, the haploidization hypothesis, which appeared capable of ex-plaining the general features of somatic assortment, becomes encumbered with two major restrictions: it requires a randomization of genetic markers, even those on the same chromosome, and a selective replication at specific times of alternative genetic units concerned with a variety of cellular properties. The subnucleus becomes in effect a single genetic locus.

Other objections to this hypothesis come from comparative studies. The problem of macronuclear structure was first posed for *Paramecium aurelia* and efforts were made to resolve it there. In particular, extensive studies were made in the attempt to detect genetic assortment in clones of this ciliate (Sonneborn *et al.*, 1956). Although phenotypic variability was observed, the loss of a genetic determinant could not be demonstrated. The concept of the diploid subnucleus in *Tetrahymena* was initially based on these studies. But one must accept the possibility that different ciliates organize their affairs in different ways; *Paramecium* may have macronuclei with diploid subnuclei, whereas *Tetrahymena* undergoes haploidization. It is perhaps significant that "allelic repression" has been found repeatedly in *Tetrahymena* and generally has not been observed in *Paramecium*. This interpretation will not bear close scrutiny, however. The total compoundness of *P. aurelia* macronuclei is much higher than that of *T. pyriformis,* and the assortment rates would be expected to be much lower. Moreover, *P. aurelia* has a relatively short life cycle which is usually terminated by autogamy at a time before *T. pyriformis* has even become sexually mature. The time available for assortment is relatively short and, nevertheless, considerable phenotypic variability in heterozygotes has been noted. Quite possibly allelic repression occurs commonly in *P. aurelia*.

In this connection we may draw attention to a recent report by Finger and Heller (1964) of allelic serotype exclusion in syngen 2 of *P. aurelia*. The differentiation occurs under special circumstances—which might be required for its detection in this form—but in principle it strongly resembles the case in *Tetrahymena*. Moreover, and very significantly, Finger reports that lineages manifesting only one allele can be induced to express the other by treating the individuals with antiserum or inhibitors of protein synthesis. Allelic exclusion of serotype potentialities in *Paramecium* does not involve the loss of the excluded determinant and hence cannot be explained by any scheme of genetic assortment. Unfortunately, the treatment of differentiated *Tetrahymena* with such agents has not yet been found to reverse either serotype or mating-type differentiations. Nevertheless, it seems doubtful that such similar phenomena in such closely related forms could have fundamentally different bases.

Finally, we may mention briefly that the plausibility of interallelic reactions of the sort postulated has been enhanced by studies on other kinds of organisms. In particular we may note the problem of sex-chromosome activity in mammals. In cells with two or more X chromosomes, the activities of many of the genes (but perhaps not all) are regulated by some exclusion principle; if an allele on one chromosome is active, that on the other is not (see, e.g., Beutler *et al.*, 1962). The mechanisms in the two cases may or may not be related, but superficial similarities may certainly be noted.

Conclusion

This presentation has been focused on a limited aspect of the problem of nuclear differentiation in ciliates and, specifically, on a rationalization of the phenomenon of subnuclear assortment. The analysis provides support for the hypothesis of diploid subnuclei as the architectural sub-unit of the ciliate macronucleus and, coincidentally, for the hypothesis of "allelic repression" as the basis for certain examples of subnuclear differentiation. If some means can be found for releasing repressions and demonstrating the persistence of both alleles in all lineages or if additional genes with more conventional manifestations can be located, the hypothesis will be considerably strengthened. Even now, however, it provides the simplest and most consistent interpretation of the observations.

A disturbing question still remains, however. Why should allelic repression be observed for all genic differences thus far studied in *Tetrahymena,* when it is not commonly observed in other organisms? One possible answer is that it has not been sought properly elsewhere; relatively few cell lineage studies have been conducted on heterozygous mammalian cells, for example. Another factor of possible importance concerns the nature and the origin of the allelic differences. All the allelic variants in *Tetrahymena* have been isolated from natural populations, are "active" alleles, and may be supposed to have existed in those populations over a period of time during which regulatory devices for their manifestation might have been evolved. New mutants and "null" alleles might have different properties, even in *Tetrahymena.* Another possible kind of explanation lies in the still incompletely resolved nature of the diploid subnucleus, which might impose certain constraints on genic expression.

In discussing the physical bases of these differentiations, we should also mention briefly their possible biological significance. Ciliates, like bacteria, fungi, and unicellular algae, are capable of more or less indefinite reproduction by fission. In one major respect, however, their biological economies are very different. All these forms have the capacity to modify their activities in response to commonly encountered environmental variables. The uninucleate—and particularly the haploid forms—have, in addition, the facility to adapt genetically to sudden or unexpected environmental vicissitudes. Rare mutants in a large population provide a means of escape from otherwise lethal conditions. In contrast, the ciliates—like multicellular organisms—can expose mutations effectively only after a sexual act; the compound macronucleus is an effective buffer to the expression of new genetic variants. Macronuclear mutations are usually swamped beyond detection in the presence of the original alleles in the mass of subnuclei, and mutations in the micronucleus are not effectively exposed to selective pressures until after nuclear reorganization. Under these circumstances the ciliates may have been pressed to develop means of achieving population diversity by epigenetic rather than genetic means. Whether this is a correct rationalization, the fact of extensive epigenetic diversification in ciliate clones is well documented. Its biological ends may be different from those of epigenetic differentiation in a multicellular form, but the mechanisms employed may be similar.

ACKNOWLEDGMENTS

These investigations were supported by grants from the United States Public Health Service.

The figures were prepared by Miss Alice Boatright.

REFERENCES

ALLEN, S. L. (1960). Inherited variations in the esterases of Tetrahymena. *Genetics* **45**, 1051-1070.

ALLEN, S. L. (1961). Genetic control of the esterases in the protozoan *Tetrahymena pyriformis*. *Ann. N. Y. Acad. Sci.* **94**, 753-773.

ALLEN, S. L. (1964a). Linkage studies in variety 1 of *Tetrahymena pyriformis:* a first case of linkage in the ciliated protozoa. *Genetics* **49**, 617-627.

ALLEN, S. L. (1964b). Unpublished material.

ALLEN, S. L., AND NANNEY, D. L. (1958). An analysis of nuclear differentiation in the selfers of Tetrahymena. *Am. Naturalist* **92**, 139-160.

ALLEN, S. L., MISCH, M. S., AND MORRISON, B. M. (1963). Genetic control of an acid phosphatase in Tetrahymena: Formation of a hybrid enzyme. *Genetics* **48**, 1635-1658.

BEUTLER, E., YEH, M., AND FAIRBANKS, V. F. (1962). The normal human female as a mosaic of X-chromosome activity: studies using the gene for G-6-PD-deficiency as a marker. *Proc. Natl. Acad. Sci. U. S.* **48**, 9-16.

ELLIOTT, A. M., AND HAYES, R. E. (1953). Mating types in Tetrahymena. *Biol. Bull.* **105**, 269-284.

FINGER, I., AND HELLER, C. (1964). Cytoplasmic control of gene expression in Paramecium. I. Preferential expression of a single allele in heterozygotes. *Genetics* **49**, 485-498.

NANNEY, D. L. (1953). Nucleocytoplasmic interaction during conjugation in Tetrahymena. *Biol. Bull.* **105**, 133-148.

NANNEY, D. L. (1956). Caryonidal inheritance and nuclear differentiation. *Am. Naturalist* **90**, 291-307.

NANNEY, D. L. (1959). Genetic factors affecting mating type frequencies in variety 1 of *Tetrahymena pyriformis*. *Genetics* **44**, 1173-1184.

NANNEY, D. L. (1963). Aspects of mutual exclusion in Tetrahymena. In "Biological Organization at Cellular and Supercellular Levels" (R. J. C. Harris, ed.), pp. 91-109. Academic Press, New York.

NANNEY, D. L., AND ALLEN, S. L. (1959). Intranuclear coordination in Tetrahymena. *Physiol. Zool.* **32**, 221-229.

NANNEY, D. L., AND DUBERT, J. M. (1960). The genetics of the H serotype system in variety 1 of *Tetrahymena pyriformis*. *Genetics* **45**, 1335-1349.

NANNEY, D. L., AND NAGEL, J. (1964). Nuclear misbehavior in an aberrant inbred Tetrahymena. *J. Protozool.* (in press).

NANNEY, D. L., CAUGHEY, P. A., AND TEFANKJIAN, A. (1955). The genetic control of mating type potentialities in *Tetrahymena pyriformis. Genetics* **40**, 668-680.

NANNEY, D. L., REEVE, S. J., NAGEL, J., AND DEPINTO, S. (1963). H serotype differentiation in Tetrahymena. *Genetics* **48**, 803-813.

NANNEY, D. L., NAGEL, J., AND TOUCHBERRY, R. W. (1964). The timing of H antigenic differentiation in Tetrahymena. *J. Exptl. Zool.* **155**, 25-42.

RAY, C., JR. (1956). Meiosis and nuclear behavior in *Tetrahymena pyriformis. J. Protozool.* **3**, 88-96.

SCHENSTED, I. V. (1958). Appendix: Model of subnuclear segregation in the macronucleus of ciliates. *Am. Naturalist* **92**, 161-170.

SONNEBORN, T. M. (1937). Sex, sex inheritance and sex determination in *Paramecium aurelia. Proc. Natl. Acad. Sci. U. S.* **23**, 378-385.

SONNEBORN, T. M. (1947). Recent advances in the genetics of Paramecium and Euplotes. *Advan. Genet.* **1**, 263-358.

SONNEBORN, T. M. (1954). Patterns of nucleocytoplasmic integration in Paramecium. *Caryologia* **6**, Suppl. 1, 307-325.

SONNEBORN, T. M. (1957). Breeding systems, reproductive methods and species problems in protozoa. *In* "The Species Problem" (E. Mayr, ed.), pp. 155-324. Am. Assoc. Advan. Sci., Washington, D. C.

SONNEBORN, T. M., SCHNELLER, M. V., AND CRAIG, M. F. (1956). The basis of variation in phenotype of gene-controlled traits in heterozygotes of *Paramecium aurelia. J. Protozool.* **3**, Suppl. 1, 8.

Author Index

Numbers in italics indicate the pages on which the complete references are listed.

Subject Index

A

Aceto-orcein, 120, 124, 127, 129
Acidic nuclear proteins, 51ff, 66
  amino acid analysis, 53
  (glutamic acid rich) amino acid composition of, 57
Acidic proteins, 56
Acidic proteins and gene modulation, 55
Acidic protein and histones
  interaction of, 56
Acridines, 74
Actinomycin, 74, 145
  binding of DNA, 73ff
  spectra of, 77
Actinomycin C_1 (D)
  structure of, 75
Adenine, 138, 140
Ag, 74
Alanine, 53, 54, 57, 62
Albumin, 74
Aleurone color, 189
Aleurone color scores, 188, 197, 216
Aleurone pigmentation, 212
Alkaline fast green (AFG), 41, 43
Allelic repression, 264ff, 268, 270, 271
  genic basis for, 266
Amethopterin, 86
Amino acid analysis
  of acidic nuclear proteins, 53
  of N-proline histone, 62
Amino acid composition
  of glutamic acid-rich acidic nuclear protein, 57
  of peptides of N-proline histone, 64
  of protein of the nuclear sap, 54
Amino acids in DNA, 51
Amino acid sequences in the peptides of N-proline histone, 64
Aminopterin, 86, 102
Amphibian lampbrush chromosomes, 142
  see also chromosomes
Amphibian oocyte nuclear sap, 148
Anaphase,
  see chromosomes
Anteroposterior gradient in mitotic division, 251

B

Arginine, 41, 53, 54, 57, 62
Arginine-containing protein, 43
Arginine-rich histones, 61
Aspartic acid, 51, 53, 54, 57, 62
Aspergillus, 218
Asymmetric RNA, 139, 148
Asynchronous DNA replication, 83
Asynchrony between homologous chromosomes, 97
Asynchrony in homologs, 129
Au, 74
Autosomal homologs
  asynchrony in, 129
Autosomes, 157

Balbiani ring, 137, 139, 141
  see also chromosomes, polytene
Balbiani ring RNA, 140
Beaded chromosomes, 98
Bean bag analysis, 256
Bithorax, 232ff, 237
Bithorax loci, 237
Bithorax mutants
  developmental effects of, 234
Bithorax-postbithorax
  body segmentation plan of, 239
Bithorax pseudoallelic series, 233ff
  polarity to the, 245
Bithoraxoid, 237
Bivalent chromosome, 30, 32, 33
Bombyx, 248
Brown, 158, 164

C

Ca++, 102
C14-thymidine, 122
Caryonidal distribution, 256ff
Cat
  sex chromosomes in, 88
  spermatocytes of, 31
Cave cricket
  sperm head of, 22
Cell-lethal, 175, 179
Cell synchronization and pulse labeling, 85ff